THE HUMAN TESTIS

ITS GROSS ANATOMY, HISTOLOGY, PHYSIOLOGY,
PATHOLOGY, WITH PARTICULAR REFERENCE TO ITS
ENDOCRINOLOGY, ABERRATIONS OF FUNCTION AND
CORRELATION TO OTHER ENDOCRINES, AS WELL
AS THE TREATMENT OF DISEASES OF THE TESTES
AND STUDIES IN TESTICULAR TRANSPLANTATION
AND THE EFFECTS OF THE TESTICULAR SECRETIONS
ON THE ORGANISM

BY

MAX THOREK, M.D.

SURGEON-IN-CHIEF, AMERICAN HOSPITAL; CONSULTING SURGEON, COOK COUNTY HOSPITAL,
CHICAGO, ILL.; PRESIDENT, INTERNATIONAL CONGRESS OF COMPARATIVE
PATHOLOGY, ROME, ITALY, 1924, ETC., ETC., ETC.

308 ILLUSTRATIONS

PHILADELPHIA & LONDON
J. B. LIPPINCOTT COMPANY

PRINTED BY J. B. LIPPINCOTT COMPANY
AT THE WASHINGTON SQUARE PRESS
PHILADELPHIA, U. S. A.

TO MY NUMEROUS FRIENDS IN THE PROFESSION HERE AND ABROAD, WHOSE ENCOURAGEMENT HAS PROMPTED ME TO UNDERTAKE THE WRITING OF THIS BOOK AND TO ENTER THE DIFFICULT FIELD OF RESEARCH ON THE ENDOCRINOLOGY OF THE TESTES, I PRESENT MY LABORS IN THE FORM OF THIS VOLUME WHICH IS GRATEFULLY INSCRIBED TO THEM.

—THE AUTHOR

CONTENTS

v

CONTENTS

CONTENTS

INTRODUCTION

THE author is convinced that there is great need for a compact work that embraces and elucidates the important questions pertaining to the anatomy, functions, pathology, dystrophias, endocrinology, aberrations, and other important questions concerning the human testes.

While it is true that much has been written on the subjects mentioned, the information obtainable is only fragmentary and is scattered in various textbooks and scientific publications in English and foreign languages, and there does not exist presently a work in English or in any other language which embraces the information sought in one volume.

A multitude of questions pertaining to the various phases of the work under discussion are still nebulous, unsettled, and controverted. Particularly is this true when one considers the endocrinology of the testes. The great interest aroused by the discussion of these subjects in various circles has led members of the medical profession to become quite bewildered by the various impressions conveyed to them. Many of the statements are founded on what has been or actually is being accomplished in this field of research, while other statements are sensational, exaggerated, not based on facts, and thereby actually tend to harm and inhibit the progress of scientific investigation.

The truly scientific spirit belongs to all times; in all ages conscientious and scientific men have rebelled against the theory of *laissez faire* and *laissez mourir*. Dogmatism and cloudy information can only be clarified by the conscientious coöperation between the laboratory worker and the clinician. Only too often, sad, though true it is, the laboratory worker does not take the trouble to check his results with data gained by the clinician, and the latter usually is too much engrossed at the bedside of patients and in his clinical work to permit of his spending much time in the laboratory or in the experimental room. To obviate such conditions the author for a number of years past has been striving, successfully, to create for himself conditions which would enable him to work in the laboratory and check up his data with clinical manifestations and facts. Many of the conclusions, therefore, embodied in this volume are the results of a combination of painstaking personal observation, much labor and research, and have not hitherto been published. All obtainable data contained in the literature as a contribution of other workers have, insofar as possible, been brought down to date.

One of the main objects of this work having been the study of the endocrinology of the testis, the basis of the work in connection consists in presenting facts as far as knowledge of the literature and the most recent results of strictly scientific investigation in this field of research permits. The work is presented with all obtainable proofs so there should be no difficulty in arriving at an exact conclusion of the scientific value of the work accomplished to date. In conjunction with these data the author publishes his own findings, all of his investigations pursued for some years past, and also the surgical application of knowledge gained in sex gland transplantation, coupled with details of his technic and the results as shown by microscopic examination and clinical findings.

The author considers that his personal acquaintance and constant communication with many of the serious-minded contemporary investigators in this field of research, particularly Voronoff, Steinach, the late G. Frank Lydston, Lipschütz, Weil, Massaglia, Bolognesi, Ceni and others, has contributed in no small degree to the value of this work.

The author wishes to take this opportunity to express his appreciation to Sanitätsrat Dr. Magnus Hirschfeld, Dr. Peter Bassoe, Dr. Frank Hinman, Dr. Arthur Dean Bevan and others who have so kindly permitted the reproduction of photographs from their works, and to N. M. LaPorte for the photographs of gross specimens and the microphotographs which illuminate the text.

It is hoped that the work embodied in this volume will stimulate further interest and research on the part of the profession at large.

Max Thorek, M.D.

American Hospital,
    Chicago, Illinois.

HUMAN TESTIS

CHAPTER I

GROSS ANATOMY OF THE REPRODUCTIVE
ORGANS IN MAN

THE reproductive organs in the male consist of two *testes* with their *ducti deferentes* (the latter being partly enclosed in the *spermatic cord*); the *seminal vesicles;* the *penis,* including the *urethra,* into which the various ducts discharge through the *penis;* the *prostate gland;* and *Cowper's* glands, or the *bulbo-urethral* glands.

Of the above, for the purpose of this treatise, we are more particularly interested in the *testes,* which are the essential organs of reproduction in the male. (Fig. 1.) They are two in number, of flattened ovoid form. Up to the third month of fetal life, the testis is strictly an abdominal organ; it begins its descent then, reaches the inguinal ring about the sixth month, and it is only shortly before birth that it reaches its true location in the scrotum.

The average dimensions of the testis are: 4 cm. to 5 cm. in length; 2.5 cm. in breadth, and 3 cm. in antero-posterior diameter.

The anterior and lateral surfaces and both extremities are covered by the visceral layer of the *tunica vaginalis propria;* the posterior border is only partially covered by it.

The *epididymis* consists of a tortuous canal which forms the first part of the efferent duct of the testis. It is tightly folded on itself, and is attached to the lateral part of the posterior border of the testis. It consists of a central part, *the body,* and upper enlarged extremity, the *head* or *globus major,* and a lower pointed extremity, the *tail* or *globus minor.* The tail is connected with the lower end of the testis by cellular tissue and a reflection of the tunica vaginalis. (Fig. 2.)

The lateral surfaces are free and covered by the tunica vaginalis, the body being also covered by it except at the posterior border.

The *appendix of the testis* is a minute oval sessile body, situated laterally on the upper extremity of the *testis,* just beneath the head of the

1

epididymis; it is a remnant of the Muellerian duct. On the head of the epididymis is a similar small-stalked appendage, *the appendix of the epididymis.*

The *ductulus aberrans,* or vas aberrans of Haller, is given off from the

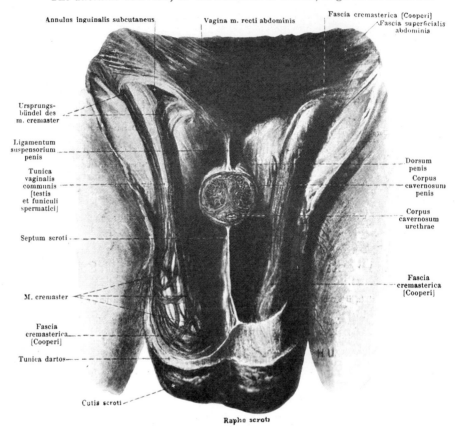

Annulus inguinalis subcutaneus   Vagina m. recti abdominis   Fascia cremasterica [Cooperi]
Fascia superficialis abdominis

Ursprungs-
bündel des
m. cremaster

Ligamentum
suspensorium
penis

Tunica
vaginalis
communis
[testis
et funiculi
spermatici]

Septum scroti

M. cremaster

Fascia
cremasterica
[Cooperi]

Tunica dartos

Cutis scroti

Dorsum
penis

Corpus
cavernosum
penis

Corpus
cavernosum
urethrae

Fascia
cremasterica
[Cooperi]

Raphe scroti

FIG. 1.—SCROTUM AND CONTENTS.
(After Spalteholtz.)
The skin and *tunica dartos* have been removed on both sides; on the right the cremasteric (Cooper's) fascia, as well as the superficial abdominal fascia, has also been ablated.   The penis is divided transversely.

ductus epididymidis near its termination in the globus minor.   It is a diverticulum or blind tubule with walls of vascular connective tissue lined with ciliated columnar or cuboid epithelium.

The *paradidymis,* or *organ of Giraldés,* is connected with the vas aberrans, and the two are identical in structure.   Both the paradidymis and the vas aberrans are functionless remains of the fetal mesonephron, or main portion of the Wolffian body.

The testis is covered by three tunics: the *tunica vaginalis, tunica albuginea,* and the *tunica vasculosa.*

The *tunica vaginalis* arises from the peritoneum. It is a closed sac which invests the surface of the testis, and is reflected on to the internal surface of the scrotum, and hence consists of a visceral and a parietal

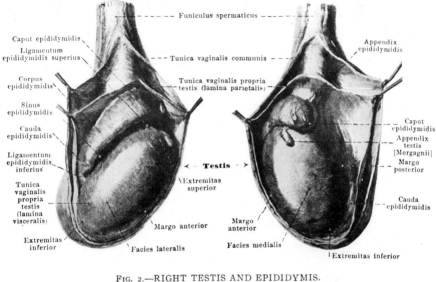

FIG. 2.—RIGHT TESTIS AND EPIDIDYMIS.
(After Spalteholtz.)
Lateral View.   Median View.
Coverings of the testes have been removed.

lamina. The visceral lamina covers the greater part of the testis and epididymis. The parietal lamina extends upwards for some distance in front of and on the medial side of the spermatic cord, and reaches below the testis.

The inner surface of the tunica vaginalis is smooth and covered with a layer of endothelial cells.

The *tunica albuginea* is a fibrous covering for the testis, and is itself covered by the tunica vaginalis, except at the head and tail of the epididymis and along the posterior border of the testis, where the testicular vessels and nerves enter the gland. At its posterior border, it is reflected into the interior of the gland, forming an incomplete vertical septum called the *mediastinum testis* (*corpus Highmori*). (Fig. 3.)

The mediastinum testis extends from the upper to near the lower extremity of the gland, and is wider above than below; from its front and sides, numerous imperfect septa branch off, radiating toward the surface of the testis and which are attached to the tunica albuginea. These completely divide the testis into a number of lobules, the bases of which are

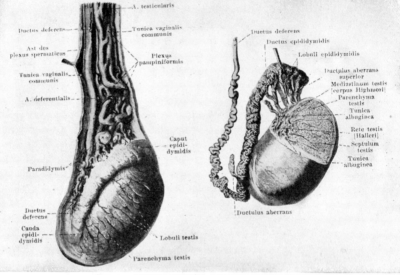

FIG. 3.—RIGHT TESTIS AND EPIDIDYMIS.
(After Spalteholz.)
A. Lateral view after removal of *tunica albuginea* and dissection of spermatic cord.
B. After removal of portion of testis and dissection of epididymis.

toward the surface and apex and converge to the mediastinum testis. The mediastinum also carries the vessels and ducts of the testis in their passage to and from the substance of the gland.

The *tunica vasculosa* is the vascular layer of the testis, and consists of a plexus of blood vessels held together by a delicate areolar tissue. It lines the tunica albuginea, and forms also an investment of all the lobules of the testis. (Fig. 4.)

The *lobules* form the glandular substance of the testis. Their number has been variously estimated at from 250 to 400. Each lobule consists of one or more small convoluted tubes, the *tubuli seminiferi contorti*.

These tubes are supported by loose connective tissue, which here and there contains groups of *interstitial cells*.

The total number of tubes is said to be about 840, the average length of each being about 70 to 80 cms., and the diameter varying from 0.12 to 0.3 mm. Each tubule consists of a basement layer of connective tissue covered externally by flattened e p i t h e l o i d cells. Within the basement membrane, epithelial cells are arranged in three irregular layers: (1) An outer layer of cubical cells, some of which enlarge to become *spermatogonia;* (2) layer of polyhedral cells in two or three strata, the intermediate cells, or *spermatocytes;* (3) the *spermatid cells,* each of which becomes a *spermatozoon.* (Figs. 5 and 6.)

In addition to the foregoing three layers of cells, other cells, called supporting or *Sertoli cells,* may be observed. These cells are elongated and columnar, and project inward from the basement membrane toward the lumen of the tube.

In the apices of the lobules, the tubules become less convoluted, and join together to form the *tubuli seminiferi recti* which enter the fibrous tissue of the mediastinum, forming a close network of anastomosing tubes, which is called the *rete testis.* These terminate at the upper end of the mediastinum, forming about twelve to twenty ducts, the *ducti efferentes testis,* which perforate the tunica albuginea and carry the seminal secretion from the testis to the epididymis.

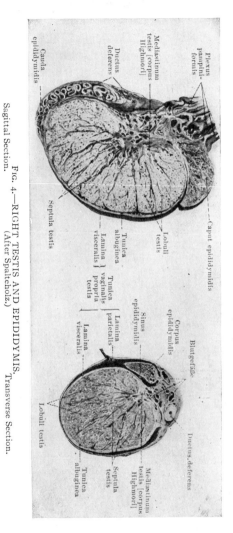

FIG. 4.—RIGHT TESTIS AND EPIDIDYMIS.
(After Spalteholz.)
Sagittal Section. Transverse Section.

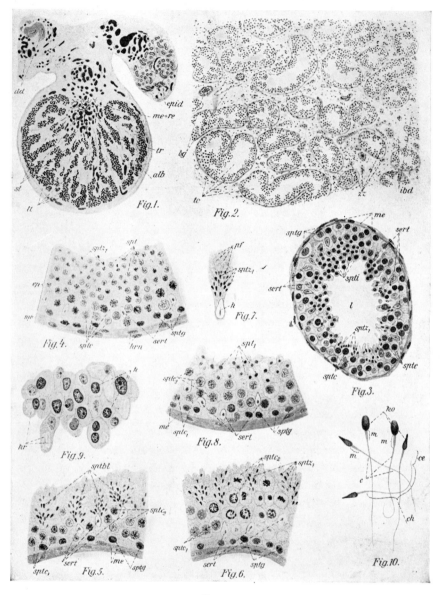

FIG. 5.

Fig. 5.—HISTOLOGY OF THE TESTES.

(After Sobotta.)

Fig. 1.—Transverse section of testis, epididymis and vas deferens of a boy. Enlargement 10 x.

Fig. 2.—Transverse section of lobule of the testis of a man dead at the age of 22 years. Observe the position and the enlargement of the tubuli seminiferi contorti and the position of the interstitial tissue of the testes. Enlarged 60 x.

Fig. 3.—Transverse section of tubulus seminiferus contortus. Man dead at the age of 22 years. Observe concentric arrangement of connective tissue sheath of tubule and arrangement of seminal epithelium. In the upper portion of the picture the spermatids are relatively enlarged; in the lower section, however, the transformation into spermatozoa may be observed. Enlarged 260 x.

Figs. 4-8.—Sections of wall of tubulus contortus of mature man (material of Prof. Benda, Berlin). Observe in section all phases of spermatogenesis. Externally the concentric layers of connective tissue may be seen; followed toward the lumen by the various cell phases. The oldest ones, the *spermatogonia* are located externally toward the periphery followed centralwards by the *spermatocytes* of first and second type, then by the *spermatids*, which transform themselves into *spermatozoa*. Observe also toward the periphery the transparent cells with the pear-shaped nuclei. These are the supporting cells or the cells of Sertoli. Fig. 4 shows all three cell types at rest (one generation has just been discharged into the lumen of the tubule, remnants in the superficial epithelial layers). Fig. 8 shows the beginning transformation of the *spermatids* into *spermatozoa*. Fig. 5 shows the formation of spermatoblasts resulting through 'copulation' of a number of maturing spermatozoa with a Sertoli cell. Fig. 6 shows mitoses in the spermatocytes, that serve to form the spermatids. Fig. 7 shows a spermatoblast 420 x enlarged.

Fig. 9.—Cross section of a group of interstitial cells of the testis. Crystalloids are seen in some of the epithelioids. Magnified 550 x. Fig. 10.—Human spermatozoa magnified 900 x.

Explanation of Abbreviations:—*Alb.* albuginea testis; *bg,* blood vessels; *ce,* end portion of tail filament; *ch,* main portion of tail filament; *ep,* epithelial layer; *epid,* epididymis; *dd,* vas deferens; *ibd,* interstitial tissue; *k,* nuclei; *ko,* heads of spermatozoa; *kr,* crystalloids; *km,* nuclei of cells of tubular membrane; *l,* lumen; *ll,* tubule of testicle; *m,* median or connecting portion; *me,* membrane of tubule; *me re,* mediastinum and rete-testes; *pf,* protoplasmic prolongation of spermatoblasts; *sert,* Sertoli cells and nuclei; *spt,* spermatids; *spt I,* spermatids in transformation into spermatozoa; *sptbl,* spermatoblasts; *sptc,* spermatocytes; *sptc I,* spermatocytes, type I; *sptc II,* spermatocytes, type II; *sptg,* spermatogonia; *st,* septula testis; *sptz I,* mature spermatozoa; *tc,* tubuli contorti; *tr,* tubuli recti; *zz,* interstitial cells.

FIG. 6.—Histologic Structures of Epididymis, Vas Deferens and Spermatic Cord.

(After Sobotta.)

Fig. 1.—Section of head of human epididymis (man dead at 22 years). Observe a number of *ducti efferentes testis* in cross section magnified 80 x.

Fig. 2.—Section of body of epididymis of man (aged 22 years). On the much convoluted *ductus epididymidis* is seen cut a number of times in various directions. Observe large peculiar epithelium with its stereociliæ, magnified 80 x.

Fig. 3.—Cross section of *ductulus efferentis testis* (man aged 22 years). Observe the cryptic depressions in the epithelium. No ciliæ in the remote recesses of the crypts. Magnified 175 x.

Fig. 4.—Cross section of lower section (toward the bladder) of the *ductus deferens* (man aged 28 years) showing outlines of wall arrangement of the seminal duct. In the lumen we find spermatozoa, magnified 25 x.

Fig. 5.—Portion of mucous membrane of section depicted in Fig. 4, magnified 140 diameters. Two layers of ciliated epithelium can be noted very distinctly.

Fig. 6.—*Cross Section of Human Spermatic Cord.* Man aged 22 years, showing the cord and its vessels held together by envelope of adipose and connective tissue. Magnified 10 x. The coverings of the cord are not shown.

Explanation of Abbreviations:—Abm, outer longitudinal muscle fibers; *art c,* arteries; *bd,* connective tissue; *bd l,* loose connective tissue between passages; *bdh, rm* or *m,* connective tissue sheath with circular muscle; *bg,* blood vessels; *cry,* crypts; *dd, ductus deferens; dep, ductus epididymis; cp,* epithelium; *cpi,* ciliated epithelium of the efferent ducts; *fe,* adipose tissue; *ilm,* inner longitudinal muscle fibers; *l,* lumen; *lm,* longitudinal muscles; *n,* nerves; *rm,* circular muscle fibers; *se,* secretion; *ta, tunica adventitia; tp, tunica propria; ve,* veins.

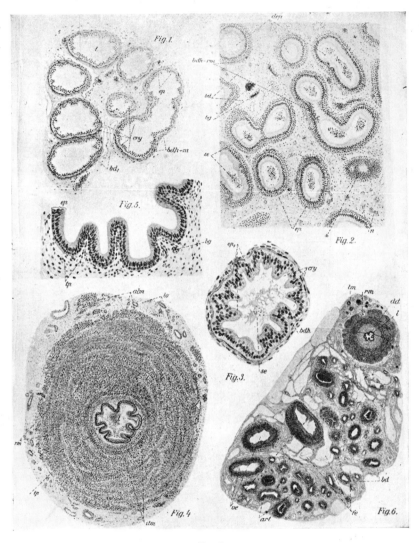

Fig. 6.

The tunica vaginalis continues with the transversalis fascia at the inguinal ring. The *tunica vaginalis propria,* which forms the serous invest-ment of the testis is, as stated, of peritoneal origin. This has the form of a double sac, the outer or parietal layer of which is closely adherent to the *tunica vaginalis communis,* containing numerous nonstriped muscle fibres forming the internal cremaster muscle. The inner or visceral layer closely invests the testis and a portion of the epididymis being reflected from the inferior and posterior parts of the latter to be continuous with the parietal layer. The lips of the *sinus epididymis* form the *ligamenta epididymis.*

The *blood supply* of the deeper structures of the scrotum comes especially from the spermatic branch of the inferior epigastric artery.

Nerves.—The external spermatic branch of the genito-femoral gives sensory nerve branches to the anterior and lateral surfaces, and also supplies the external cremaster muscle; the posterior surface is supplied by the perineal branch of the pudendal nerve, and the inferior surface by the perineal branches of the posterior femoral cutaneous, and the renal, aortic, and hypogastric plexuses of the sympathetic. However, the exact manner of the terminal innervation of the testis is not as yet definitely known.

The *principal artery* supplying the testis is the spermatic, a branch of the aorta from which branches are sent to the epididymis. The *deferential artery,* a branch of the super-vesical, also sends branches to the epididymis, and enters into extensive anastomoses with the testicular branches of the internal spermatic; anastomoses also occur with the vessels supplying the scrotum. The venous return is through the *pampiniform plexus,* a series of veins which pass out and up from the posterior portion of the testis and later unite to form the spermatic vein, which on the right side empties into the inferior vena cava and on the left side into the renal vein.

The *lymphatics* arise from a plexus in the tunica vasculosa and termi-nate in the lumbar lymph nodes.

The *ductus deferens* is the continuation of the epididymis and extends from the tail of the epididymis to the prostatic part of the urethra. In its first portion, it is slender and tortuous, but when it reaches the level of the head of the epididymis, it becomes straighter and thicker. Thence it continues upward as one of the constituents of the spermatic cord to the inguinal ring, and on entering this, traverses the inguinal canal as part of the cord. At the abdominal ring, it separates and passes downward and backward over the lateral surface of the bladder, until it reaches the *prostate gland,* which it traverses as the *ductus ejaculatorius* to open into the prostatic portion of the urethra. Just before reaching the prostatic gland, each ductus deferens widens out into a spindle-shaped enlargement called the *ampulla.* Just beyond this, it is joined by a lobulated structure, the *vesiculus seminalis,* which measures about 4.5 cms. x 2 cms. These vesicles are situated between the fundus of the bladder and the rectum, and form reservoirs for the storage of semen. They secrete a special fluid which is added to the product of the testicle. Each vesicle consists of a tube coiled upon itself, and which is about the diameter of a goose quill, and varies in length from 10 to 15 cms. Both the ductus deferens and the vesiculæ seminales consist of three coats; an external areolar coat, a middle or muscular coat and an inner or mucous coat.

Structures Connected with the Testis

Penis.—Composed of three cylindrical masses bound together by fibrous tissue and covered with skin. Two of the masses are lateral and are known as the *corpora cavernosa penis;* the third is median and is called *corpus cavernosum urethræ.* This latter, which is also termed the *corpus spongiosum* contains the urethra. Posteriorly, this is expanded to form the urethral bulb. Anteriorly, it is also greatly expanded in the form of a flattened cone and forms the *glans penis,* which is molded on the rounded ends of the corpora cavernosa penis. At the summit of the glans is a slit, the external urethral orifice. The urethra widens in the glans to form the navicular fossa.

The penis is also often described as consisting of three regions, *i.e.,* the root, the body, and the extremity. The root comprises the urethral bulb and the crura, one on each side. The body of the penis extends from the root to the anterior end of the corpora cavernosa. The extremity consists of the glans penis. The skin covering the penis at the root is continuous with that of the pubis and scrotum. At the junction of the corpora cavernosa and glans, the skin is folded upon itself to form the prepuce or foreskin. The integument covering the glans is continuous with the urethral mucous membrane at the orifice.

Prostate Gland.—The prostate is situated in the pelvic cavity above and behind the lower part of the symphysis pubis, and surrounds the commencement of the urethra. It is roughly about the size of an average horse chestnut, and anatomically consists of a base and apex, a posterior, an anterior, and two lateral lobes. The prostate measures about 4 cm. at its base, 2 cm. in diameter and 3 cm. in vertical height. It weighs about 8 gm. It is perforated by the urethra and ejaculatory ducts. The sub-stance of the prostate consists of glandular and muscular tissue. The

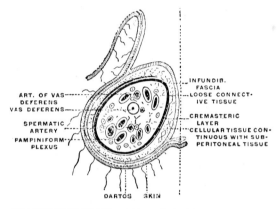

Fig. 7.—TRANSVERSE SECTION OF THE RIGHT SPERMATIC CORD.
(After Woolsey.)

glandular tissue contains a number of small excretory ducts through which the secretion of the gland passes.

Bulbo-Urethral Glands or Cowper's Glands.—These are two small lobulated bodies, about the size of peas, placed behind and laterally to the membranous portion of the urethra and closed about the urethral bulb. Each has a small excretory duct opening on the floor of the cavernous portion of the urethra.

The Spermatic Cords.—These are two in number, each about the size of a little finger, by which the testes and epididymides are suspended in the scrotum. The left cord is somewhat longer than the right, so that the left testis hangs the lower. Each cord is composed of: the vas deferens, the spermatic artery, the artery of the vas deferens, the pampiniform plexus of veins, the lymphatics, and the spermatic plexus of nerves. (Fig. 7.)

The Vas Deferens.—The vas deferens, the terminal excretory duct of the testis, is continuous with the ductus epididymis at the lower portion of the globus minor. It is about two feet long and 2 mm. in diameter, and consists, from without inward, of the following layers: a fibro-elastic adventitia; a longitudinal layer of smooth muscle; a circular layer of smooth muscle; a submucosa containing smooth muscle; a tunica propria of connective tissue and a mucosa of two layers of columnar epithelium. It will be seen that the walls are relatively very thick and the lumen of the duct very small. (Cf. Fig. 6.)

The Spermatic Artery.—

The Artery of the Vas Deferens.—This is a branch of the superior vesical.

The Pampiniform Plexus of Veins.—These unite to form the spermatic vein.

The lymphatics are the same as those of the testis.

The Nerves.—(See above.)

All these elements are bound together by areolar tissue into a single structure—the spermatic cord. Leaving the scrotum at the external inguinal ring, the cord passes through the inguinal canal to the internal inguinal ring, where its components diverge subperitoneally. The vas deferens hooks around the outer side of the deep epigastric vessels near their point of origin, crosses the internal iliac vessels, and dips down into the pelvis to the base of the bladder, crossing the obliterated hypogastric artery, passing between the ureter and the posterior bladder wall. Here it becomes first sacculated, then narrowed, and finally unites with the duct of the seminal vesicle on the corresponding side.

Descent of the Testes.—In early fetal life, the testes and epididymides, which are developed respectively from the embryonic genital folds and Wolffian bodies, lie below the kidneys in the retroperitoneal space. Attached to the lower pole of each testis is a fibrous cord, containing also some muscle tissue, which passes down through the inguinal canal to be inserted into the base of the scrotum. This cord, which is called the gubernaculum testis, receives accessory fibres from Scarpa's triangle, from the perineum, and from the root of the penis. Toward the end of fetal life, testis and epididymis begin to descend through the inguinal canal, whether merely guided by the gubernaculum or aided by its actual contraction is not definitely known. As they pass through the canal, the spermatic cord is for the first time formed behind them; and testis, epididymis, and cord in their progress become invested with a series of coverings

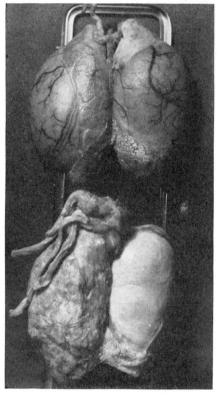 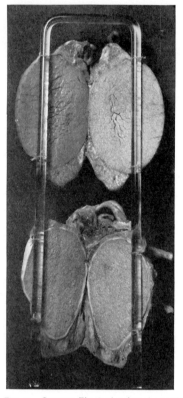

FIG. 8.—Gross anatomy of testis of macacus nemestrinus, upper, and of man aged 33 years, lower picture. In the latter the *tunica vaginalis* had been removed on the right half of the testis.

FIG. 9.—Same as Fig. 8, showing the testis split, disclosing internal gross appearance.

derived from the tissue layers through or past which they go. The process of descent is normally complete at or shortly after birth.

Scrotum.—The scrotum is the cutaneous sac containing the testes and parts of the spermatic cord. Its surface is divided into two equal parts by a ridge or raphe running from the anus to the under surface of the penis. It consists of the skin, the tunica dartos, and the intercrural cremasteric and infundibular fasciæ. The blood supply of the scrotum comes from the pudendal branch of the femoral artery, the superficial perineal branch of the internal pudendal artery, and the cremasteric branch of the internal epigastric artery. It will be observed that this blood supply is quite different from that supplying the testicle and its immediate connections.

Figs. 8 and 9 depict the gross anatomy of a testis of a monkey (Macacus nemestrinus) and that of a man 33 years of age.

CHAPTER II

HISTOLOGY OF THE TESTICLE *

THE wall of the seminiferous tubules (*tubuli contorti*) consists of three layers: (a) an outer layer of several rows of flattened connective tissue cells; (b) a thin basement layer, and (c) a lining epithelium.

The epithelial lining of the tubules consists of two kinds of cells, the so-called supporting or sustentacular cells, and the glandular cells proper, or spermatogenic cells. (See Fig. 5.)

The *sustentacular cells*, which are also known as *Sertoli cells*, are epithelial structures irregularly columnar in form, with their bases resting on the basement membrane. The nuclei of these cells, ovoid in form, are clear, being poor in chromatin, and their protoplasm contains fat droplets. Some have suggested that these Sertoli cells are derived from the spermatogenic cells, but that instead of ultimately developing by evolution into spermatozoa, they undergo retrograde changes, their protoplasm mingling with the intercellular substance; their nuclei becoming lost and the cells finally disappearing.

In the spermatogenic cells proper, several distinct layers can be differentiated: (1) *spermatogones,* small cuboidal cells which lie against the basement membrane. Their nuclei are rich in chromatin. These spermatogones multiply by mitotic division to form the second layer of seminal cells, the (2) *spermatocytes.* (Fig 10.)

The spermatocytes are large spherical cells which form two to four layers to the inner side of the spermatogones. They have abundant cytoplasm and large nuclei. Again by mitotic subdivision, the spermatocytes give rise to the (3) *spermatids.* Ferguson [1] states that there is a process of union between spermatids and the Sertoli cells to form spermatoblasts. These *spermatoblasts* consist of the nucleus of the Sertoli cell, a protoplasmic pedicle, and a protoplasmic mass consisting of the fused cell bodies of the spermatids. The spermatids thus transformed are the direct progenitors of the spermatozoa, which are the specific and final secretion of the seminiferous tubules.

On uniting with the Sertoli cells, the spermatids change their form;

---

* See also Chapter on the Function of the Testicular Secretions.

14

the nucleus becomes elongated and assumes the figure of the head of the spermatozoon, and a part of the protoplasm, in continuation with the head, is drawn out in a filament which forms the body and tail of the spermatozoon. The rest of the protoplasm undergoes dissolution, and the complete spermatozoon is set free. Thus the contents of the seminiferous tubules not only contain the figured elements or spermatozoa, but also the fluidified protoplasm of the cells having elaborated these figured elements.

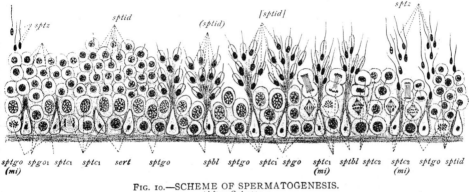

FIG. 10.—SCHEME OF SPERMATOGENESIS.
(After Sobotta.)

The left and right ends of illustration depict the process alike. To follow stages of spermatogenesis commence at left and follow to right. *Mi*, cells in mitosis; *sert*, supporting cells of Sertoli; *sptbl*, spermatoblast; *sptc₁*, spermatocytes first type; *sptc₂*, spermatocytes second type; *sptgo*, spermatogonia; *sptid*, spermatids; *(sptid)*, spermatids in first stage of development into spermatozoa; *[sptid]*, spermatids in second stage of development into spermatozoa; *sptz*, spermatozoa.

Human *spermatozoa* are long, slender, flagellate bodies, of from 50 mm. to 70 mm. in length, and suspended in the semen. Their general aspect is that of a tadpole. The accompanying schematic drawing given by Bailey [2] shows the general structure. Each spermatozoon consists of a head, body, and tail. By undulatory movement of the long tail, the spermatozoon is capable of swimming freely in a suitable medium. In man, it is estimated that there are about 60,000 spermatozoa per cubic millimeter of semen. (Fig. 11.)

The head consists mainly of chromatin, which is enclosed in a thin cytoplasmic membrane (*galea capitis*). The body, united to the head by the neck, is about the same length as the head, and consists of an axial core surrounded by a protoplasmic capsule. The tail, which is by far the longest part, being 40 m. to 60 m. in length, has an axial thread continuous with that of the body, and is also enclosed in a capsule continuous with the body.

The head and body of the spermatozoa, which alone contain chromatin and centrosomes, are the parts essential to fertilization of the female
ovum; the tail is necessary for motility of
the spermatozoon. Considering their
minuteness, the speed of the spermatozoa is
very great, and is sufficient to overcome the
adverse resistance of the cilia in the female
tube. In a suitable medium, the spermatozoa are capable of sustaining vitality for
a considerable time; they have been found
alive in the uterus and tube three and a half
weeks after coitus.

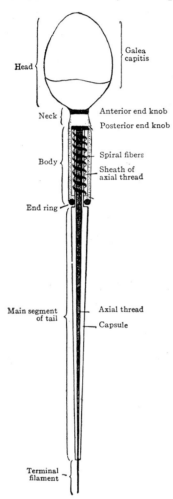

The spermatozoa are motionless until
the secretion of the testis is diluted with
the secretion of the prostate, when they
become very active.

The semen, which forms the vehicle by
which the spermatozoa are ejected from
the seminiferous tubules of the testicle, is
a viscous milky fluid, whitish-yellow in
color, heavier than water, alkaline in reaction, containing protein, etc., and possessing a peculiar odor. Chemically, it
contains 9.7 per cent. solids, 0.9 per cent.
inorganic, and 8.8 per cent. organic substance and 2.3 per cent. proteins. The
inorganic constituents consist principally
of calcium, phosphorus, sodium and potassium. Semen, when ejected from the glans
penis, differs from that in the vas deferens,
by possessing a characteristic odor which
is conferred on it by admixture with

FIG. 11.—Diagram of human spermatozoon. (Bailey after Meves and
Bonnet.)

the secretion of the prostate gland especially. This odor is said to be due
to decomposition of a phosphorous compound of the prostate known as
" Böttcher's " spermine crystals. Thus the semen, when ejected, contains

not only the spermatozoa, and the products of the seminiferous tubuli, but also the secretions of the accessory genital glands, and many coarse protoplasmic granules. Whatever differences of opinion may exist concerning the functions and value of other products of the seminiferous elements, it is universally admitted that the spermatozoa alone are concerned in the fertilization of the ovum.

Returning to consideration of the seminiferous tubules, histological investigation shows that separating and supporting these tubules, there is a limited amount of interstitial connective tissue, which carries the blood vessels and nerves. In the midst of this connective tissue are found groups of large spherical cells with large nuclei, the so-called *interstitial cells,* which some consider are remnants of the Wolffian body. Much controversy has arisen concerning the evolution and function of these cells. They were first described by Leydig in 1850 and are frequently referred to as the *Leydig cells.* Leydig [3] regarded the interstitial cells as a type of connective tissue cell which supplied nutriment to the spermatogenic cells, and down to the year 1900 authors generally agreed with this view. The interstitial cells are known to be present in the primitive genital tract of almost all mammalians. In man they are abundant at birth and rather diminished as age progresses. Loisel [4] considered that the *interstitial cells* were of two types: one arising from connective tissue cells and producing pigment, the other type being a true sexual cell formed from the same primordial source as that producing the seminiferous tubules and producing a proper secretion. Fat is found in both the interstitial cells, and as stated, in certain of the seminiferous cells of most mammalians. This fat is mostly a phosphated lipoid material. Besides fat, mammalian interstitial cells contain various granules, pigments and crystalloids, which some consider to be an internal secretion of the cells.

The interstitial cells are imbedded in a meshwork of fibrous reticulum, which is abundant and tightly woven in some animals, scanty and loose in others. Nussbaum [5] described these cells as arranged in isolated nests and strands, each such collection being surrounded by a membrane similar to the walls of the seminal tube.

Mott's [6] study of the testes in one hundred subjects, at ages varying from birth to eighty-six years, shows that at birth there is a large amount of interstitial tissue between the seminiferous tubules; the interstitial cells

2

of Leydig are numerous and contain a substance like lutein and lipoid granules. Up to the time of puberty the interstitial cells are diminishing and at puberty the seminiferous tubules are closely approximated. Active spermatogenesis is then seen in all stages; the interstitial cells contain much lipoid. The immature spermatids dive into the Sertoli cells and there acquire their tails, which consist almost entirely of lipoid, lecithin and cholesterin. Patients dying of chronic diseases before puberty show an arrest of granule formation in the interstitial cells.

Evidence is given that the lipoid granules seen in the interstitial tissue and in the cells lining the basement membrane of the tubules constitute the raw material from which the nucleic acid necessary for active nuclear proliferation and spermatogenesis is formed.

According to Cowdry [7] the interstitial cells in adult human testes vary in number in different individuals. They occur singly or in groups, which may or may not be related to blood vessels.

The interstitial cells may be distinguished from connective tissue cells by their general appearance as well as by the fact that they do not stain with vital dyes like trypan blue. The nuclei are poor in chromatin and rarely contain distinct nucleoli.

The centrosomes of interstitial cells may be either spherical or rodlike. Two centrosomes may occur in a cell with a single nucleus, and in binucleated cells four centrosomes may be found. Fat and pigment granules are frequent in interstitial cells. The presence of varying crystalloids is usual, those known as *Reinecke's* being the most frequent in human interstitial cells.

The interstitial cells of the testis have a very generous blood supply. Small branches of the spermatic artery enter from the tunica albuginea and interlobular spaces, which are largely occupied by the interstitial cells. While these vessels are usually well separated from the cells by the accompanying connective tissue, and have no particular relation to the cells, they give off a copious network of capillaries which come into very intimate relation with the interstitial cells.

Assertions to the effect that the Leydig cells are controlled by centres situated in the subthalamic region or elsewhere are not at all convincing in view of the fact that other investigators in this field as well as the author have been successful in transplanting testicular tissue and finding it to live. It seems, therefore, that for the discharge of their duties the interstitial cells are not necessarily dependent upon the nervous system.

Ishibashi [8] has shown that the interstitial cells in men are of variable structure according to age. They are conspicuously numerous in children and at certain stages closely resemble fibroblasts.

Whether the Leydig cells divide by mitosis or amitosis has not definitely been established as yet. Nucleoli are only rarely encountered within the nucleus.

Winiwarter [9] has studied the Leydig cells very carefully and the *mitochondria* observed by other investigators in the cell bodies of Leydig cells have been closely scrutinized by this observer. They appear in granular and round form, sometimes evenly distributed through the cell body and at other times gathered in clusters. Mitochondria may be stained in fresh, living cells in dilute solution of Janus green. This same observer claims to have followed the transition between mitochondria and crystalloids.

Winiwarter has fully described *centrosomes* within human Leydig cells. (Cf. illustration.) In cells with a single nucleus two· centrosomes may occur and in cells with two nuclei often four of these bodies are observed.

J. Duesberg [10] has made a control study of the interstitial cells of the testicle in didelphys (opossum), paying particular attention to the reticular apparatus of Gogli of these interstitial cells by using Cajal's uranium nitrate method. Study of the accompanying plates, prepared by Duesberg will illustrate these premises to a full extent. (Figs. 12 and 13.)

The researches of Iscovesco [11] as well as those of Mulon [12] are strongly suggestive of an internal secretion elaborated by the interstitial cells, and while the studies of Duesberg and the last named observers are very convincing the substances elaborated have not as yet been isolated from the tissues. There is no doubt in the mind of the author that continued research will soon establish definitely the identity of the internal secretion and its chemical composition.

The interstitial cells occur especially in the irregular connective tissue intervals between the seminiferous tubules; they also occur among the *tubuli recti* and immediately beneath the tunica albuginea. They are supported by a fine mesh of fibrous reticulum. (Figs. 14–21.)

The interstitial cells will be further considered in the chapter on the functions of the testicular secretions. (Page 35.)

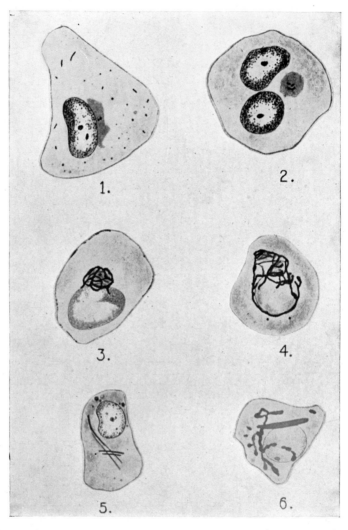

FIG. 12.—Structure of the interstitial cell of the testicle of the didelphys.   (J. Duesberg.)

Explanation of Plate I.—All figures were outlined with a Zeiss camera-lucida, at the level of the stage of the microscope. Lenses used: for Figs. 1–12, Zeiss apochr. immers. 2 mm. (ap. I, 40), in combination with ocular 12; for Fig. 13, Zeiss apochr. imm. 1 mm. 5 (ap. I, 30), and ocular 6. Artificial light (gas).

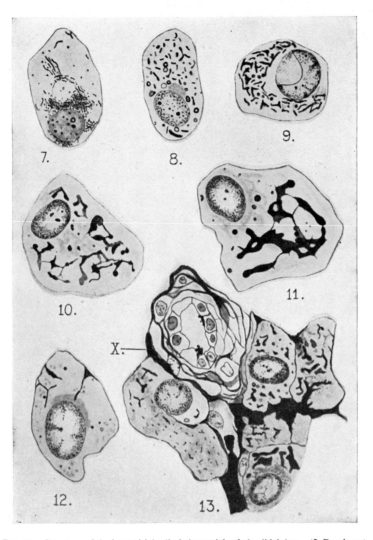

FIG. 13.—Structure of the interstitial cell of the testicle of the didelphys. (J. Duesberg.)

Explanation of Plate II.—7, binucleated cell with normal chondriosomes, fixation and stain after Benda; 8, cell with modified chondriosomes. Same fixation and stain; 9, 10 and 11, different types of networks formed of modified chondriosomes. Same fixation and stain; 12, an interstitial cell with several exogenous processes. Same fixation and stain; 13. a group of interstitial cells, with intracellular and intercellular accumulation of secretion-product. The capillary, filled with the same product, extends, as the next section shows, up to the point marked X. Same fixation and stain.

The spermatogenetic tissue of the gland ends at the termination of the seminiferous tubules (*tubuli contorti*) where the products enter the tubuli recti and proceed toward the epididymis and vas deferens. These are only excretory ducts. The *tubuli recti* and the rete testis are lined with a single layer only of cuboidal cells (flattened epithelial cells). The *tubuli recti* are much smaller than the *tubuli contorti;* these latter have a diameter of from 150 to 250 m., while the diameter of the *tubuli recti* is only from 20 to 40 m.

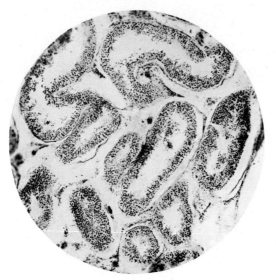

FIG. 14.—Normal human testicle. (Man aged 33 years.)
7.5x16 Leitz. Magnified 95x. Stained with hematoxylin and eosin. (Author's observation.)

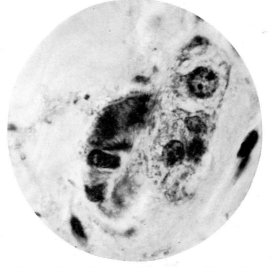

FIG. 15.—Normal human testicle. (Man aged 33 years.)
Typical Leydig cell, magnified 2400x. Stained with hematoxylin and eosin. Observe cell body and its histologic composition as well as the nucleus, granules, vacuoles and nucleolus. (Author's observation.)

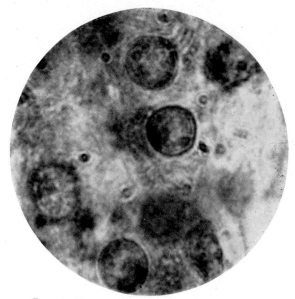

FIG. 16.—Normal human testicle. (Man aged 33 years.)
Leydig cells, magnified 3080x. 15x2. Oil immersion. Leitz apochromatic. Stained with
hematoxylin and eosin. (Author's observation.)

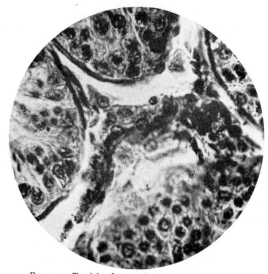

FIG. 17.—Testicle of normal macacus nemestrinus.
Oc. 7-½, obj. 2. Leitz apochromatic. Stained with hematoxylin and eosin. Observe islands of
interstitial cells. (Author's observation.)

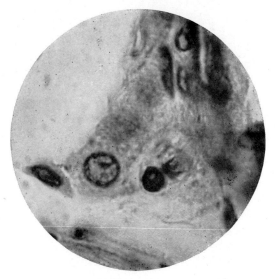

FIG. 18.—Testicle of normal macacus nemestrinus.

Leydig cells, magnified 2350x. Oc. 15, obj. 2. Leitz apochromatic. Stained with hematoxylin and eosin. Observe nuclear wall, nuclear granules; vacuoles and granules in cytoplasm; outline of cell wall. (Author's observation.)

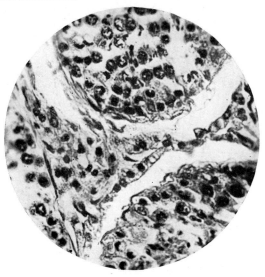

FIG. 19.—Testicle of normal dog.

Magnified 386x. Oc. 7-½, obj. 4. Leitz apochromatic. Stained with hematoxylin and eosin. Observe islands of interstitial cells between seminiferous tubules in full spermatogenesis. (Author's observation.)

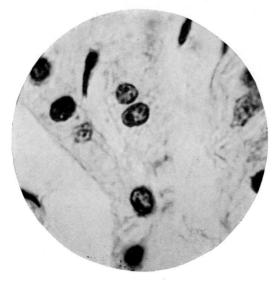

FIG. 20.—Testicle of normal dog.

Magnified 2250x. Oc. 15, obj. 2. Stained with hematoxylin and eosin. Note Leydig cells, disposition of nuclei, chromatin granules and vacuoles. (Author's observation.)

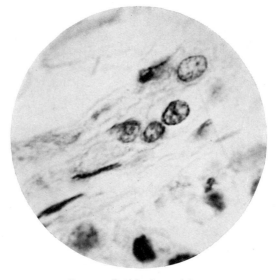

FIG. 21.—Testicle of normal dog.

Magnified 2250x. Oc. 15, obj. 2. Leitz apochromatic. Stained with hematoxylin and eosin. Note granular cell bodies, nucleus, nucleolus and nuclear chromatin net work. (Author's observation.)

BIBLIOGRAPHY

[1] FERGUSON: Normal Histology. New York, 1905, p. 376.

[2] BAILEY: Text Book of Histology. New York, 1916 (p. 339 et seq.).

[3] LEYDIG, FRANZ: On the Anatomy of the Mammalian Generative Organs. 1850.

[4] LOISEL: C. R. Soc. de biol. Paris, 1901, iv, 952, etc.

[5] NUSSBAUM: Zur Differenzierung des Geschlechts im Thierreich V, Von der Bedeutung der Hodenzwischensubstanz. Arch. f. mikr. Anat., 1880, xviii, 1–121, 4 pl.

[6] MOTT: Brit. Med. Jour., 1919, Lond. Normal and Morbid Conditions of the Testis, ii, 655–659; 698–700; 737–742.

[7] COWDRY: Endocrinology and Metabolism, 1922, ii, p. 424.

[8] ISHIBASHI, M.: Über die Zwischenzellen mit besonderer Berücksichtigung ihrer pathologischen Verhältnisse. Mitt. a. d. med. Fak. d. k. Univ., Tokyo, 1919, xxii, 39–120.

[9] VON WINIWARTER: (a) Das Interstitielle Gewebe der Menschlichen ovarien. Anat. Anz. Jena, 1908–09, xxxiii, 1–9. (b) Observations cytologiques sur les cellules interstitilles du testicule humaine. Anat. Anz. Jena, 1912, xli, 309–320.

[10] DUESBERG, J.: On the Interstitial Cells of the Testicle in Didelphys. Biol. Bull. of Woods Hole, Bost., 1918, xxxv, 175–197.

[11] ISCOVESCO, H.: Action physiologique d'un lipoide (11Bb) extrait du testicule. Compt. rend. soc. de biol., Paris, 1913, lxxv, 445–447.

[12] MULON: Sur une sécrétion lipoide nouvelle de la glande interstitielle ovarienne C. R. Soc. de Biol. Par., 1910, lxii, 423–24.

CHAPTER III

THE PHYSIOLOGY AND FUNCTIONS OF THE TESTICULAR SECRETIONS

The Rôle of the Leydig, Seminiferous and Sertoli Cells

FROM the time of Hippocrates and Aristotle, it has been believed that there was a co-relation between the testicular fluids and the nervous system, brain and cord. Modern researches have done little toward a positive proof that such direct influence does or does not exist; the findings, such as they are, rather point toward a negative view, although recent experimental work by Ceni [1] has demonstrated that in fowls, at least, lesions of the cortical centres of the brain produced sterility, quite independently of the sexual instinct and power to fulfill the sexual act which were preserved. That psychic factors intervene is well understood, but the mechanism of such action through the nervous system is by no means clear.

The anatomists and physiologists of the sixteenth and seventeenth centuries understood that there was a connection between the functional organs of generation and other parts of the economy. Ambroise Paré states that eunuchs and the castrated degenerated into a feminine condition. Such facts were of course evident from observation. Riolan also recognized a sympathy between the testicles and nervous system, arising principally from the distribution of the costal nerves. In this period the belief was general that the strength and courage of men were derived from the testicles, a view arising from humoral medicine, which saw humors and vapors arising from these organs and influencing the blood and nerve force. It was a correct, though a clouded view of the existence of internal secretions which modified temperament and character; eunuchs and the castrated failed to show the fierceness and virility which distinguished the man with testicles in full functional vigor. And it was not even considered necessary that the testicles should be in the scrotum in order that a man should have virility and the power to engender his kind.

Among earlier medicinal writers also, there was a certain amount of metaphysical speculation necessarily connected with the testicles and the part their product played in the rôle of generation. Swedenborg in his posthumous work, *The Generative Organs* (translated Dr. J. J. Garth Wilkinson, 1852) may be taken as giving the popular general current views up to a century ago regarding the testicles and their functions.

Swedenborg says that it was commonly supposed that the testes were the only organs that prepared the semen, but that this view arose from not knowing what the semen was. The semen was not a humor of simple composition, but a humor compounded in regular order and succession. Many organs were constructed for preparing this humor, the testicles, epididymis, vesiculæ seminales, prostate gland and urethra, every one of which contributed its share. Although the semen was elaborated in the testicles, yet the material which forms it was taken out of the spermatic vessels.

It was only toward the end of the seventeenth century that the testicle, which previously had been considered an amorphous mass, was observed to be composed of tubules folded on themselves, and that the seminal fluid was prepared in these tubules. While being prepared, it produced vapors which spread into the whole organism and produced the beard, change of voice and other characteristics of virility. After castration, such vapors were no longer produced and the organism became debilitated.

In the eighteenth century, the view was taken that the sexual characteristics and virility arose not from any vapors, but by virtue of the sperm itself. Bordeu, writing in 1775, remarked that the semen from the testicles renewed and restored life and temperament and furnished the necessary vigorous tone. Such a daily stimulus was lacking in eunuchs and the aged, in which the sources of the semen have degenerated, and who are sustained only by the recollection of their former vigor.

It was toward the end of the seventeenth century also that the discovery of mobile filaments, or spermatozoids, in the semen was made, and that such were deficient in the semen of testicles not occupying their normal situation. Also, without any exact knowledge of the interaction of the various secretions, the sympathy or co-relation of the different regions of the body as between the uterus and breasts for example, was well known. John Hunter [2] distinguished the secondary sexual characters as quite independent of the reproductive act, and that castration prevented their development. Such views were generally held up to the time that

Brown-Séquard [3] made his celebrated experimental auto-injections of testicular extracts.

The view held, therefore, up to the dawn of scientific research, was that the testicular secretion, as we know it now, was a product elaborated from the blood, first in the testicle, and thence in the other generative organs, each of which added some vital quality. Apparently, whatever was characteristic in any individual, either sexual or personal attributes, was considered to be a particular element in that individual's blood. As Swedenborg says: " The inmost essence of the seed which is the inmost of the man or of whatever animal the seed belongs to, is not prepared in the testicles, but is drawn out in abundance from the blood and from the juice of the nervous fibers," and again, " the semen is the complex of all the possible essences in the body; that is to say, it not only consists of vastly numerous elements and principles from the elemental world, but moreover, its inmost essence is the animal spirit, and the inmost of this is the soul itself which is the first and the proper substance of the body."

Such metaphysical explanations could scarcely, however, be expected to satisfy the modern awakened spirit of scientific inquiry, which sought its results in deductions from experimental investigations rather than from metaphysical reasoning and generalities.

In regard to the testicle and its functions, one of the earliest scientific investigations was that of Berthold [4] of Göttingen in 1849, who transplanted the testicles from four domestic cocks into their abdominal cavities. He found that the masculine sex characteristics were preserved in these birds, through, as he asserted, an effect on the blood which traversed the grafts, and thence on the whole organism. The view is precisely that which is held today, though Berthold had no idea of internal secretions. Berthold believed that his transplants became vascularized. Nussbaum [5] in 1849 repeated these experiments on frogs and found that fragments of transplanted testicles continued to elaborate spermatozoa for more than a year. Since then a multitude of investigators have carried out similar work with varying results. Some of these will be referred to in the Chapter on Experimental Researches on the Testicular Secretion.

The view that the testicle is an organ with a double glandular function is an old one. It was long known, or rather suspected, that in addition to its seminiferous output, the testicle secreted substances which specially affected the organism as a whole.   It could not fail to be observed that where the testicles did not develop, or were lost or destroyed in any manner, the individual was not only incapable of procreating, but that his organic structure was variously modified from that of an individual with normally functioning testicles.

But the point that has caused particular dispute is not the question of a separate testicular secretion, which influences sex characters, but rather what particular structure of the testicle was responsible for such secretion, and how it acted.

There are, in general, two broad views on the question of internal secretions of the testicle.   There are those who maintain that the spermatogenetic portions of the testicular structures are alone concerned, not only with spermatogenesis and the elaboration and ejection of ripe spermatozoa, but that these same structures also prepare and discharge substances into the blood and lymphatics which act as a hormone, and are responsible for distinct sex characters, as well as sexual desire and potency.   On the other hand, there are those who say that the spermatogenous portions of the testicles are concerned only with spermatogenesis, and who attribute to the so-called interstitial cells, Leydig cells or " puberty gland," a distinct glandular function.   They consider that these cells form a gland which secretes the hormone which is responsible for sex characters and sex functioning.

As these views are antagonistic, it will be necessary to spend some little time in presenting some of the arguments advanced by both sides in favor of the view held.

No definite opinion should be formed from studying one of the lower animals and deductions drawn therefrom in applying conclusions to the human being, for it has been proven conclusively that the relationship between the testis and the male secondary sexual characters differs to quite an extent in insects, crustaceans, trytons, birds and mammals.   For instance, in birds the relationship between the gonads and plumage is apparently the reverse of the relationship in the crab.

Goodale has shown that different parts of the soma react differently to the influence of the gonads in certain birds.   Some characters, such as size in females, voice, mandible color in ducks, and certain phases of behavior, are independent of either ovary or testis, while others depend entirely or to some extent upon the proper functioning of the gonads. For instance, the comb and wattles, fat disposition, size in males, and summer plumage in some instances in ducks are influenced by the ovary. This conclusively proves that the secondary sexual characters in birds are not equally affected by the primary sex organs.

It has been observed in a great many animals that have a rutting season that there is an appreciable increase in the size of the testes at this time.

LeCallion and others believe that the seasonal increase in the size of the testes is due to increased proliferation of the interstitial cells. In the hibernating marmot spermatogenesis ceases and the interstitial cells almost completely disappear, according to von Hansemann,[6] but with the assumption of spermatogenesis in the spring the interstitial cells reappear in great numbers.

The relation of the spermatic nerves to the interstitial cells has been exhaustively studied by Kuntz,[7] who has shown that atrophy of the interstitial cells does not result from section of the nerve supply to the testis. It is only the seminal cells that then degenerate, while there is a distinct hypertrophy of the interstitial tissue. Kuntz believes that these degenerative changes are due, in all probability, to vascular changes resulting because of paralysis of the blood vessels. The author's experiments corroborate these findings, as will be shown in a later chapter.

That the sex hormone in animals has a great deal to do with metabolism in general has been conclusively proven by a great many investigators. That this hormone influences a great many tissues is undoubtedly true and in fact well established. The changes observed in man at puberty, with its increase of physical and psychical activity, can be directly traced to increased hormone activity. Again, should there be changes in the hormone activity of the interstitial tissues, regressive changes are at once noted, as shown in eunuchs, due to all causes, or to pathologic conditions stunting interstitial function to a greater or lesser degree, and it may be correctly argued that senile changes are largely dependent upon regressive metamorphosis in the interstitial cells.

Tandler and Grosz [8] have shown that the interstitial cells of the testes have a *marked influence upon bone growth*.

Sellheim [9] has shown that castration of cocks has a modifying influence upon the growth of the osseous structures. Changes take place in the skull, pelvis and bones of the extremities which consist of increased longitudinal growth with retarded ossification of the epiphyseal cartilage. Similar results have been observed in mammals.

The studies of Launois and Roy,[10] Tandler and Grosz, Gruber,[11] Lortet,[12] Pittard,[13] Pelikan,[14] Weil and others have conclusively proven that castration in mammals, including man, is followed by excessive longitudinal growth in the bones, with a lack of proportion between the length of the extremities and that of the trunk and persistence of the epiphyseal synarthrosis beyond the normal age. After castration enchondral ossification is stimulated and prolonged. This does not affect all the cartilages equally and therefore the disproportion of the resulting growth is unequal. The bones most markedly affected are those of the legs, forearms, arms, thigh, pelvic girdle, and, last, the vertebral column. There are marked alterations in the skull with the result that the cranial capacity develops less completely than normal.

Swale Vincent is of the opinion that the subnormal bone growth is not due to the fact that the testis is not acting as an organ of reproduction, but to the fact that the normal internal secretion of the organ is not available for the control of bony growth in the body. That gonadectomy is frequently followed by an increased deposit of fat is a well known fact, and this is also true when senility sets in. Capons are excessively fat.

It has already been shown in considering the histology of the testicle that in the midst of the connective tissue between the seminiferous tubes of nearly all mammalians, there are special cells which have been termed " interstitial cells."

Kölliker's claim in 1854 of having discovered the interstitial cell of the testicle has finally been definitely settled by various workers in the field by giving credit for its discovery to Leydig, who described the cells in 1850. It will be seen that priority of the cell of Leydig antedated Kölliker by four years. Confirmation of Leydig's work was then given by von Ebner in 1871, who believed with his predecessor that the interstitial cell is of connective tissue origin, until Hofmeister, in 1872, leaned to the view that the cell is of epithelial nature.

Plato,[15] Beissner[16] and Friedmann,[17] who were some of the earliest to investigate these interstitial cells, considered that they had a trophic function; that their function was to insure nourishment to the seminiferous

3

tubules, accumulating the nourishing materials brought by the blood, elaborating them in their cytoplasm, and then yielding the product to the Sertoli syncytium. This syncytium, which was intimately associated with

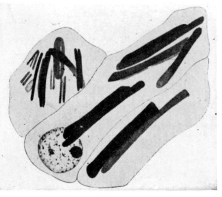

FIG. 22.—Groups of interstitial cells, showing large and small crystalloids. Human testicle, man aged 41 years. (After Winiwarter.)

the seminal cells proper, absorbed the materials and distributed them to the different constituents of the spermatogenetic complex, especially the spermatids, during their transformation into spermatozoa.

The interstitial cells, or the cells of Leydig (Figs. 22 and 23), were known to contain many substances, fat, pigment, etc., which gave them

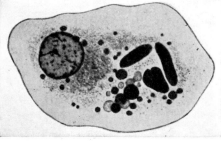

FIG. 23.—Interstitial cell from human testicle of man 25 years of age. Cell shows idiosomes, centrosomes, fat and crystalloids. (After Winiwarter.)

the character of glandular cells. In 1876, Reinecke [18] discovered in these cells certain crystalloids, which he observed passed into the lymphatics and capillaries, and which he considered testified to a separate secretion from the cells in question, which produced sexual excitation.

The majority of histological and biological investigators of these cells still, however, considered that their rôle was trophic in regard to the seminiferous tubes. Other investigators, however, saw more in these interstitial cells. They considered that they were instrumental in the elaborations of a special internal secretion. Such a hypothesis was advanced by Regaud and Policard [19] (1901) and Loisel [20] (1901–02). Mosselmann and Rubay [21] formally adopted this view, and extending the opinions of Reinecke, thought further that the internal secretion of the interstitial cells was concerned in the determination and maintenance of the secondary male sex characters.

By *primary sexual characters* is meant the progerminative factors which result in the anatomical and physiological differentiation of male and female. By the *secondary sexual characters* is meant special attributes, physical and psychical, inherent to the male or female; such as in the man, genital ardor, virility, the occurrence of hair on the face, changes of voice, and all other physical characters, distinct from genital organs proper, which make up the figure of human masculinity.

The controversy on the question of the origin of the special internal secretion of the testicles gave impetus to the special researches and findings of Ancel and Bouin.[22] These authors showed in 1904 *that in mammals the interstitial testicular tissue is a true gland of internal secretion, which alone exercised on the organism the function of determining male sexual characters, libido, and sexual potentiality, which had hitherto been ascribed as the function of the testicle as a whole.*

The histology of the interstitial cell, considered in a previous chapter, (Cf. Chapter II) needs more detail, which is given herewith.

Its microscopic appearance, while conforming to certain set characteristics, changes its aspect nevertheless from time to time. The capillaries of the testicle are surrounded by interstitial cells. In other words, groups of these cells are frequently found around the blood spaces. This arrangement is strikingly represented also in the suprarenal body, and we find the cortical cells surrounding the capillaries leading to the medulla. They bear frequently a close resemblance to the cells of the liver and the cells of the corpus luteum of the ovary. The eccentric location of its nucleus, which may be double, has already been alluded to. The nuclei are surrounded by a condensed *endoplasm* which merges, as the periphery is approached, into a thinner vacuolated *ectoplasm* (Fig. 24).

The granular structure of the protoplasm (Altmann's) granules can be brought out beautifully by special staining processes. That is, by fixing small pieces of testicle by Altmann's method or some of its modifications, the principal of which is to use oxydizing agents, such as

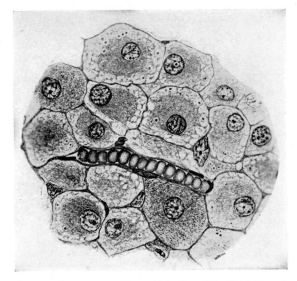

FIG. 24.—Arrangement of interstitial cells. (After F. M. Hanes.)

Zenker's fluid. Hematoxylin and eosin. This section is from a cryptorchid pig's testis, showing the interstitial cells surrounding a capillary. Some of the cells are homogeneous throughout, but most of them show a dense *endoplasm* and a vacuolated peripheral *ectoplasm* containing definite granules. 1x1000.

potassium dichromate or osmium tetroxid, followed by staining the bits of tissue thus prepared by the methods of Altmann, Benda and Weigert. The reproduction of photographs from Hanes (Fig. 25) beautifully show the protoplasmic arrangement of sections thus prepared. It brings into view this endoplasm around the nucleus composed of granules of various sizes and close grouping. The ectoplasm is clear and concise with fewer granules. These granules are thought by Hanes to be identical with certain granules described by Whitehead. Fixed in formol and sectioned after imbedding in paraffin and counterstained in methylene blue, these granules are beautifully shown up. Stained with the acid fuchsin of Altmann they become a distinctly clear red within the other cell granules.

These granules usually are surrounded by a narrow vacuolated space. They can also be brought out in black by treating them with Weigert's method of myelin staining or Heidenhain's iron-hematoxylin.

In 1896 Reinecke [18] discovered in the testicle of an executed criminal the crystals which are known by his name. These were situated in the interstitial cells and caused Reinecke to think that these crystalloid bodies represent the true internal secretion of the cells under consideration.

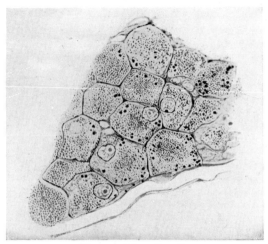

FIG. 25.—Altmann's stain.

The granules of the protoplasm are stained red, the fat droplets black. As in the preceding figure the *endoplasm* as well as the *ectoplasm* are sharply contrasted, due to their granular contents. (Hanes.)

Bouin and Ancel [22] considered the testicle as essentially composed of three parts: (1) the seminal gland; (2) the nutritive or Sertoli syncytium; (3) the *interstitial gland*. Histological study by these authors of cryptorchids showed that the seminal gland alone was lacking. Such animals possessed sexual *libido* and power, but failed to procreate. The other elements of the testicle were quite normal.

Closure of the excretory sperm ducts brought about precisely the same effects in animals as ectopic testicle (cryptorchidism). The animals still possessed sexual libido and power. Bouin and Ancel reason from this that the seminal cells have no influence on the maintenance of sexual characters, or of sexual instinct, and that cryptorchids, or ligatured animals, are similar to normal animals, except that their testicles do not enclose seminal cells. The integrity of the sexual characters and of the sexual instinct, is always associated with the integrity of the interstitial gland, and of the nutritive syncytium.

In order to prove that the nutritive syncytium of Sertoli had no action on the organism, Bouin and Ancel removed one testicle from animals and resected a length of the deferent canal of the opposite side. The animals were left in this condition for a period up to 10 months before removing

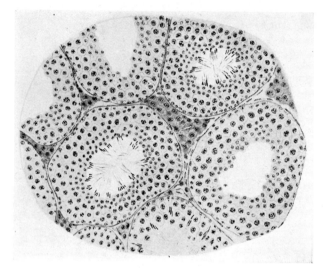

Fig. 26.—Section of a testicle of an adult rabbit.

Between the seminiferous tubules in which spermatogenesis is seen, one observes interstitial cells grouped in small masses in the connective tissue. Magnified 250x. (After Bouin and Ancel).

and examining the remaining testicle. Basing themselves on the known biological law of compensatory hypertrophy in the remaining organ of any organic pair when one is destroyed, there would be observed under the above conditions a compensatory hypertrophy of both the nutritive syncytium and of the interstitial gland if both were necessary for the production of the sexual characters and desire, both of which continued undiminished in these animals. Examination of the remaining testicle, however, showed complete disappearance of the seminal gland, very advanced degeneration of the Sertoli elements, and a compensatory hypertrophy of the interstitial gland. The number of these latter cells was increased by the transformation of intertubal connective tissue cells. The interstitial gland had about doubled in volume.

Studies of unilateral cryptorchids also showed Bouin and Ancel that ectopic testicles increased in size and weight at the expense of the interstitial gland alone. They concluded, therefore, that *neither the seminal gland nor the Sertoli nutritive elements of the testicle have any general action upon the organism since neither show any phenomena of compensatory hypertrophy, and that their presence or absence makes no difference on the showing of sexual characters in the organism. That the interstitial*

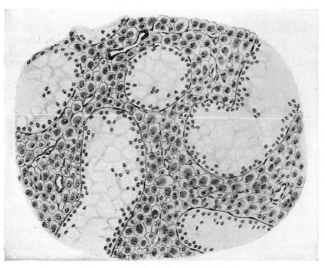

FIG. 27.—Section of testicle of rabbit.

Rabbit had been castrated on one side and whose *vas deferens* had been ligated on the other side. The animal remained under observation twelve months. One observes in the section an absence of seminal cells within the seminiferous tubules. The internal surface of the basement membrane is lined with nourishing syncytium alone. Between the seminal tubules the "interstitial gland" presents considerable development, much greater than in normal testicles or in testicles which have been subjected to bilateral stenosis of the deferent canals. Magnified 250x. (After Bouin and Ancel.)

gland alone presents the phenomena of compensatory hypertrophy, and that consequently to it alone, is due the rôle of maintaining sexual characters and sexual instinct in the male.

Bouin and Ancel give two histological illustrations in support of these views. Fig. 26 shows a section of the testicle of an adult rabbit. Between the seminal tubes in full spermatogenesis are seen the interstitial cells which form small masses situated in the intertubal spaces.

Fig. 27 is the section of a testicle from a rabbit which had been castrated on one side and had the deferent canal on the other side ligated. This animal remained under observation for twelve months. The seminal tubes are seen to be devoid of contents. The internal surface of their membrane proper is lined by nutritive syncytium alone. Between these seminal tubes, the interstitial gland is seen considerably developed, and the space occupied is much more voluminous than in the normal testicle or in testicles which had been submitted to bilateral castration.

From their extensive animal and human experiments, Bouin and Ancel formulated the following conclusions, which, until quite recently, have been more or less accepted unchallenged by the majority of physiologists:

(1) That ectopic testicles are characterized by seminiferous tubules which do not contain seminal cells, but only their syncytium; between these tubules, the interstitial element or gland is normally developed. But such cryptorchids preserve their sex instincts and characters. Castration abates the instinct and character.

(2) That experimental occlusion of the excretory ducts realized the same effects and demonstrated that integrity of the sex characters and of sex instinct is always associated with integrity of the interstitial gland and of the nourishing syncytium.

(3) Further, animal experimentation established that the nourishing syncytium has no more general effect on the organism than has the seminal cells; its presence or absence has no effect on the sex characters or instinct.

(4) That the interstitial gland alone in the testicle possesses a general action, since it alone presents the phenomena of compensatory hypertrophy, and that to this gland alone belongs the function of maintaining the integrity of sex characters and of sex instinct.

(5) That in the testicles of old men, the interstitial cells are less voluminous than in the adult; Reinecke's crystalloids completely disappear, and similarly to other products of cellular activity; the senile interstitial gland shows progress with diminution, then abolition of secretory activity and the elaboration of abnormal (pigmental) products.

These conclusions meant that the seminal cells and Sertoli cells and syncytium had no action on the general organism, and that the interstitial cells alone exercised such an action which was possible after experimental or pathological occlusion of the sperm outlets. But in addition to its general effect on the organism, the interstitial gland had a nutritive rôle toward the seminal elements of the testicle.

But the greatest strength was given to Bouin and Ancel's hypothesis by Steinach [24] who published the results of his animal researches in 1912. These experiments showed that the sexual elements degenerated while the interstitial elements increased; moreover, Steinach showed that sexual puberty was dependent upon the internal secretion furnished as he alleged by the Leydig interstitial cells alone which he hence termed the " puberty gland." Steinach's subsequent " rejuvenation " surgical work by ligature of the vas deferens, which will be described later, was based on his full

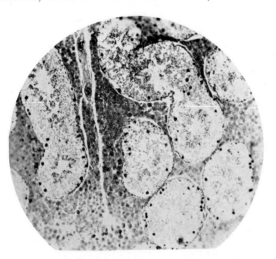

FIG. 28.—Normal testis of pig.

The actively functionating seminiferous tubules dominate the picture; the interstitial cells occupy the interstices of the contiguous tubules. (Hanes.)

belief that the interstitial cells alone furnished the particular internal secretion governing sex characters and virility.

Hanes' [23] studies upon the question of the function of the interstitial cells in relation to internal secretion were very thorough and comprehensive. He endeavored to answer the question, " Does the mammalian testicle in addition to the formation of sperm furnish an internal secretion essential to the normal development of the organism, and if so, which cells of the testicle have this function?" by a series of brilliant experiments which will be narrated directly and the conclusions drawn therefrom noted. " A study of the conditions of cryptorchidism will partially elucidate the problem," says Hanes. He has examined fifty-six cryptorchid testes from pigs, seven from sheep and six from men. In not a single instance has he found spermatozoa and only in very young cryptorchid pig testes could he demonstrate spermatogonia. These animals were all sterile and a most careful search of the literature could not furnish a single authentic case of a fertile cryptorchid. Most writers, of course, agree upon the infertility of the double cryptorchid animal. It must be kept in mind that a truly cryptorchid testicle lies completely within the internal abdominal ring, and a great deal of confusion has arisen, according to Hanes, through

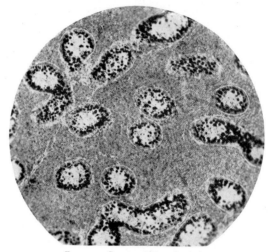

FIG. 29.—Cryptorchid testis of pig.

Exactly the reverse is observed here; the seminal tubules are shrunken and the interstitial cells greatly predominate. Both sections are stained to show fat (Sudan III). Same magnification. The round droplets of fat form a peripheral fringe in the normal seminal tubules, while in the tubules of the cryptorchid testis the fat droplets are very abundant, filling the Sertoli cells. (Hanes.)

the lack of appreciation between funicular and incompletely descended testes. It is agreed universally that every double and true cryptorchid animal develops every attribute of the normal male save the power of propagation. In the normal testicle (Fig. 28) the spermatic tubules greatly predominate over the interstitial cells while in the cryptorchid testicle the reverse is true. (Fig. 29.) The interstitial cells of the cryptorchid testicle are usually larger than those of the normal testicle, but otherwise their structure is the same. The seminiferous tubules, on the other hand, show marked abnormalities. The basement membrane of the tubule is thickened and it is lined only by a single layer of Sertoli cells. While in the adult cryptorchid testicle not a trace of spermatogenesis is to be found, in the very young cryptorchid animal there are large primary sperm cells (*Ursamenzellen*). These, however, do not develop further but soon disappear.

The external genitalia of adult but castrated animals are distinctly undeveloped and atrophic in appearance (Figs. 30, 31A and 32A). However, no such changes are found between the genitalia of normal and cryptorchid animals. " Since then," remarks Hanes, " in the absence of the sperm from cells secondary sexual characters develop quite normally, one may safely eliminate these cells from the problem of determining which element of the testicle furnishes an internal secretion to the organism."

The next phase to be studied is, which of the parenchymatous elements, the interstitial cell or the Sertoli cell, is supplying the hormone? No method has as yet been found which will cause the disappearance of one while leaving intact the other. The occlusion of the vas deferens, röntgenization of the testicle, freezing, have all been tried with the result that the spermatogenic cells disappear, but the Sertoli and interstitial cells persist. In transplantation of pieces of dog's testicle under the rectus muscle of castrated dogs the same condition obtained. Here Hanes was able to find that the Sertoli cells and the interstitial cells retained their viability. In commenting on his views in this respect Hanes has the following to say: " We have seen that embryologically the interstitial cell is mesenchymal. Histologically it presents the type of the gland cell with a plentiful cytoplasm rich in cell granules. The histologic resemblance of the interstitial cell to the cells of the liver is worthy of emphasis, and especially is this true when both are stained to demonstrate their rich content of cell granules. The interstitial cells stand in the closest possible relation to the rich capillary mesh work of the testicle. They surround the capillaries in their course to the tubules and are bathed in the large intertubular lymph spaces. A compensatory hypertrophy can be demonstrated in the interstitial cells under certain conditions. In a pig from which one testicle has been removed at an early age the interstitial cells of the remaining organ are present in markedly increased numbers."

Plato in 1896, advanced the thought that the interstitial cells furnished nutriment in the form of fat to the Sertoli and spermatogenic cells. This view was soon discarded by Beissner,[16] in 1898. Von Lenhossek, in 1897,

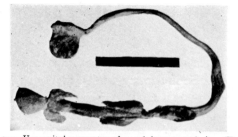

FIG. 30.—Urogenital apparatus of an adult castrated pig. (Hanes.)
Figs. 30 to 32 show bladder, prostate, seminal vesicles, glands of Cowper and penis. The organs of the castrated pig are small and atrophic, whereas the organs of the cryptorchid pig are as well developed as in the normal animal.

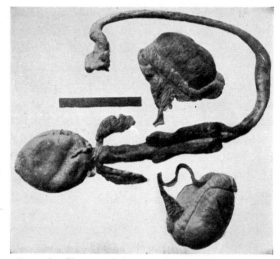

FIG. 31A.—The urogenital organs of a normal pig. (Hanes.)

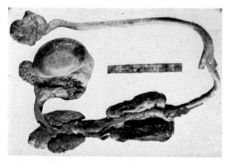

FIG. 32A.—The urogenital organs of a mono-cryptorchid pig.
(The other testicle had descended normally and had been removed.) (Hanes.)

advanced the view that the interstitial cells furnished pabulum for the use of the cells of the seminiferous tubules. This is refuted by Hanes and others. In 1875 Harvey thought that the interstitial cells represent nerve cells. This view has also been successfully contradicted. In 1897 von Bardeleben saw a resemblance between the Sertoli cell and the Leydig cell, and advanced the thought that " worn out Sertoli cells were in time replaced by young Leydig cells." In 1909 Goldman, using the vital stains of von Bardeleben, claimed that he demonstrated the passage of the Leydig cells through the wall of the seminiferous tubules, but Hanes repeated with great care the work of Goldman and concludes that " in the course of an enumeration of 1000 Leydig cells in sections from the testicles of rats which had been vitally stained with trypan blue and pyrrol blue no suggestion of the phenomenon described by Goldman was observed. It must be very rare, for among the many careful histological studies of many observers of the easily staining Leydig cells no one has described a similar picture."

A heated controversy has existed among various scientific investigators on the functions of these cells since the time Sertoli described his cell in 1865. The latter are also known as " sustentacular cells " (F. Merkel); " follicle cells " (LaValette St. George); " Nährzellen " (Peter); and " sperm nourishing cells " (Grobben). Regaud described the Sertoli cells in 1910 as forming a syncytium. Von Ebner, in 1902, thought that the Sertoli cells supply food in the form of fat during the process of spermatogenesis. Von Ebner's views have been answered by Hanes and Rosenbloom as follows: " During the development of the spermatids from the spermatogonia, and their subsequent conjugation with the Sertoli cells, important changes have taken place in the fats in the Sertoli cells. Von Ebner (1902) has described a ' circulation ' of the fat of the Sertoli cell, during the course of a spermatic generation, from the base of the Sertoli cell toward the lumen of the tubules, and noted that *pari passu* with the development of the sperm the fat diminished. He concluded that it was utilized as nutriment for the developing spermatozoa. His clear and convincing descriptions are based upon histological changes in the normal testes, but no evidence of a physiological nature has, so far as I am aware, been brought forward in its support. Such evidence, obtained from a microchemical and chemical study of normal and cryptorchitic testes is presented elsewhere and may be summarized very briefly at this point. If seminal tubules in various stages of spermatogenesis proceeds the large fat droplets which are present in the basal portions of the Sertoli cells in the beginning, divide into very much smaller droplets and pass centralward in the protoplasmic prolongations of the Sertoli cells, and thence into the spermatids after their union with the Sertoli cells. During its migration the fat can be shown by appropriate staining methods to have changed in its chemical character from neutral fat to a lipoid. Using Weigert's method for the staining of myelin, Regaud (1910) has also demonstrated lipoids in the Sertoli cells and spermatids. The exact manner in which the fat furnished by the Sertoli cells is eventually utilized by the spermatids and sperm, shares the obscurity which envelops the question of the ultimate metabolism of fats by the cells throughout the body. In cryptorchid testes it has been pointed out that the sperm-forming cells have completely disappeared. If the fat of the Sertoli cells is destined for the nutriment of the spermatids and sperm, the absence from the seminal tubules of these elements should result in the presence of an excessive amount of fat in the Sertoli cells. That such is strikingly the case will be seen from a section of a cryptorchid testis stained to demonstrate fat. The Sertoli cells are seen to be loaded with large neutral fat droplets. Upon chemical analysis of normal and cryptorchid testes, the micro-chemical findings are corroborated. Of the dried weight of normal pig testes, 19 per cent. was found to be fatty material, whereas the percentage of fatty substances present in cryptorchid testes was found to amount to 31 per cent. of their dried weight. In other words, the fat contents of the cryptorchid testicle is almost double that of the normal. We conclude, therefore, that fat accumulates in the Sertoli cells of the cryptorchid testis because of the absence of the spermatogenic cells which normally utilize this fat." (Figs. 31 and 32.)

These scientific investigators are supported in their views by the researches of Miescher. Hanes and Rosenbloom from their studies, therefore conclude "that one function of the Sertoli cell is the providing of the nutriment to the peculiarly situated spermatogenic cells. Histological, chemical and physiological evidence amply supports this conclusion.

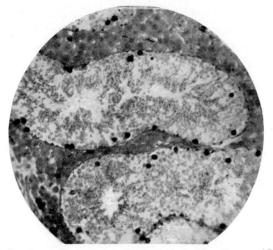

FIG. 31.—Section of normal pig testis in active spermatogenesis. (Hanes and Rosenbloom.)
   Altmann fixation (osmic acid and potassium dichromate) stained with Bensley's neutral gentian. The droplets of neutral fat lying in the Sertoli cells form an outline of the seminiferous tubule. Numerous small droplets of fatty material are seen toward the lumen.

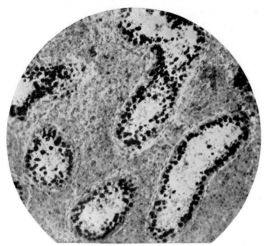

FIG. 32.—Section of cryptorchid pig testis. (Hanes and Rosenbloom.)
   Stained with Sudan III. and hematoxylin. The tubules are very much smaller than in the normal testicle, and are lined only by a layer of Sertoli cells which contain a large number of fat droplets. No sperm forming cells are present. Leydig cells greatly increased in numbers.

Whether or not the Sertoli cells furnish in addition an internal secretion to the body, we cannot say with absolute certainty. There is no evidence whatever that they elaborate an internal secretion, whereas an abundance of facts point to their functioning solely as sperm nourishing cells. The interstitial cells of Leydig, on the other hand, present the characters of active gland cells, and the evidence which I have presented has led me to believe that they furnish an internal secretion to the male body necessary for its normal development."

Massaglia [25] not being satisfied with the experimental work of Ancel and Bouin in regard to the function of the interstitial cells, has repeated those experiments using roosters instead of rabbits as experimental animals, as in the former the secondary sexual characters are much more marked. Massaglia believed that for some time following the operation of ligature and resection of the *ductus deferens,* the rooster, while alive, keeps all the secondary sexual characters of the male, but the testes have become small, and, on microscopic examination, atrophy of the cells of the seminiferous tubules is noted. While the interstitial cells of Leydig show no lesions, one would be justified in agreeing with Ancel and Bouin that the interstitial cells have the function of internal secretion of the testis.

In addition to simple ligation of the ductus deferens, Massaglia made further experiments. Three or four months after the initial ligature, when atrophy of the cells of the seminiferous tubules had occurred, the testes were removed. This, in effect, amounted to extirpation of the Leydig cells; and any changes in the secondary sex characters could then be ascribed to loss of these cells.

The secondary sex character changes, if any, subsequent to abdominal testicular transplants, were also studied.

In the ligature experiments, in order to obviate reconstruction of the *ductus deferens,* it was resected for about 2 cms. and ligated at each extremity. (Figs. 33 and 34.)

Massaglia, from his experiments, found that after ligation and resection of the *ductus deferens,* there may be:

1. Spontaneous reconstruction of the *ductus.* In such cases, there are no changes in the testis.

2. The *ductus* may remain obstructed, but the consequences in the testis are not always the same: (a) sometimes following the operation, the vas deferens and testis increase in volume. On microscopic examination of the gland, the seminiferous tubules may be greatly dilated, and contain

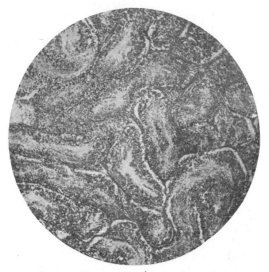

FIG. 33.—Normal testis of cock. (Massaglia.)

Note seminiferous tubules full of spermatozoa. The spaces limited between two or three seminiferous tubules show the interstitial cells. Fixation, formalin; staining, hematoxylin-eosin; magnification, 60 diameters.

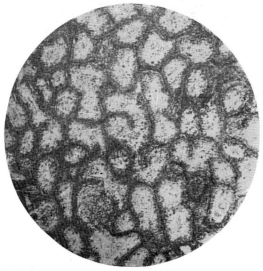

FIG. 34.—Testis of cock. (Massaglia.)

After ligation and resection of spermatic duct. Shows some spermatozoa in a few seminiferous tubules and degenerative changes in its epithelium, slight increase of the interstitial connective tissue and the Leydig's cells. Fixation, Bouin's fluid; staining, hematoxylin-eosin; magnification, 60 diameters.

4

an enormous number of spermatozoa three months after ligation. (Fig. 35.)

In the epithelium of the seminiferous tubules, there is hydropic degeneration and the Leydig cells are normal or increased after four or five months' time. This first period follows a second marked by increase of the interstitial connective tissue, followed by atrophy of the testis; the

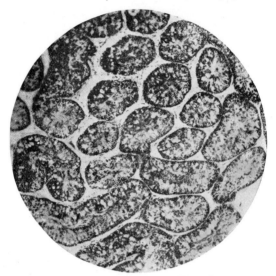

FIG. 35.—Left testis of cock. (Massaglia.)

After ligation and resection of spermatic duct. Seminiferous tubules dilatated and full of spermatozoa; hydropic degeneration of the epithelium of the seminiferous tubules; interstitial connective tissue increased; Leydig's cells in normal number; edema. Fixation, formalin; staining, hematoxylin-eosin; magnification, 60 diameters.

spermatogenous function is either greatly diminished or has disappeared. Atrophy of the testis and degeneration of the spermatogenetic cells may be much earlier, and few of the latter may complete their cycle so as to become spermatozoa, but then the Leydig cells remain normal or increase. Massaglia, following Massarman, thinks that such a result may follow injury of the nerves during operation.

The important observation in Massaglia's study, was that in no case in roosters, after ligation and resection of the *ductus deferens,* did there occur changes in the secondary sexual characters, and in case of young animals, development was normal. Ancel and Bouin's conclusions, as regards the rabbit, were thus confirmed by Massaglia in the case of the rooster. But removal of the atrophic testes, in which the Leydig cells were in good condition, caused in the adult animals a sudden cessation of crowing, a loss of the sexual instinct, and desire to fight.

The " interstitial gland internal secretion " theory has not, however, gone unchallenged. The most recent histological researches rather deny the existence of an internal secretion affecting sex characters being due to the interstitial cells, and attribute such effects entirely to the work of the seminiferous elements proper of the testicle. Voronoff and Retterer [27] are the most prominent protagonists of this view, which they have supported in two recently published monographs upon the subject, Retterer being responsible for the histological researches and Voronoff for the experimental surgical work.

Voronoff's first experimental work by testicular grafting in animals was carried out from 1917 to 1920 in the Physiological Station of the College of France. When such grafts survived, the vascular nutrition was weakened, but they still showed some tubules, the epithelial cells of which evolved in such a way as to produce spermatozoa. Generally, the epithelial cells were changed into a mass of protoplasm containing numerous nuclei (syncytium), which filled the lumen of the tube. Instead of producing spermatids and spermatozoa, such protoplasm evolved into reticulated tissue. Therefore, following grafting, the epithelial elements of the seminiferous tubes, being less well nourished than before, change the structure and cycle of evolution; instead of producing spermatozoa, the greater part is transformed into a reticulated tissue which represents their second evolution stage.

The protoplasm or cytoplasm into which the large mass of epithelial cells changed, may be differentiated into: (1) a fine network of reticulum; and (2) into a clear mass contained in the meshes of the network (hyaloplasma). This hyaloplasma ultimately melts away and the reticulated meshes are seen empty. It is owing to this process that the interseminal reticulated tissue becomes more abundant. No mitotic phenomena have ever been observed in the interseminiferous tissue, and it is therefore not proliferation of the connective tissue which increases the mass of the interseminiferous tissue.

In view of such deviation from ordinary evolution Retterer and Voronoff try to find what are the elements in a grafted testicle which change the general habitus of the grafted animal and give him virile characteristics (*libido* and *potentia cœundi*). Cryptorchids show similar characters, and they are equally observed after ligature of the deferent canals, and after the action of X-rays. Since in these latter conditions the interseminiferous tissue becomes more abundant and richer in interstitial cells, some authors attributed to these latter cells the function of elaborating an internal secretion which is absorbed and acts on the whole organism. But in the grafted tissue, cellular division, according to Voronoff and Retterer, is seen to be absent in the interseminiferous tissue; therefore, its hypertrophy does not cause proliferation of the connective cells. The interseminiferous connective tissue becomes more abundant simply because the epithelial cells of the seminiferous tubes are transformed into reticulated tissue. Interstitial cells are rare in normal animals. None has been found in grafted testicles, and such therefore, cannot be responsible for an internal secretion.

Summing up the situation according to their findings in testicular grafts, Retterer and Voronoff say that in grafted testicles, the interseminiferous tissue becomes more abundant accordingly as the seminiferous tubes become thinner. Simultaneously the epithelium of these tubules is transformed into reticulated tissue with the meshes filled with hyaloplasma. This hyaloplasma fluidifies and becomes absorbed leaving the reticulum with empty meshes. It is to the production and absorption of this hyaloplasma elaborated by the testicular cells of epithelial origin that the influence which a grafted testicle exerts on the organism is due.

Retterer and Voronoff, therefore, conclude from the grafting experimental work that *the epithelial cells of the seminiferous tubes, when they become transformed into reticulated tissue, furnish a plasma, the absorption of which into the organism determines secondary sexual characteristics and desire.*

In an article quite recently published, Voronoff and Retterer [27] consider the same subject based upon resection of the deferent canals. They resected 6 to 10 cms. of the deferent canal in dogs, and made a histological study of the subsequent effects upon the testicular elements, checking their findings with a similar histological study in normal control animals.

Examination of the seminiferous tubes in dogs, with the deferent canal resected for about a year, compared with a normal dog, showed that the epithelial lining was thicker, and that the lumen of the tubule was reduced to a slit, which was occupied by a small mass of clear cytoplasm. In the normal dog, loose connective tissue was abundant in the intervals between the seminiferous tubuli; in the resected dog, the tubuli were approximated, and the interval between them much reduced. In the resected dog, the seminiferous tubuli, which were reduced to closely approximated cords, recalled, from the morphological point of view, the tube of an infant or of a child who had not yet reached puberty, or perhaps that of an old man. But the evolution of the epithelial lining of the tube was quite different. The nuclei continue to multiply and the smaller nucleoli to which they give origin become transformed into heads of spermatozoa. The epithelial lining of the seminiferous tubules survives after resection of the deferent canal, the cells forming the lining are greatly multiplied, resulting in a much thickened epithelial lining which transforms the tube into a more or less compact cord.

Thus in the resected dog, spermatogenic evolution continues in the absence of excretion; also animals, which have had their deferent canals resected, continue to experience *libido* and *potentia cœundi*. Internal secretion therefore continues after resection of the deferent canals.

In the testicle with resected deferent canal, the seminal cells evolve in the same manner as in a testicle with a free canal, but the evolution is slower and the successive forms of the cells remain in the same places where they were produced. Sertoli cells are not present in the testicle with a resected deferent canal. The cells which fill the tubes show little or no spermatozoa. The previous observers who noted these modifications, were satisfied to conclude that the seminal layer of cells degenerated or atrophied while the sustentacular or Sertoli cells multiplied. But Voronoff and Retterer say that if these observers had prolonged their experimental work and had further examined those apparently Sertoli cells, they would have seen that after eight to twelve months, they again evolved into a line of seminal cells. The cytoplasm becomes more dense; and in the absence of ejaculation, it shows little or no fluidification to allow spermatozoa a vehicle for ejection. But this cytoplasm elaborates certain plasmas which pass into the blood and influences all the organisms and preserves to the animal his genital desire and power.

There is no hypertrophy of the interseminiferous tissue a year after resection of the canals. If this interseminiferous tissue seems to increase in the first period following resection, it is because the seminal tubuli then diminish in caliber.

Resection of the deferent canal suppresses excretion of the sperm alone. The epithelial elements of the seminiferous tubuli, which at the time of the resection were in an advanced stage of evolution, degenerate; but those which were in a state of repose, or in the earlier stages of their evolution, continue to survive and pursue their evolution. This evolution is, however, different from that in normal conditions.

Voronoff and Retterer from their ligature experiments thus arrive at the same results that they reached from their testicular transplantation, i.e., that the seminal elements alone, and not the interstitial cells, are concerned with secondary sex character and desire. They say that Steinach [32] only recognized the degenerative phenomena occurring within the first few months following ligature of the deferent canal. At the end of several months, at least in the dog, the epithelium again proliferates and produces a new generation of seminal elements. The interstitial connective tissue instead of increasing decreases after resection of the deferent canal.

Apart from his actual histological findings, Retterer argues that in all the endocrine glands (thyroid, suprarenals, hypophysis) it is the epithelial cell which is charged with the secretory function. Why should there be an exception in the case of the testicle by ascribing to that gland such a function and to the interstitial cells which are connective tissue cells. according to Retterer? The fact that the same epithelial cells can fulfill two functions—endocrine and exocrine—in the testicle is no more surprising than in the case of the liver which secretes bile and elaborates sugar.

The views of Retterer and Voronoff are substantiated by Gley [30] who finds that in batracins and birds the secondary male characters develop when the interstitial cells are absent from the testicles, and that such cells are abundant at early age before the sexual characters develop. The same thing is observed in man; the sexual male characters appear at puberty when spermatozoa are elaborated by the seminiferous canals, *i.e.*, when the spermatogenic function is established. These views are consistent only with a nutrient rôle being assigned to the interstitial cells.

The views of Hanes that the Sertoli cells may have something to do with internal secretion is corroborated by the opinions held by Steinach, who believes the Sertoli cells belong to the incretory system. He says: [33] " After vasoligation and during the progress of the atrophy of the seminal canal the Sertoli cells suffer less and a great part remain intact. It is, therefore, not as yet definitely settled whether these cells also, together with the Leydig cells, give rise to internal secretion or not. Certain characteristics of structure and, furthermore, the resisting power of these cells would permit of analogy as far as function is concerned."

In another place Steinach,[33] examining and commenting on some of his successful transplants, says: " In the transplants I find in the wall of the tubuli a closely arranged layer of epithelial cells preserved. Further researches and microscopic examination of transplants at various periods after their transplantation will decide whether this epithelium is of importance with reference to internal secretion or not."

He maintains that while it has not as yet been definitely proven that the Sertoli cells play an important part as cells of internal secretion, at the same time he believes in such possibility but thus far nothing definite has been proven with reference to the Sertoli cells one way or another.[34]

To ascertain the important rôle of the Leydig cell in the development of secondary sex characteristics and the lack of predisposition of the seminal cells in this direction, Steinach conducted the following experiment:

In an infantile animal he created a bilateral artificial cryptorchidism and a few days after the wound had healed he divided the spermatic cord. In this manner he was successful in retaining a testis in full form and size and having it heal in its new surroundings. By this method he was enabled to study the histologic picture of the transplant and at the same time watch the development of secondary sex characteristics. After the transplant remained *in situ* for over a year the secondary sex characteristics had progressed to full development. It is self-evident that in this instance the great majority of the seminal canals had entirely disappeared. Their only component part was the Sertoli cell but the Leydig cells persisted in great numbers. This is, of course, another link in the chain of evidence that the Leydig cell is responsible for the development of the secondary sex characteristics. Still another fact strengthening that belief is, quoting Steinach, " it is possible in infantile castrates to preserve secondary sex characteristics and develop them by the implantation of isolated substances of puberty gland. This experiment was successful in my hands in the case of many infantile castrated male rats into which I have transplanted isolated puberty glands."

Steinach did not conclude the functional value of the Leydig cell through his vasoligation experiments. On the contrary, he has reached his conclusions entirely through transplantations, and from the wealth of material which he studied he has drawn his conclusions and then attempted to verify them through his vasoligation experiments. The masculinization of young female animals through implants containing exclusively Leydig cells, has resulted not only in the development of secondary sex characters, but also in the elongation of the clitoris, that assumed the characteristics and corresponding proportions of a sort of a penis. These experiments have been carried out and substantiated by Lipschütz.[35]

Furthermore, the pertinent question that presents itself to those who believe that the seminal cell in the normal individual and in the transplants is responsible for the development of the secondary sex characters and other manifestations resulting from the incretion of the testicular hormone can be best met with by the studies of Sand,[43] Lipschütz and Ottow,[37] Wagner,[38] Moore, [45] Kuntz [7] and Bormann,[40] who have conclusively shown that even in the presence of seminal cells and in the absence of interstitial tissue by reason of its under-development the manifestations of castration may develop.

In this connection it may be well to recall that Peter Schmidt called attention to the report at the Urologic Congress of 1921, where Kriser and Lenk added their conclusions to the mass of convincing evidence already accumulated. Cases of organic impotency of aged individuals were subjected to the action of the X-ray, carefully graded until azoöspermia was produced. After weeks, and in some cases after months, the potency and general physical power of these individuals reappeared. The sperm examined prior to röntgenization which contained numerous spermatozoa has shown the latter to have completely disappeared. This was substantiated by repeated examinations. It is a well-known fact that röntgenization of the male sex gland of röntgenologists for a considerable period of time, without taking any special precautions to protect their genital apparatus from the X-ray, will in due time produce sterility, although their potency is normally preserved. The most convincing work on this particular subject has been recently published by Aron of Strassburg.[46] This careful observer

studied the influences of the internal secretion on the development of secondary sex characters on Tritons. It is well known that up to the present time
in Urodels no interstitial cells or Leydig cells could ever be demonstrated,
and this was a very strong argument for those scientific investigators who
believed and maintained that no interstitial cells are necessary for the
development of secondary sex characters because in Tritons and Urodels
these cells were not present. Aron, however, was recently successful in
proving that in these animals the testicle contains at its hilus a special
gland which gives rise to the internal secretions. The composition of this
gland consists of large cells containing lipoids. The ingenious manner in
which Aron worked on the solution of this problem contributed a great
deal to clearing up this much-discussed question. Aron destroyed the
organ of internal secretion of these animals with a thermocautery, after
which the manifestations of castration at once became evident. The comb
drooped and the sexual impulse disappeared. Furthermore, in these very
animals that have evinced these manifestations of castration spermatogenesis was in progress in full sway. It is, therefore, believed that all
theories built on a structure of the seminal cell as the important part in
the determination of secondary sex characters and internal secretion
inevitably collapse in view of these striking and convincing proofs.

Schmidt cites Steinach's conclusions in this respect as follows:[47]

" 1. The sexual gland exercises specific sex functions.

" 2. The elaboration of the hormone in the sexual gland is independent of the formation and discharge of the seminal cells.

" 3. The sex gland hormones are of utmost importance for the formation and perpetuation of the somatic and psychic sex characters.

" 4. Transplantation, vasoligation and röntgenization result in the
accentuation or reëstablishment of hormone production.

" 5. A rise in the hormone production in individuals with precocious
senility, or even senility on a physiologic basis, causes a regeneration which
may in a sense be looked upon as a rejuvenation."

Harms [26] in a recent work considers that Bouin and Ancel, Steinach
and others have exaggerated the importance of the interstitial cells. These
authors believed that the sperm cells had no endocrine function, but that
this was alone the prerogative of the interstitial cells. Plato and others,
however, believed that the interstitial cells were only trophic elements for

the spermatogenous cells. Steinach admitted that a certain parallelism existed between the number of interstitial cells and the intensity of the secondary sexual characters and that autoplastically grafted testicles remained infantile, had no sperm cells and therefore showed their endocrine functions by the interstitial cells alone. This view has not, however, been proved as the grafted testicles contain many unripe spermatogones and Sertoli cells to which the endocrine function may be attributed. The same is true with testicles transplanted in castrated female animals. Harms always found Sertoli cells or cells derived from these in the graft. Some animals are without interstitial cells and yet have secondary sexual characters. It is, however, quite possible that the interstitial cells may have an endocrine function. Harms often observed in histological pictures that interstitial cells yielded substances to the capillaries. Harms believes that the endocrine substance of the testicle is created by degenerating or secreting spermatogones and Sertoli cells, that it is stored up in the interstitial cells in the form of a *Pro-sekret* (preliminary secretion), and that in these cells this *Pro-sekret* is changed into the real secretion. In the Bidder organ, in toads especially, there are many structures which sustain this theory.

Author's Researches.

In an endeavor to throw additional light on the question as to the internal secretion of the Leydig cells, that is, whether this cell is responsible for the internal secretion or the seminal cell is endowed with this function, and in view of the still existing controversy the author carried on a series of experiments which will be described forthwith:

Animal Experiments

Six male apes (cynocephali) were selected. They were at the age of full sexual maturity and very active sexually when placed with females of the same species. They were all castrated. Gradual impotence set in, and while a hyperstimulation, as it were, of sex activity ensued for the first two or three weeks after castration, the sexual ardor gradually declined, so that about the end of four or more months all the animals were thoroughly sexually impotent and unable to react with an erection in the presence of females. Homotransplantations were then performed on five animals, and a sixth had a cryptorchitic human testicle implanted into

AUTHOR'S EXPERIMENTS TO ASCERTAIN FUNCTION OF TESTIS.

Lab. No. Animal	Type of Animal	Date of Castration	Effects of Castration	Implantation*	Results
1	Macacus rhesus	Feb. 10, 1921	Hyperstimulation. Gradual sexual decline. Impotent by August, 1921	Feb., 1922. Homotransplantation. Testis of macacus nemestrinus	Gradual return of potency. Normal sex activity, April, 1922
2	Macacus nemestrinus	Feb. 10, 1921	Hyperstimulation. Gradual sexual decline. Impotent by Oct., 1921	Feb., 1922. Homotransplantation. Cynocephalus porcarius	Potent June, 1922. Potency uninterrupted and continuous
3	Cyrcopithecus	Feb. 10, 1921	No hyperstimulation. Gradual sexual decline. Impotent by June, 1921. Marked loss of weight	Feb., 1922. Homotransplantation. Cynocephalus porcarius	Gained weight; potent May, 1922
4	Cynocephalus	Feb. 10, 1921	Gradual sexual decline. Impotent by Sept., 1921. Appreciable loss of weight	Feb., 1922. Homotransplantation. Macacus rhesus	Gained weight; gradual return of potency; viz., feeble one year after implantation. Imperfect erections, loss of libido
5	Macacus nemestrinus	Feb. 10, 1921	Hyperstimulation. Impotent by Dec., 1921	Feb., 1922, transplant cynocephalus	Remains impotent, April, 1923
6	Macacus nemestrinus	Feb. 10, 1921	Sudden impotence; complete by Dec., 1921	Feb., 1922, heterotransplant: cryptorchid testis from human	Potent six weeks after implantation, violent pederasty with another monkey. Died Jan., 1923 in struggle with another monkey

*The transplanted testes were converted into "interstitialoma" by exposing them to the action of the X-ray prior to implantation.

him. Similar animals were subjected to the action of the X-ray sufficiently to destroy all seminiferous cells but not strong enough to devitalize the Leydig cells. Subsequent to the röntgenization of the testes, removal of specimens from same for microscopic study has proved them to have become " interstitialomas " in the sense of Bolognesi (composed of interstitial cells alone). In this manner every element of doubt as to the absence of the spermatogenic cell has been eliminated. These interstitialomas were then implanted into the castrates. Gradually the animals became potent and cohabited with females of the same species. The cynocephalus in whom the cryptorchitic testis had been transplanted showed a reappearance of sexual ardor about six weeks after implantation. Removal from the cage in which the female was stationed, into a cage where another male shared quarters with him, caused his sexual ardor to become so great that very active pederasty was practiced between the two, the animal (male) carrying the transplant playing the active part and the other male a passive rôle. A study of the cryptorchitic testis, removed two months after its implantation, showed the following microscopic picture. (Fig. 36.)

The cryptorchid testicle transplanted into monkey No. 6 (Cf. table) showed the characteristic cryptorchid picture (Fig. 37) with the well-known thickening of the seminiferous tubules, the disappearance of the characteristic contents and the extraordinarily hypertrophied interstitium.

Figs. 38–40 show a transplanted human testis into a macacus nemestrinus, and eloquently illustrate and emphasize the total absence of seminiferous structure and the substitution of Leydig cells and newly-formed blood vessels in the implant, which was removed after two months. Very few Sertoli cells were found, and it stands to reason that the Leydig cells contributed to the incretory function in these experiments and that the other elements may be excluded as having furnished any hormone whatever.

Analysis of Table

These experiments show 66–2/3 per cent. of successes (return of potency after hetero- and homotransplantations) ; 16–1/6 per cent. failure (No. 5) and 16–1/6 per cent. partial failure (No. 4). Or, expressed differently, of the homotransplants we had 75 per cent. successes and 25 per cent. failure. The transplant from the cynocephalus to the macacus nemestrinus was a complete failure, while the heterotransplant of the cryptorchid testis

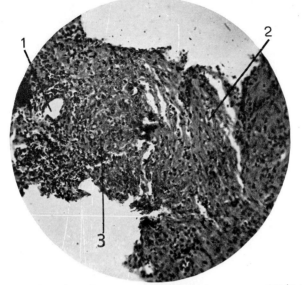

FIG. 36.—Transplanted human cryptorchid testis into macacus nemestrinus.
Two months after transplantation. Magnified 240x; ocular 7.5; objective 8. Leitz apochromatic. Hematoxylin and eosin. 1, bloodvessel; 2, connective tissue and Leydig cells; 3, same plus leucocytic infiltration.

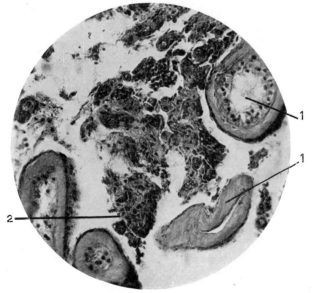

FIG. 37.—Human cryptorchid testis (transplanted into macacus nemestrinus).
1, typical cryptorchid tubules; 2, much hypertrophied interstitium.

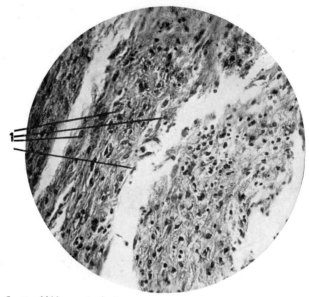

FIG. 38.—Cryptorchid human testis after two months transplantation into macacus nemestrinus. 1, Leydig cells. Total absence of tubules and seminal elements.

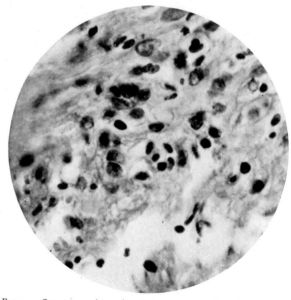

FIG. 39.—Same as previous microphotograph, magnified 768 diameters.

from the human was a thorough success. Following castration, 50 per cent. of the animals show a transitory hyperstimulation of sexual activity, followed in a shorter or longer period by complete impotence.

Evidence from Human Testis

The following observation will perhaps throw some additional light on the question at issue. It concerns an individual, colored, a porter by occu-

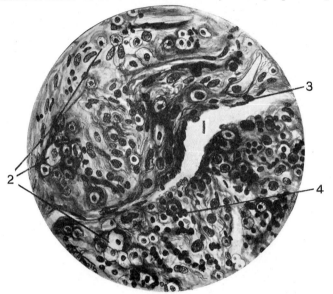

FIG. 40.—Same as previous specimen. Drawn on larger scale.
1, bloodvessel; 2, Leydig cells; 3, endothelial cells; 4, leucocytes.

pation, American, twenty-three years of age. His family history is negative.

Past History.—In 1906 the patient had pneumonia. In 1912 he developed mumps, which was followed by swelling of both testicles. He remained in bed for sixteen days. His *vita sexualis* was normal, so far as he could determine. He cohabited normally from the age of twelve years on. In 1916 he contracted syphilis, from which, he says, he was cured. He married in 1919 and at that time he observed that the sexual act lasted longer than usual. He gradually found that he could not succeed in inducing an orgasm. This condition became gradually worse and more pronounced until at the present time the patient is unable to produce an emission no matter how hard he tries. The sexual act is sometimes greatly prolonged. In order to test himself the patient often prolongs the act of coition to a period of about two hours when, weakened from the strenuous exertion, he has to desist, and with penis

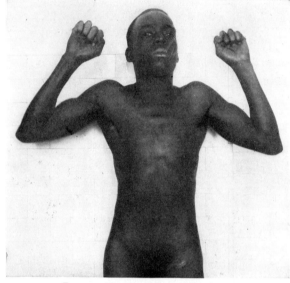

Fig. 41.—Chest development of patient.
Note general contour, muscular development and freedom from adiposity.

still erect to give up the attempt, as he expresses it, in despair. In other words, his *libido* is intact and his sex characteristics absolutely normal.

This being a case of great importance as to the question at issue, the author decided to examine the testis of this man microscopically to ascertain the condition of the spermatogenic elements and also to study the cells of Leydig as well as those of Sertoli. The general appearance of the patient is that of a perfectly normal masculine individual, with testicles smaller in appearance than is normal for an individual of his size. This observation is corroborated by the statement of the patient that he had observed a gradual diminution in size of his scrotal contents, since he had the parotitis. We find no accumulation of fat, no effeminacy, no earmark of eunuchoidism. (Figs. 41 and 44.)

The patient was anæsthetized with gas-oxygen, the *tunica vaginalis* opened and the testicles exposed to view. A thorough examination of the deferent ducts showed them to be normal; the epididymis was also normal

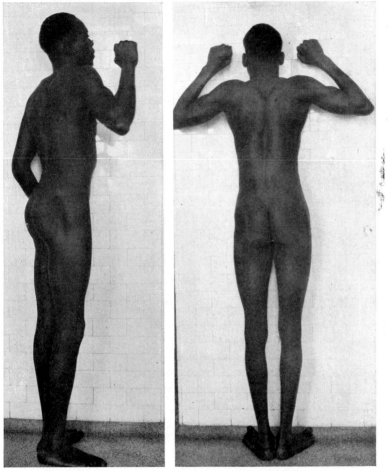

FIGS. 42 and 43.—Showing lateral and posterior views of the patient.

Note strong muscular development and absolute freedom from fat; perfect proportions and marked masculine habitus.

but diminished in size. The consistency of the testicle was softer than is normally the case and much smaller than normal for an individual of his age and body dimensions. A section was removed for microscopic study.

5

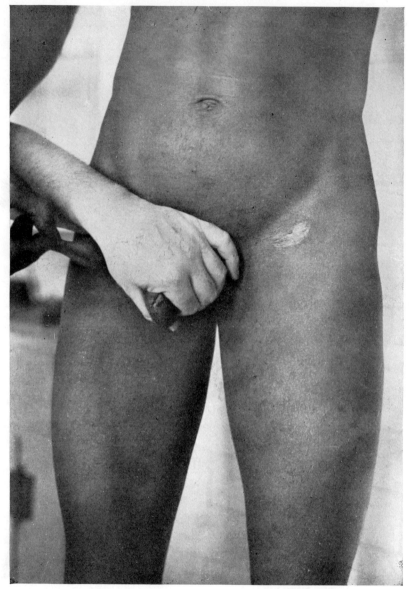

FIG. 44.—Showing small size of testicles compared to height and general strong muscular development of the rest of the body.

The gross appearance of the cut surface of the testicle was yellow, resembling closely in appearance a homo- or heterotransplant. The specimen was prepared in formol and its microscopic study disclosed the following (Figs. 45–48):

The appearance on the low magnification of the specimen stained with hematoxylin-eosin gives the appearance of a eunuchoid testis.

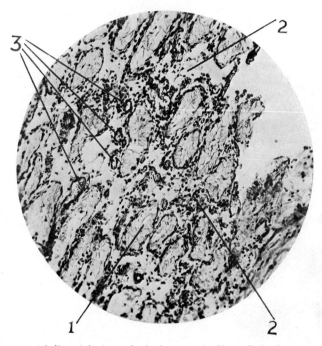

Fig. 45.—1, *tubuli seminiferi* completely degenerated. No seminal cells; 2, *interstitium* increased in quantity; 3 blood vessels. Objective 7.5; ocular 8 (Leitz apochromatic). Magnified 205 diameters. Hematoxylin and eosin.

On higher magnification the findings were as follows: The seminiferous tubules are very much smaller than in the normal testes of a man of his age and their contents are *completely degenerated*. They are composed of a wall of very thin connective tissue. The lumen of the tubule contains a hyalin substance stained with the eosin. *Not a single seminal cell is to be found upon studying a great many sections.* In the interstitial spaces there is a great deal of infiltration with leukocytes. The vessels in the interstitium are numerous and filled with red blood corpuscles.

The tubules are widely separated from one another. The structure separating them consists of hypertrophic interstitium the main composition of which is chiefly lymphocytes, leukocytes, blood vessels and Leydig cells. The number of Leydig cells seems to be increased and their protoplasm is

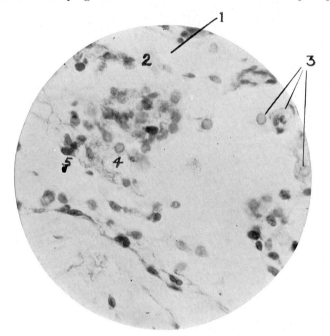

FIG. 46.—1, *tubulus seminiferus;* 2, wall of tubule composed of connective tissue; 3, 4 and 5, Leydig cells. Objective 7.5; ocular 2. Leitz apochromatic. Hematoxylin and eosin stain.

markedly granular. The nuclear wall is very strongly stained, sharply circumscribed and of normal size.

Comment.—To the mind of the author the studies recited herein conclusively prove, basing his opinion on clinical symptoms coupled with microscopic examination, that neither the seminal cells nor the Sertoli cells have anything to do in these cases with the production of *libido,* sex potency, and the retention of secondary sex characters. Not a single cell representing the lining of normal tubules nor an isolated Sertoli cell could be detected in studying a great many sections in the last case recited. On the other hand, the Leydig cells were found to be increased in number and there was a good deal of leukocytic invasion in the field. For our intents and purposes the question to be decided is what causes, at least in the individual under discussion, the clinical manifestations enumerated above? Surely not the tubular elements, for they do not exist. The cerebral centres of the patient are certainly eroticized, as shown by the forceful and prolonged

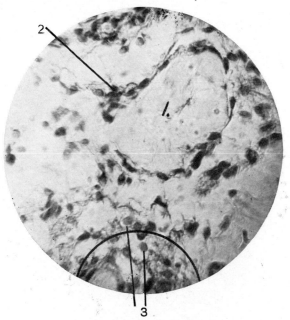

FIG. 47.—Testis of D. W.

1, interior of seminiferous tubule; 2, wall of tubule composed of a single layer of connective tissue cells. No Sertoli cells in any portion of the testis examined; 3, interstitial cells. Ocular 8; objective 4. Leitz apochromatic. Hematoxylin and eosin. Magnification 511x. Semicircular area outlined shows in higher magnification in the following microphotograph.

erections and the existence of marked *libido;* and, hand in hand with this we find the presence of an element in the sections studied and that is the Leydig cells. What other conclusion can be reached? None other than that the existing cellular elements are responsible for the internal secretion and clinical manifestation so clearly manifest here. If we couple our findings in the last cited case with those related in the preceding group, in which by röntgenization the author was able to destroy all tubular elements and transplant pure interstitialomas into the bodies of previously castrated and impotent animals, in whom a return of *libido* and sex potency became manifest, it accentuates and proves the premises set forth in this thesis in favor of the Leydig cells as the incretory apparatus for masculinization, erotization and sex potency.

The following case will further tend to illustrate with even greater force, the relative functions of the various component parts of the testis.

Cryptorchidism.—Mr. J. K., aged seventy years, was admitted to the American Hospital complaining of dragging and painful sensations in the

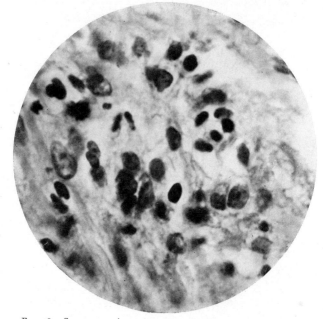

Fig. 48.—Same as previous microphotograph magnified 940 diameters.

lower part of the abdomen, particularly in the lower section of the inguinal region, on both sides.

Family History.—Irrelevant.

Previous Diseases.—The patient has always been in perfect health.

Habits.—Used alcohol up until ten years ago, during which time he imbibed liquor to excess. Used tobacco all of his life, in moderation.

Sexual History.—Patient arrived at sexual maturity at a rather early age. Masturbated occasionally. Had his first intercourse when fifteen years old, since which time he has been given occasionally to sexual excess, cohabiting almost nightly. He has been married, divorced his wife, who has never been pregnant. His *vita sexualis* at the time of admission to the hospital, while not as active as in his younger days, is still very pronounced and he has sexual intercourse regularly once or twice weekly.

Previous Operations.—Four years ago he was operated upon for the relief of a bilateral cryptorchidism. This operation, however, proved unsuccessful.

Physical Examination.—The patient does not betray his age, looking more like a man in the late fifties than his real age. His hair is gray; mustache black; general nutrition and physical development normal. Wears an upper dental plate, some bridge work in the lower section of the mouth. Chest well formed; expansion of the lungs normal. Thoracic organs negative. Blood pressure, systolic 190; diastolic 100. Examination of the abdomen discloses a soft rounded tumor at the site of the internal abdominal ring on each side. These masses are displacable upward but cannot be brought downward. There is impulse on coughing on both sides. Palpation of the tumors, which in all probability are the testicles, is not painful. The examination of the urine shows a trace of albumin and many hyaline, fine and coarsely granular casts. Hemoglobin 80 per cent. Coagulation time of the blood four minutes. Blood Wassermann negative. Leukocytes 11,200 per c.mm. The patient is very anxious to be relieved of the dragging sensations and discomfort in the region of the incisions resulting from the previous operation and the frequently appearing " shooting " pains in that locality which make him suffer to no small degree.

Diagnosis.—Bilateral cryptorchidism; incipient bilateral inguinal hernia; neuralgia of the ilioinguinal and iliohypogastric nerves, possibly due to scar tissue involvement resulting from previous operative procedure.

Operation.—Under scopolamin-morphin anæsthesia supplemented by gas oxygen, the patient was operated on the twenty-ninth of April, 1923, by the author.

Operative Findings.—The exposure of the tumor through an inguino-abdominal incision on the right side disclosed it to be the testicle which was converted into a necrotic mass of calcareo-sebaceous consistency, intimately adherent to the parietal peritoneum and contiguous structures. This necrotic mass was ablated and found upon miscroscopic examination to consist of dead testicular tissue of degenerated and calcified debris.

(Fig. 49.) On the left side the exposure of the mass showed it to be a cryptorchitic testicle which was freed from the surrounding structures and brought down to the scrotum after resorting to the operative technic the author is using in cases of undescended testes. Sections of the testes were submitted to microscopic examination.

Postoperative Course.—After a fortnight the incisions were found to have healed *per primam* and the patient left the hospital.

Microscopic Findings of Specimens from Testes.—The general appearance presented under low power magnification (Fig. 50), is that of

FIG. 49.—Gross appearance of calcified and degenerated abdominal testis.

a cryptorchitic testis. Close scrutiny of the picture shows that the seminiferous tubules were empty and their walls consisted of only a *single layer of connective tissue cells*. The spaces between the tubules are filled with islands of syncytium composed of Leydig cells surrounded by a vacuolar reticulum. Here and there blood vessels which are very much thickened are seen in the intertubular spaces.

Fig. 51 shows the tubules in high magnification. It displays to great advantage the thin unicellular connective tissue walls of the tubules, the outlines of which are not regular but wavy. Here and there one meets, occasionally, a Sertoli cell.

Observing carefully Fig. 52, one sees a group of mono- and binuclear Leydig cells with distinct outlines resting in a bed of reticulated syncytium. On the periphery of these islands of Leydig cells, one can discern a transformation of the outermost Leydig cells into the reticulated syncytium.

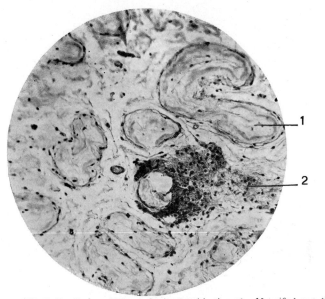

FIG. 50.—Mr. J. K. Cryptorchidism. Ocular 8; objective 16. Magnified 105 diameters. Leitz apochromatic. Hardened in formalin, stained with hematoxylin and eosin. 1, empty tubuli seminiferi; 2, intertubular syncytium containing Leydig cells.

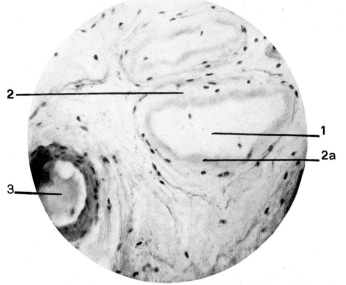

FIG. 51.—Mr. J. K. Cryptorchidism. Ocular 8; objective 8. Magnified 215 diameters. Leitz apochromatic. 1, empty tubuli seminiferi; 2, wall of tubuli composed of one layer of connective tissue cells. Total absence of spermatogenetic elements; 3, much thickness of blood vessel walls.

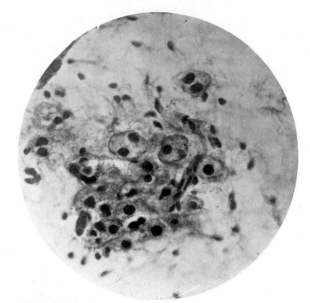

FIG. 52.—Mr. J. K. Cryptorchidism. Ocular 8; objective 4. Magnified 511 diameters. Leitz apochromatic. Island of syncytium and Leydig cells between the seminal tubules. Observe peripheral Leydig cells in act of dissolution and their close relationship to reticulum.

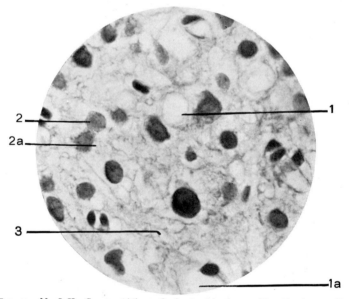

FIG. 53.—Mr. J. K. Cryptorchidism. Ocular 8; objective 2. Magnification 965 diameters. Leitz apochromatic. High magnification of reticulum and hyaloplasm surrounding apparently active Leydig cells. 1 and 1a, vacuoles; 2 and 2a, Leydig cells; 3, reticulum.

The delicate reticular meshwork which contains the numerous vacuolated spaces is beautifully illustrated in Fig. 53. In some parts leukocytes are found in abundance. While normally the nuclei of Leydig cells stain a faint blue, some of the nuclei found here display a deeper color than usual. Upon a close-up study of the Leydig cells themselves, shown in Fig. 54, the granular protoplasm of the cell bodies, their mono- and binuclear struc-

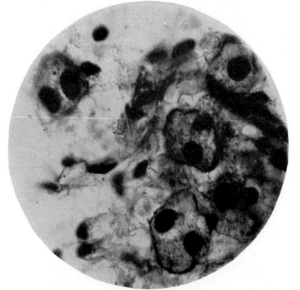

FIG. 54.—Mr. J. K. Cryptorchidism. Ocular 12; objective 2. Magnification 1250 diameters. Leitz apochromatic. High power appearance of Leydig cells; observe granular protoplasm; binuclear cells, of which 3 are represented in the field and 1 mononuclear Leydig cell.

ture is clearly depicted. In some of the spaces an epithelial cell is observed here and there, occasionally between the tubules.

Comment.

A critical study of this case brings the following facts vividly and emphatically before us: *First,* the total absence of spermatogenetic elements in the tubules; *second,* the abundance of reticulated syncytium with well developed normal Leydig cells; *third,* the apparent transformation of Leydig cells into vacuolated syncytium; and, *fourth,* the persistence of marked sexual potency, normal secondary sex characters and remarkable virility in the patient. All these factors can lead to *one conclusion only,* and that is: the Leydig cells with their reticulated syncytium *alone* are, in this case, responsible for the clinical manifestations, and no incretory functions at all can possibly be ascribed to any other of the testicular elements.

Conclusions.—From a review of the literature and from experimental studies with auto-, homo-, and heterotransplants carried on by the author for the last number of years he draws the following conclusions:

1. The spermatogenic function of the mammalian testicle seems to be limited to the tubules harboring the seminal cells.

2. It seems that the Leydig cells are alone responsible for the production of the internal secretion that gives rise to the secondary sex characters, sexual potency and cerebral eroticizing products.

3. The spermatogenic cells do not seem to play any part in the formation of such internal secretion; the function of the Sertoli cells and spermatogonia may, however, play some rôle in that respect.

4. Whether or not the Sertoli cells carry nutrition in the form of fat to supply the spermatogenic function of the tubules, whether they do or do not have a part in the production of an internal secretion, is questioned by many, but the author is inclined to look at them as nutritional and storage cells only until further definite proof to the contrary is furnished by investigators in this field of research.

5. The syncytial transformation of the transplanted male sex gland the author believes to spring, first, from the seminal cells, and after their disappearance, from the Leydig cells which are the most resistant of the testicular elements and have been observed by the author to disappear last in transplanted gonads.

Fortunately, in regard to therapy, surgical therapy especially, the question is not of such great moment. From the clinician's point of view it matters but little to what mechanism good effects are ascribed if good effects actually occur from testicular transplantation.

BIBLIOGRAPHY

[1] CENI: Rioist, Exper. di freniat, 1908, xxxiv, 57.

[2] HUNTER, JOHN: A Treatise on the Venereal Diseases, 1786.

[3] BROWN-SÉQUARD: Effets physiologiques et therap. d'un liquide extraite de la gland sexuelle male. C. R. Acad. d. Sc., Paris, 1893, cxvi, 856.

[4] BERTHOLD: Transplantation der Hoden. Arch. f. Anat. u. Physiol, 1849, p. 42.

[5] NUSSBAUM: Arch. f. Mikros. Anat., 1906, lxviii.

[6] HANSEMANN, VON: Ueber die sogenannten Zwischenzellen des Hodens und

deren Bedeutung bei pathologischen Veränderungen. Arch. f. path. Anat., u. Physiol., u. f. klin. Med. Berl., 1895, cxlii, 538–546.

[7] KUNTZ, A.: (a) The innervation of the gonads in the dog. Anat. Rec., Phila., 1919, xvii, 203–219; (b) Experimental Degeneration in the Testis of the Dog. Anat. Rec., Phila., 1919, xvii, 221–234. Endocrinology, v, Nr. 2 März, 1921.

[8] TANDLER and GROSZ: (a) Ueber den einfluss der kastration auf den Organismus. Wien. klin. Wchnschr., 1907, xx, 1596–1597.

[9] SELLHEIM: (b) Kastration and Knochenwachstum. Beitr. z. Geburtsh. u. Gynäk., Leipz., 1899, ii, 236–259, 6 tables.

[10] LAUNOIS and ROY: (a) Gigantisme et infantisme. Rev. Neurol., Par., 1902, x, 1054–1058; (b) Gigantisme et castration, les modifications du squelette consecutives a l'atrophie testiculaire et a la castration. Rev. Internat. de med. et de chir., Par., 1902, xiii, 397–399., ,

[11] GRUBER: Beobact. a. d. Menschl. u. Vergleich. Anat., Berlin, 1879.

[12] LORTET: (a) Allongement des membres posterieurs du a la castration. Compt. rend. Acad. d. sci., Par., 1896, cxxii, 819; (b) Allongement des membres inferieurs du a la castration. Arch. d'anthrop. crim., Lyon and Par., 1896, xi, 316–364; (c) Un squelette d'eunuque. Lyon med., 1896. lxxxi, 435–438.

[13] PITTARD: (a) La Castration chez l'homme et les modifications qu'elle apporte. Compt., rend. Acad. d. Sc., Par., 1903, cxxxvi, 1411–1413.

[14] PELIKAN: Gerichtl. med. Untersuch. u.d. Skopzenthum in Russland, 1876.

[15] PLATO: Arch. f. Mikros. Anat., 1896, xlviii, 280.

[16] BEISSNER: Arch. f. Mikros. Anat., 1898, li, 794.

[17] FRIEDMANN: Arch. f. Mikros. Anat., 1902, lii.

[18] REINECKE: Arch. f. Mikros. Anat., 1896, xlvii.

[19] REGAUD and POLICARD: C. R. Soc. de biol., Par., 1901, iii, 450.

[20] LOISEL: C. R. Soc. de biol., Par., 1902, iv, 346.

[21] MOSSELMANN and RUBAY: Ann. de Méd. Veterin. Bruxelles, 1902.

[22] ANCEL and BOUIN: Sur les Celles Interstitielles du Testicle. C. R. Soc. de biol., Paris, 1903, lv. 1397.

[23] HANES: Jour. Exper. Med., 1911, xiii, 338.

[24] STEINACH: Pflügers Arch., 1912, cxliv, 71.

[25] MASSAGLIA: Endocrinology, 1920, iv, 547.

[26] HARMS: Fortsch. d. Naturwissensch, Forsch, 1922. lxxvii, 189.

[27] VORONOFF and RETTERER: Jour. d'Urol. Med. et Chir., Par., 1922, xiv, 81; La Glande Génital Male, Paris, Doin., 1920.

[28] VORONOFF: "Congrés Franc de Chir," 1919.

[29] RETTERER: C. R. Soc. de Biol., Par., 1919, lxxxii, 1022.

[30] GLEY: "Physiologie," Paris, 1921.

[31] STEINACH und HOLZKNECHT: Pubertätsdrüse und Zwitterbildung. Archiv. f. Entwicklungs-Mechanik, Bd. 42, 1916; Erhöhte Wirkungen der inneren Sekretion bei Hypertrophie der Pubertätsdrüse. Archiv. f. Entwicklungs-Mechanik, Bd. 42, 3 Heft.

[32] STEINACH: Verjüngung durch experimentelle Neubelebung der alternden Pubertätsdüse. Sonderuck aus dem "Archiv. für Entwicklungs-Mechanik," Bd. 46, 1920, J. Springer, Berlin.

[33] STEINACH : Geschlechtstrieb und echt sekundäre Geschlechtsmerkmale als Folge der innersekretorischen Funktion der Keimdrüsen. "Zentralblatt f. Psychologie," Bd. 24, Nr. 13, 1910.

[34] STEINACH : Pubertätsdrüse und Zwitterbildung. "Archiv. für Entwicklungs-Mechanik," Bd. 42, 1916.

[35] LIPSCHÜTZ, A.: Quantitative Untersuchungen über die innersekretorische Funktion der Testikel. "Deutsche medizin, Wochenschr," 1921, Nr. 13.

[36] LIPSCHÜTZ, A.: Innere Sekretion und Sexualität: "Umschau," xxv, Nr. 44.

[37] LIPSCHÜTZ und OTTOW : Sur. les conséquences de la castration partielle. "Comptes rendus de la Soc. de Biologie," October, 1920.

[38] LIPSCHÜTZ, OTTOW und WAGNER : Nouvelles observations sur la castration partielle. "Comptes rendus de la Soc. de Biologie," June, 1921.

[39] LIPSCHÜTZ, OTTOW und WAGNER : Sur le ralentissement de la masculinisation dans la castration partielle. "Comptes rendus de la Soc. de Biologie," October, 1921.

[40] LIPSCHÜTZ, BORMANN und WAGNER : Über Eunuchoïdismus beim Kaninchen in Gegenwart von Spermatozoën in den Hodenkanälchen und unterentwickelten Zwischenzellen. "Deutsche medizin. Wochenschrift," 1922/10.

[41] LIPSCHÜTZ, A.: Deut. Med. Wchnschr., 1921, xliv, 1247.

[42] LIPSCHÜTZ, A.: Über die Abhängigkeit der Körpertemperatur von der Pubertätsdrüsen. Arch. f. d. ges. Physiol., Bonn, 1917, clxviii, 177–192.

[43] SAND : (S. auch 50, 51 u. 63) Moderne Sexualforschung, besonders Verjüngung. "Zeitschr. f. Sexualwissenschaft," Bd. 7, Heft 6.

[44] SAND : Ètudes experimentales sur les glandes sexueles chez les mammiferes. Journ. de Physiologie et de Pathalogie Générale," 1921, S. 305.

[45] MOORE : Journ. of Experimental Zoology, Bd. 33. Nr. 2.

[46] ARON, M.: Sur le conditionnement des caractéres sexuelles secondaires chez les batraciens urodéles. "Comptes rendus de la Soc. de Biologie," July, 1921.

[47] SCHMIDT, PETER : Theorie und Praxis der Steinachschen Operation. Rikola Verlag, A. G., Wien., 1922.

CHAPTER IV

PATHOLOGY OF THE TESTICLE

A. *Anatomical Anomalies.*
    Anomalies of Formation.
    Anomalies of Growth.
    Atrophy and Hypertrophy of the Testicle.
    Anomalies of Migration.
    Ectopic Testicle.
    Cryptorchidism.
    Anomalies of Position.
    Changes in the Testicle in Constitutional Diseases.
    Torsion of the Spermatic Cord.

B. *Tumors.*

C. *Inflammatory Conditions of the Testes.*

D. *Diseases of the Coverings of the Testicle and of the Spermatic Cord.*

E. *Tuberculosis of the Testes and Epididymis.*

F. *Syphilis of the Testes.*

G. *Functional Pathology; Dystrophias.*
    a. Effects of internal secretion of the testes upon growth and metabolism.
    b. Effects of Castration; Eunuchism.
    c. Eunuchoidism; Retarded Puberty and Infantilism; genito-glandular dystrophies.
    d. Precocious Puberty.
    e. Dwarfism and giantism.
    f. Adiposity and the endocrines.
    g. Fröhlich's disease (Dystrophia-adiposogenitalis).

H. *Functional Variations.*
    a. Hermaphroditism.
    Homo-sexuality.

A. Anatomical Anomalies of the Testicle.

Anatomically, the testicle may show any of four kinds of anomalies. *Anomalies of formation; anomalies of growth; anomalies of migration;* and *anomalies of position.*

Anomalies of Formation.—In the human embryo, the testicles and appendages arise from the two Wolffian bodies placed at either side of the

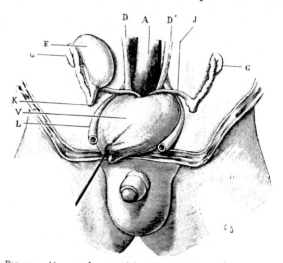

Fig. 55.—Absence of one testicle. (Anorchidism.) (After Godard.)

a, rectum; *d*, right ureter; *d'*, left ureter; *e*, right testicle. On the left side the testicle was completely absent. In its place one finds, along the internal border of the epididymis, a reddish body composed of blood vessels. *g*, right epididymis, of which the head is turned back and hooked; *g'*, left epididymis; same disposition of the head; *j*, left deferent canal (the right deferent canal occupies a position symmetrical to its opposite fellow); *k*, right gubernaculum testis (the left gubernaculum testis is seen in symmetrical position with the one on the opposite side); *l*, right umbilical artery (the left umbilical artery is symmetrical with opposite artery; *v*, bladder.

vertebral column. There are thus normally two glands and two excretory canals. The simple anomalies which may arise from some error of development may be: (a) fusion of the two normally independent testicles; (b) one or both of the testicles may be split or subdivided; (c) the gland and its excretory canal normally united may become separated, or one may be absent.

Saint-Hilaire [1] reported a case of testicular, kidney, etc., fusion in an infant. Cases of three testicles have been reported. Vanvaerts [2] reported such a case in 1908 in which the right testicle was duplicated, but there was no left testicle.

Ciulla[3] reports two cases of the very rare anomaly of two testicles in one half of the scrotum; in one of these cases the inguinal canal was also absent and there was only one ureteral orifice in the bladder.

Day[4] reported the case of a young man of nineteen who showed two scrota with two normal testes in each and a fifth testis in certain redundant tissue posterior to one pair. The only symptom apparently was super-

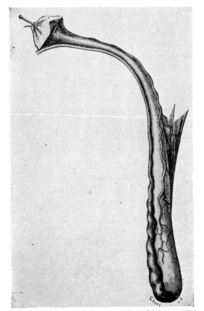

FIG. 56.—(After Godard.) Absence of the testicle, of the epididymis and of the terminal portion of the deferent canal. The figure shows the deferent canal attached to the vaginal pouch (vagino-peritoneal sac),which has been inflated and in which neither testicle nor epididymis could be found. The vas deferens could be followed only to a line corresponding to the trajectory of the inguinal canal, after which it could not be further traced. The seminal vesicle was also absent on that side.

abundant sexual desire. Several other more or less similar cases have been reported.

Separation of the testicle from its excretory canal may result in one of three conditions, *absence of the testicle,* absence of the excretory canal, or simultaneous absence of testicle and canal. The first is termed *anorchidism,* which may be unilateral or bilateral. (Fig. 55.)

The epididymis alone is very rarely found absent, and its absence is generally accompanied by a number of other anomalies; similarly with the deferent canal. (Figs. 56 and 57.)

6

Simultaneous absence of the testicle and its excretory canal is the most frequently observed variety of anomalies of the male genital apparatus. It may be uni- or bilateral.

As a general rule, anomalies of the epididymotesticular organs are accompanied by anomalies of the whole genitourinary apparatus, and occur in individuals who are more or less examples of incomplete monstrosity. A male individual with failure of development of both testicles is a true eunuch, who has the feminine aspect and development of form; but the monorchid loses nothing or little of his genital faculties. Similarly with him, who having the gland intact, he simply fails to develop an outlet for the sperm, on condition that the gland does not cease to develop. An individual deprived of his excretory apparatus, whether by vicious formation, or by a pathological process, acquires or preserves the characters of a male; he is sterile or azoöspermic in regard to propagating his kind, but is not impotent.

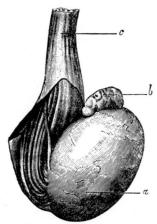

FIG. 57.—(After Godard.) Absence of the greatest portion of the epididymis (only the head exists) and the vas deferens. *a*, testicle; *b*, head of the epididymis (the body and the tail are missing); *c*, spermatic cord.

When the testicles are in the scrotum, it is easy to find by exploration if the excretory ducts are absent, but if the scrotum is empty it is impossible to say whether the case is one of anorchidism or cryptorchidism.

Anomalies of Growth.—There may be either *atrophy or hypertrophy of the testicle*. If atrophy occurs during fœtal life, the result later may be a small fibrous nodule in the scrotum which can scarcely be termed a testicle; if the atrophy results from any cause later in life, the testicles of an adult may be infantile in type. Such a one is both sterile and impotent, there being an entire failure of testicular secretion if the defect is bilateral. Without being common, the anomaly is seen with a fair degree of frequency.

Hypertrophy of the Testicle.—The weight of the testicle in an adult varies from about 15 to 30 gms. When hypertrophy is found, it usually has a pathologic origin, or else there is a developmental failure in one of the two testicles when the other may hypertrophy. Thus there may be hypertrophy in cases of monorchidism or unilateral ectopic testicle, as in a case reported by Curling [5] of a monorchid aged seventeen years, whose testicle weighed 70 gms.

Ectopic Testicles: Anomalies of Migration.—In ectopic testicles, the organ does not reach its proper destination—the scrotum. There are three types of anomaly, viz: (a) *arrested migration;* (b) *aberrant migration;* (c) *intermittent migration.*

In *arrested migration,* the testicle remains in some part of the trajectory which it traverses in its descent toward the scrotum, thus it may be in the abdominal, lumbar, in the iliac, or in the inguinal region. In such a case, the individual is a *true cryptorchid.*

David M. Davis gives the following classification of aberrant migration: " When the testicle seeks an abnormal position, it may be considered that (1) the implantation of the gubernaculum has been faulty, or (2) pressure or trauma have caused the ectopia. The ectopias resulting from aberrant migration may be classified as follows:

" *Intra-Abdominal.*

"(a) Pelvic—in the small pelvis.

"(b) Deep crural—the testis descends through the femoral ring to lie under the cribriform fascia (like femoral hernia).

" *Extra-Abdominal.*

" (a) Superficial crural—usually caused by pressure on a normally descending testis; fairly common.

"(b) Cruro-scrotal—the testis lies in the cruro-scrotal fold; rare.

"(c) Pubo-penile—at the base of the penis, in front of the pubis; rare.

"(d) Penile—beneath the skin of the penis; very rare.

"(e) Subcutaneous abdominal—the testis slides out under the skin at varying distances from the external ring; sometimes it reënters the muscles higher up.

"(f) Perineal—the testis lies beneath the skin of the perineum; eighty-seven cases reported.

"(g) Transverse—lies in the opposite side of the scrotum; five cases reported."

In *aberrant migration,* the testicle deviates from its normal path of descent and remains in some neighboring region, such as the iliac fossa, or the retrovesical pelvic space. These are cases of irregular testicular ectopia. In some very rare cases there has been observed a migration of the testicle into the penile or adjacent regions. (Fig. 58.)

Intermittent ectopia or migration is very rare, and is due to complete permeability of the peritoneo-vaginal canal, and a long, free, testicular pedicle. The anomaly consists in alternating immigration and emigration of the testicle.

Murad [6] reported a case of intermittent abdominal testicle in a boy of sixteen years. There was migration of the testicle in the lumen of a

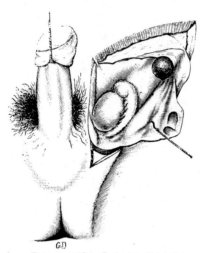

FIG. 58.—(After Godard.) *Ectopoi cruro-scrotale.* The testicle is situated entirely in the cruro-scrotal fold on the outside of the inguinal canal. The latter is opened on the posterior wall, of which one observes the outlines of the spermatic cord. Above and on the outside a small loop of strangulated bowel is seen on the abdominal orifice.

persistent peritoneo-vaginal canal. This migration was effected from below upward. Such a migration is only possible when means of intra-scrotal fixation of the testicle are absent. Normally such fixation is assured by the scrotal ligament which fixes the testicle in the fundus of the scrotum, or by adhesions of the vaginal with the other envelopes as well as by connective-cellular-tissue adhesions of the vas deferens and vessels.

Clinically this type of anomaly is characterized by two painful crises. One when the testicle slips up from the scrotum to the abdomen, the other when it again descends to its normal position.

Ectopia of the Testicle is extremely common, and has been estimated as met with in 1.25 per thousand of males, but *bilateral ectopia* is much less frequent than unilateral. The type most frequently seen is the *inguinal ectopia* and it is estimated that more than 60 per cent. of the cases are of this type, and that inguino-iliac ectopias reach 80 per cent. When the testicle is ectopic, the general rule is that the epididymis and deferent canal remain with it, but cases are known where they have become dissociated from the testicle.

From the point of view of spermatogenesis and testicular secretions, the most interesting question to us is the anatomical changes which occur in the ectopic testicle. The infantile ectopic testicle was examined histologically by Godard [7] and by Goubard and Follin [8] and the adult ectopic testicle by Monod and Arthaud [9] and Felizat and Branca.[10] (Fig. 59.)

In the child, the ectopic testicle does not show, according to these authors, any epithelial modifications, but there are abundant interstitial lesions; the connective tissue is extremely abundant. At puberty, and in the adult, the epithelial cells become granulous and undergo fatty degeneration, and the epithelium finally disappears; the seminiferous tubules undergo fibrous transformation.

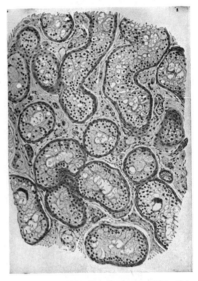

Although there is disagreement concerning the nature of the tissue changes, there is fair agreement upon one important fact, i.e., that a young ectopic testicle is not seriously compromised, but that an old ectopic testicle atrophies and degenerates; such testicle produces no spermatozoa. This latter phenomenon has a double reason: first, epithelial degeneration which prevents cellular evolution; and, second, that the increase of connective

FIG. 59.—Section of cryptorchid testicle of man aged 23 years. (After Harms.) Note absence of spermatogenesis and well-developed interstitial cells.

tissue which involves the corpus Highmori, offers an obstacle to excretion.

The therapeutic indication in misplaced testis is clear. Ectopic testicles must be operated upon to allow a proper replacement of the organs before the onset of puberty. If not operated upon and testicular atrophy has already set in, there remains only secondary operative procedures, which one can resort to, such as testicular transplantation, which we shall deal with later on. If the cosmetic element be an important one, some form of prosthesis (Cf. Chapter on Prosthesis) can be relied upon to furnish the desired result.

A point to which little attention has been paid is non-development or atrophy of the testicles, in the *interrelationship between the testicular secretions and the secretions of other internal secretory glands*. Gellin,[11] after testicular extirpation in the dog, saw the thymus increase in volume and weight. Similarly Cecca, Zoppi and Thorek [12] found that ablation of the genital glands caused thyroid hypertrophy, and that there were some changes in the suprarenals. (See Chap. on Interrelation.)

Another point of importance connected with ectopic testicles is that such are more liable to neoplastic evolution than in the case of testicles normally placed. Bland-Sutton [13] showed that of fifty-seven testicular tumors operated at the London Hospital, forty-eight, or 84 per cent., were in ectopic testicles.

Hyperplasia and hypertrophy of the interstitial cells appear to accompany both imperfect development and secondary atrophy of the seminiferous tubules.

Cryptorchids may be considered as midway between castrated animals and normal individuals in regard to the genital glands.

Observations on cryptorchid animals show absence of sustentacular cells, with the interstitial cells well developed. Bilateral arrest of descent of the testes with a lack of development as a rule means absolute sterility without loss of virility.

If sclerosis of the testes occurs, or if there is a complete compression of the spermatic cord, the individual is sterile and sexually undifferentiated. The penis is small, pubic hair shows feminine arrangement, larynx and voice remain as in boys, and there may be gynecomastia.

In the young, operative measures for the artificial descent of the testicle are usually followed by good functional and anatomical results. There need be but little apprehension in regard to the future genital life of such patients. In any ectopic patient, if it is certain that the ectopic testicle is sterile, the organ when brought down to the scrotum will remain sterile; but if the spermatogenic capacity has not been completely destroyed, the testicle in its new normal position may acquire renewed spermatogenetic power. Such opinion has the support of many cases in literature.

Griffith [16] experimented by replacing the testicles of dogs in the abdomen. The testicle so replaced continues to grow to some extent and the seminal tubules are seen to be lined with only a single layer of columnar epithelial cells, lying upon the tunica propria; spermatozoa do not exist.

The testicle of a full-grown animal so replaced soon dwindles to two-thirds normal size or even less, and, after a short time, presents the same histological picture as above. This is the same appearance as that of an arrested undescended testicle.

Anomalies of Position.—In its normal position the testicle hangs vertically in the scrotum, being suspended by its superior pole from its vessels and excretory canal. The epididymis is placed along the superior edge of the testicle. Many varieties of departure from this normal position of the testicle and epididymis occur, and with reference to the testicle the epididymis may be in anterior, horizontal, etc., inversion. Such inversion is usually unilateral.

Such inversions are of little consequence from the functional secretional standpoint.

Considered in detail, *inversion* occurs when it occupies a position in the scrotum different from that occupied normally; *i.e.*, not inclined slightly forward, the great axis being directed from above downward, the anterior border looking downward and the posterior border upward and backward. The variety called anterior inversion especially is very frequent and is said to occur in one of every twenty subjects.

The varieties of inversion are numerous: *Anterior inversion, superior* or *horizontal inversion, vertical inversion, lateral inversion, etc.* The types can be subdivided according to whether the epididymis is in front or behind. In anterior inversion, which is the only one of practical importance, the position of the testicle is exactly the opposite to that which it occupies in the normal state. Its posterior border has become anterior; its inclination is backward instead of forward. The epididymis always covering the posterior border has, like it, become anterior. Consequential to this arrangement there are minor derangements in the situation of the vaginal and the elements of the cord.

Various causes have been invoked to account for inversions of the testicle. No hypothesis is quite satisfactory. The most likely appears to be that the anomaly is due to a disturbance in development, which in this particular case is a vicious situation of the gubernaculum.

Inversions in no way interfere with the development or functioning of the testicle.   They are only of importance to the surgeon when for any reason he is called upon to explore or to operate the testicle or its adnexæ.

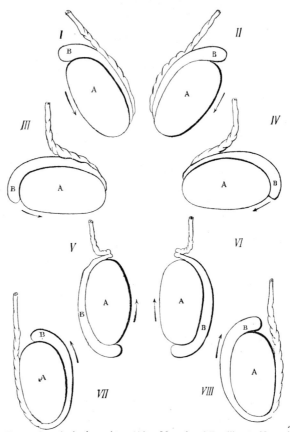

Fig. 60.—Types of testicular inversion. (After Monod and Terrillon.)   Normal type.   Great axis directed downward and backward.   Epididymis above and behind.   Free border of testicle and tunica vaginalis beneath and in front.

I, varieties deviating from the normal type.   The testicle has undergone rotation round a transverse axis; II, horizontal or superior inversion with the head of epididymis in front; III, horizontal inversion with the head of the epididymis in rear; IV, vertical inversion with epididymis in front and its head beneath; V, vertical inversion, epididymis is behind and its head beneath; VI, complete inversion, the epididymis is behind, its head is above, but the deferent canal is in front; VII, complete inversion, the epididymis is in front, its head is above, but the deferent canal is behind.

The attached table of illustrations shows schematically the various types of testicle inversions and is reproduced from the classical work of Monod and Terrillon [14] on *Diseases of the Testicle*.   (Fig. 60.)

Changes in the Testicle in Constitutional Diseases.

Jaffé [15] points out that autopsy findings in marasmus are generally negative. From a study of the testis in normal children and in marasmus Jaffé comes to the conclusion that the most certain criterion for the anatomical diagnosis in children's testes is the number of interstitial cells and their fat content. In the testicle of normal children there is but little connective tissue, the interstitial cells are few, and contain no fat or at most only traces of fat. In chronic infectious diseases there may be a secondary atrophy. In such cases one finds the stroma between the seminiferous tubules increased and edematous; the interstitial cells show no changes from normal. In children with a clinical diagnosis of constitutional inferiority one notes a definite increase in the connective tissue stroma and in the interstitial cells both in regard to number and lipoid contents. These are the changes usually found with marasmus. The increase of interstitial cells and their fat content is not looked upon as a cause of the condition, but rather as a manifestation of constitutional inferiority.

Torsion of the Spermatic Cord.

The author had the following to say in the *Interstate Medical Journal* on the question at issue: " Under the term strangulation of the testicle, or strangulation of the spermatic cord, a number of cases have been described in literature in which a mechanical torsion of the cord by interference with its vascularization has produced a sphacelous condition in itself or in the testicle, or both.

" The first case of this kind was reported by Delasiauve in 1840, and was confounded with strangulated intestinal hernia, so that the condition, though not rare, is not common. About one-third of the recorded cases occurred in frankly undescended testicles, and some evidence of this condition was given in a large number of the other cases. Indeed, several authors consider that an abnormal descent or other anomaly of testicular development is a necessary condition for torsion of the cord or testicle. A true strangulation of the cord at the ring is hardly conceivable.

" Torsion of the spermatic cord has been found to occur at all ages, but is most usual in the ten years following puberty. Vanverts,[17] who made an extensive report on the condition in 1904, collected forty-four cases. In thirty-nine of these in which the situation of the testicle was noted it was in the scrotum and normal in seventeen, in inguinal ectopia in fifteen, in abdominal ectopia in one, and in the others either lately descended or irregular in the scrotum. Similarly in thirty-four cases of torsion collected by Lapointe [18] the testicle was nonectopic in eighteen.

" The actual underlying cause producing torsion of the spermatic cord is unknown. As stated above, it is found that in about 47 per cent. of the cases the testicle is ectopic. According to Sebileau and Descomps,[19] torsion is especially favored by abnormal mobility of the testicle or by its abnormal pediculization. When the testicle is ectopic, there is usually abnormal mobility. The spermatic cord, being fixed to the abdominal wall by its superior pole, cannot well twist except by the action of the suspended testicle; and according to Bramann,[20] whenever there is any abnormality in the descent, there is more or less incomplete fixation of the testicle. Free testicular mobility is therefore looked on by many authors as a strong contributing factor of torsion. The torsion may occur either in the scrotal space within the fibrous sac or it may occur intravaginally. In the first, the testicle and cord twist with the sac containing them; in the second, owing to some unusual condition of the vaginal, the testicle floats freely and may twist within the sac. French writers distinguish between the two species, calling the first torsion and the second volvulus. Rigby and Howard [21] consider that the predisposing cause is a congenital abnormality in the attachment of the testis to the spermatic cord, joined to the voluminous condition of the tunica vaginalis.

" There may be (1) abnormal attachment of the common mesentery and vessels to the lower pole of the body of the testis and the globus minor, so that the testicle is attached by a narrow stalk instead of by a broad band; (2) the globus minor may be elongated; or (3) there may be a capacious condition of the tunica vaginalis.

" Scudder [22] found that in all reported cases of torsion with an undescended testicle the mesorchium was abnormally long. Bramann [20] found the same. Farr,[23] after an investigation of the literature found (1) that there was usually a free-lying testis with abnormally long mesorchium; (2) that the relative size and position of the testis and epididymis varied greatly, and both may be malformed or misshaped; (3) the tunica vaginalis is usually capacious; (4) cord is abnormally long or otherwise abnormal. As regards this latter, Lauenstein [24] has laid stress on a broad and flat condition of the cord, and Kocher [25] thinks that bifurcation of the cord favors torsion.

" Trauma has been looked on as an immediate factor when the foregoing predisposing causes exist. In many of the recorded cases there is a history of straining or some other effort producing intra-abdominal pressure. Farr thinks that torsion with an undescended testicle is largely due to intra-abdominal pressure acting directly or indirectly on the cord and testis, an attempt of nature's, perhaps, to force a descent.

" The natural result of torsion of the cord is to interfere with the vascular functions. The venous circulation is arrested, with consecutive congestion and intratesticular and intraepididymitic hemorrhage, which, according to the conditions, may lead to atrophy or necrosis of the organs. A suppurative or gangrenous condition can only arise if there be communication with some source of infection. The testicle becomes blackish from the gorged congested blood; histologic examination will disclose multiple hemorrhagic areas, with disappearance of all distinctive cell characteristics of the seminiferous tubules.

" The twist in the cord is generally confined to its lower part, and in the majority of cases it is from right to left in direction. In degree it may vary from half a turn to three or four complete turns.

" The onset of symptoms is almost always sudden and severe, varying according to the degree of torsion; there is usually sharp pain in the inguinal region, with exquisite tenderness on pressure; if the testicle be undescended, there will be swelling in the groin above Poupart's ligament, and the testicle will be absent from the scrotum on this side; the tumefaction has no impulse on coughing; the scrotal skin is usually red and edematous. When the testicle is in the scrotum, the latter organ is swollen and the appearance simulates epididymitis or orchitis. Vomiting is the rule, accompanied by persistent constipation, but suppression of flatus is exceptional. The intestinal symptoms are reflex in character, a reaction of the nervous system, resulting from torsion of nerves of the spermatic plexus. These intestinal conditions may occasion abdominal distention, with drawing up of the thighs, and the patient shows a facies abdominalis.

" When the testicle is fully descended, the symptoms may be mistaken for those of epididymitis or orchitis, and diagnosis may be difficult unless the case is seen very early. Epididymitis, or orchitis, may usually be excluded, however, by the absence of any cause. Gonorrhea, prostatic trouble, mumps, and other infective conditions, syphilis, and tuberculosis can generally be excluded.

" With an undescended testicle the symptoms are most easily mistaken for those of strangulated inguinal hernia. The symptoms in the two conditions are almost identical. In only a very few of this class of cases was a correct diagnosis made. In fact, in fifty-seven cases of torsion collected by Dalous and Constantin [26] a clinical diagnosis was made in three only. As Rigby and Howard,[21] however, point out, the general symptoms of torsion, while similar, are not so severe as those of strangulated hernia, and there is not the same degree of shock. Vomiting is not so persistent and is never fecal; the bowels react to purgatives and there is rarely absence of flatus. Besides, the absence of the testicle from the scrotum will offer a clue; and Scudder thinks that, with this fact known and the external abdominal ring empty, the mistake in diagnosis can hardly occur.

" Vanverts thinks that, while the two conditions can be differentiated by care, yet, if an epiploic strangulated hernia coexists with an ectopic testicle, differentiation from a torsion of the cord is impossible. It is interesting to mention that Villard and Souligoux [27] report that of six hundred and seventy patients operated at the Lariboisiere, Paris, for inguinal hernia, thirty-five were cases of ectopic testicle.

" Despite the apparent facility of distinguishing between a strangulated hernia and torsion of the cord with undescended testicle, yet in a large number of the cases, if not in the majority of the cases recorded in which diagnosis has been made preoperatively, cases of torsion with undescended testicle have been diagnosed as hernia. A tabular statement of such cases picked from the literature is appended.

" With regard to the evolution of these cases and the treatment, Putzu [28] made a number of experimental torsions of the spermatic cord in dogs. He found that a double twist effectively cut off the circulation from the testicle and that the organ atrophied. In many cases it necrosed and sloughed. Simpler torsion had results varying according to the amount of twist and the length of cord twisted. Atrophy may result, but the phenomena may be transitory. Of dogs that had suffered a double funicular twist, half had to be castrated. If operated within thirty hours of torsion, the testicle can generally be saved. In slighter twists the time can be extended.

" The clinical results observed and the operative findings generally agree with these results. Spontaneous detorsion may and often does occur, and is favored by rest, etc., but, as previously stated, the condition, if left untreated, may lead to hemorrhagic and ultimate gangrene. Atrophy is the more usual result, gangrene with sloughing being rare. In Scudder's list of cases there were seven not operated; two of these atrophied and three sloughed; the results in the other cases unknown. In nine cases observed by Rigby and Howard they saw no case of sloughing in four unoperated.

" The treatment of choice, if the case is seen early, appears to be to operate. If the testicle be undescended and in such condition that its preservation may with confidence be expected, it should be drawn down and fixed in place; if fixation is difficult, or if the vascular process of degeneration gives little hope of a good result, castration ought to be the rule, as, even though atrophy might reasonably be expected, the dangers which might arise from possible infection suggest removal of the testicle and the tunica vaginalis, with the shutting off of the peritoneal cavity. Attempts made to suture the aberrant testicle in the scrotum have generally resulted in failure.

" **Author's Case.**—Andrew P., Polish, aged fifteen years, seven months. Referred by Dr. Edward C. Seufert. Admitted to hospital with diagnosis of strangulated hernia. Diagnosis corroborated by the writer.

" **Family History.**—Negative.

" **Clinical History.**—Patient has always been well and of very active type. Parents are living and have seven children besides patient.

" **Onset of Present Complaint.**—While the patient was lifting a basket filled with potatoes he perceived a sudden pain in the left groin, which became agonizing at once. He dropped the basket and fell on the floor. Two physicians were called in, who diagnosed the case as strangulated hernia, and the patient was ordered transferred to the hospital, which was not, however, done until the following day.

" On his arrival at the American Hospital at 5 P.M. on the day following the onset the patient was found with a typical facies abdominalis, his left leg drawn up to his abdomen and strikingly shocked. He vomited only

LIST OF CASES DIAGNOSED AS STRANGULATED HERNIA, OR IN WHICH THE SYMPTOMS SUGGESTED IT AND IN WHICH TORSION OF THE SPERMATIC CORD WAS FOUND.

No. of case	Reporter and reference	Age of patient	Symptoms and diagnosis	Treatment and findings	Remarks
1	Delasiauve. Rev. med. franc et etrang, 1840, p. 363.		Strangulated hernia	Efforts to reduce by taxis; then operated; testicle ectopic and cord twisted several times; testicle gangrenous and removed	Recovery
2	Scarenzio. Ann. univers. di medicina, 1895, p. 695	41	Carried a truss for left hernia; sudden onset of pain in groin and signs of peritonization; inguinal tumefaction; strangulated hernia	Operated; testicle ectopic in vaginal, discolored; cord twisted twice; testicle edematous and full of dark blood; castration	Recovery
3	Anders. St. Petersb. med. Wchnschr., 1892, p. 437	13	Has carried a truss for hernia; tumefaction in the left inguinal canal; symptoms of strangulated hernia	Operated; tumor found within external inguinal ring; pillars of ring sectional; tumor found to be twisted and sphacelous epididymis; reduced spontaneously; castration	Recovery
4	Bryant. Med. chir. Trans., LXXV., p. 247	15	Had undescended testicle; symptoms suggested strangulated hernia	Operated; testicle in inguinal canal and discolored; cord twisted; easily untwisted; testicle was left in place	Recovery; testicle atrophied; mentions that Math had a similar case in a young child
5	Page. Lancet, Lond., 1892, I, p. 257	17	Sudden violent testicular pains on right side and vomiting; tumefaction; constipation; strangulated hernia	Operated; testicle black and sphacelous; epididymis tumefied; cord twice twisted from right to left; castration	Recovery
6	Barker. Lancet, Lond., 1893, I., 792	15	Right testicle small and incompletely descended; right inguinal hernia for seven years; sudden pains in region; vomiting and high temperature; right testicle swollen; no stools for two days, epiploic hernia	Operated; testicle flat, livid, and hard; cord twisted three half-turns; spontaneous detorsion; no hernia; castration	Recovery

7	Johnson. Ann. Surg., 1892, XVII, 282	20	Had left inguinal hernia; sudden pain and tumor in the left scrotum; vomiting	Operated three days after onset; testicle gangrenous; cord twisted several times; castration	Recovery
8	Lauenstein. Samml. klin. Vortr., 1894, No. 92	25	Sudden violent pain in right hypogastric region during an effort; tumor in groin; right testicle absent; vomiting; torsion of cord or epiploic hernia or appendicular abscess	Medical treatment but patient grew worse; operated; testicle discolored; cord twisted 180° from right to left; detorsion; castration	Recovery
9	Cohen. Deutsch. Zeitschr. f. Chir.. 1890, XXX, p. 101	21	Testicle ectopic in inguinal canal; sudden sharp pain in groin with tumefaction at site; thought to have strangulated hernia	On operation murky red fluid found in sac; swollen black testis discovered; cord twisted; orchidectomy	Recovery
10	Whipple. Nash. Brit. Med. Jour. 1891, June 6, p. 1226	16	Left testicle undescended; strain and felt something give way in groin; followed by lump in groin; vomiting; strangulated hernia	Hour-glass swelling of scrotum and groin; lower half is testis; upper sac containing bloody fluid; epididymis strangulated; cord and epididymis twisted twice; orchidectomy	Recovery
11	Keen. Med. Chir. Trans., Lond., 1892, LXXV, p. 253	23	Had a right reducible inguinal hernia and an undescended right testis; pain, vomiting tenderness and swelling in groin; thought the trouble was with the hernia	Operated; orchidectomy; testicle had been rotated three half turns; hematoma behind testis partly gangrenous	
12	Dujon and Chegut. Arch. prov. de chir., Paris, 1900, VIX, p. 653	14	After long horse-riding, colic followed by swelling of left scrotum; pain ceased for some days, but swelling persisted; pains recur. with ballooning of abdomen; constipation; symptoms become intensified; strangulated inguinal hernia	Operated; testicle found black and cord twisted twice right and left; cord replaced with testicle (which was not ectopic)	
13	Leonte. Bull. et mem. Soc. de chir. de Bucarest, 1900, p. 88 (see Bardesco, case 14)	70	Has always carried a truss for what was believed to be a left hernia and which at times had crises like strangulation; during one of such crises came to author	Operated; cord found twisted 270° from left to right; castration	Recovery No grangrene

LIST OF CASES DIAGNOSED AS STRANGULATED HERNIA, OR IN WHICH THE SYMPTOMS SUGGESTED IT AND IN WHICH TORSION OF THE SPERMATIC CORD WAS FOUND.

No. of case	Reporter and reference	Age of patient	Symptoms and diagnosis	Treatment and findings	Remarks
14	Bardesco. Bull. et mem. Soc. de chir. de Bucarest, 1900, p. 89	56	For four days showed symptoms of right strangulated hernia, following a fall; no stools; no flatus; no vomiting; no testicular ectopia	Operated; cord twisted 180° from right to left, commencing at intravaginal portion; castration	Recovery
15	Phocas. Mentioned by Vanverts, Ann. de mal. de org. genito. urin., 1904, XXII, p. 454 (case 43)	Infant	Symptoms of strangulated hernia; testicle ectopic	Operated; cord twisted; detorsion; castration	Recovery
16	Defontaine. Arch. prov. de chir., Paris, 1894, III, p. 141	8 mos.	Painful tumor in left scrotum extending to external ring; vomiting and agitation; epiplocele in a vagino-peritoneal sac	Operated; cord twisted; testicle swollen; detorsion; testicle allowed to remain	Recovery; testis atrophied five months later
17	Pillet. Rev. gen. de chir. et de therap., Paris, 1911, XXV, p. 806	32	Sudden pains in groin after heavy walk; tumor over inguinal region the size of orange; scrotum empty; one testicle ectopic; no stools; diagnosed as strangulated omental hernia in pro-peritoneal sac	Operated; sac contained edematous discolored testicle; cord twisted several times and sphacelous; castration	Recovery
18	McConnell. Dublin Jour. Med. Sc., 1912, CXXXIII, p. 337	15	Sudden pains in right groin while sitting with crossed legs in tailor-like position; tumefaction and vomiting; family physician diagnosed hernia; hospital diagnosis strangulated inguinal hernia; right testicle not ectopic	Operated; sac between pillars of external ring contained twisted spermatic cord and vas deferens; loop of cord twice twisted on self; right testis removed	Recovery; author says the customary symptoms of twisted cord, viz., edematous testicle and redness of scrotum were absent

19	Farr. Ann. Surg., 1913, LVIII, p. 838	1	Vomiting four days; constipation; pain and swelling in right groin; right testicle not felt in scrotum; strangulated right inguinal hernia	Operated; inguinal canal contained enlarged testicle and epididymis twisted on cord; castration	Recovery
20	Turner. Brit. Med. Jour., 1903, II, p. 1403	13 mos.	Sudden irreducible tumefaction in the left inguinal region; pain and agitation; no vomiting; testicle not found in scrotum; strangulated hernia with undescended testis	Operated; testis in sac edematous and discolored; cord twisted one whole turn right to left; castration	Recovery
21	Heaton. Brit. Med. Jour., 1905, II, p. 1342	24	Symptoms both constitutional and local, closely resembled those of strangulated hernia	Operated; testicle swollen and infiltrated with blood, discolored; tunica vaginalis distended with blood; castration	Recovery
22	Bruch. Bull. et mem. Soc. de chir. de Paris, 1908, XXXIV, p. 721	18	Suddenly awakened from sleep by violent pain in inguinal region; came to hospital with diagnosis of strangulated inguinal hernia; bilious vomiting; diagnosis of hernia accepted	Operated; testis and epididymis found in sac in inguinal canal; cord twisted; detorsion; castration	Recovery
23	Viscontini. Gaz. de orped. e. d. chir. Milan, 1913, XXXIV, p. 1041.	8 mos.	Vomiting; pain; agitation; scrotum enlarged on left testicle in place; brought to hospital with diagnosis of left strangulated inguinal hernia; surgical diagnosis of strangulated epiplocele	Operated; testis free in vaginal without mesorchium; vaginal distended; supra-vaginal twisting of cord from right to left three times twisted; castration	Recovery; author says that supra-vaginal torsion is very rare and that this is the fourth case on record
24	Snyder. Jour. Kansas Med. Soc., 1916, XVI, p. 195	13	Sudden pain without warning in left inguinal region; severe vomiting; shock; hospital diagnosis of strangulated omental hernia	Operated; testicle in scrotum; cord twisted in vaginal testicle; gangrenous; castration	Recovery; boy also had a simultaneous hernia in linea alba, which was rectified at the same time

7

once or twice. His abdomen was tympanitic and somewhat sensitive. Over
the left groin a swelling was found about the size of a hen's egg; the
overlying integument was edematous and actively hyperemic. Gentle
attempts at taxis promptly failed. There was no testicle in the left scrotum. Patient complained of violent pains, paroxysmal in character, radi-

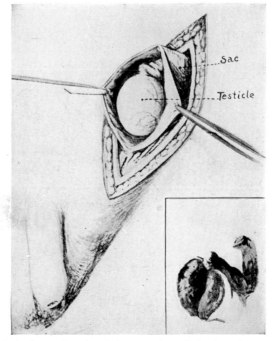

FIG. 61.—Author's case of torsion of the spermatic cord, showing point of torsion of the cord
and anatomic relations. Lower insert presents the gross appearance of the testis and cord.

ating to the left thigh, abdomen, and perineum. The temperature was
normal; pulse, 70; blood count, negative; bowel action, torpid; persistent
efforts followed by expulsion of flatus and slight bowel movement;
urinalysis, negative.

"Operation.—Ether anæsthesia. Incision over tumor. Tissues tume-
fied and infiltrated. Testicle exposed. Spermatic cord twisted once clear
around at the lower angle, causing testicle to appear brownish black. The
tunica vaginalis was free and very spacious. Considerable effusion of
serous fluid into the vaginalis. Mesorchium was abnormally long. The

cord was untwisted and packs wrung out of hot salt solution applied to testis and cord for nine minutes. No signs of return of circulation; no possibility, apparently, of bringing testicle into scrotum, as suggested by Bevan in performing operation for cryptorchidism. Testicle was then promptly removed. The wound was closed and the patient returned to bed. Uneventful convalescence and recovery. (Fig. 61.)

" Pathology.—On splitting the testicle and epididymis a brownish black color made it at once apparent that the venous circulation, as well as the arterial supply, had been seriously interfered with as a result of the shutting off of the blood supply by reason of the twisting of the cord. Here and there slight intratesticular hemorrhages were noted with the naked eye. The microscope disclosed a distinct obliteration of the normal appearance of the seminiferous tubules and sanguineous exitus into the testicular tissue by diapedesis and rhexis.

" Conclusions.—(1) Torsion of the spermatic cord must be reckoned with as a possible criterion in the differential diagnosis of apparently complicated hernia; (2) from a study of the literature it becomes plainly evident that in twisted spermatic cords, particularly when they are ectopic with short mesorchium and with clear evidence of a beginning degeneration of the testicle involved, castration seems the only rational method of procedure." [31]

BIBLIOGRAPHY

[1] SAINT-HILAIRE: Hist. des Anomal. d. Test. T. i., p. 542.
[2] VANVAERTS: Echo méd. du Nord., 1908.
[3] CIULLA: Rivist. Sanit. Siciliana, 1922, No. 16.
[4] DAY: Jour. Amer. Med. Assn., lxxi, 2055, 1918.
[5] CURLING: Diseases of the Testes, 4th edit.
[6] MURAD: Lyon Chirurg, xvi, 519.
[7] GODARD: C. R. Soc. de Biol., Paris, 1896, 2 ser. T., iii, 415.
[8] GOUBARD and FOLLIN: Soc. de Biol., Paris, 1855, p. 203.
[9] MONOD and ARTHAUD: Arch. gén. de Méd., 1887.
[10] FELIZAT and BRANCA: Jour. de l'anat. et de physiol, 1902.
[11] GELLIN: Zeitschr. f. exper. Path. u. Therap., 1910, p. 416.
[12] CECCA and ZOPPI:
[13] BLAND-SUTTON: Practitioner, Jan., 1910.
[14] MONOD and TERRILLON: Mal. du Test., p. 90.
[15] JAFFÉ: Frankfurt Zeitsch. f. Path., 1921, xxvi, 250.
[16] GRIFFITH: Jour. of Anat. and Physiol., 1892, xxv, 99, 483.
[17] VANVERTS: Torsion du cordon spermatique (Ann. d. mal. d. org. genitourin., Paris, 1904, xxii, p. 401)

[18] LAPOINTE : La Torsion du cordon spermatique, Paris, 1904.

[19] SEBILEAU and DESCOMPS : Maladies des organes genitaux des hommes. Nouveau traite de chir., Paris, xxxii, 1916, pp. 606–629.

[20] BRAMANN : Der Processus vaginalis und sein Verhalten der Störungen des Descensus testiculorum. Arch. f. klin. Chir., xl, p. 137.

[21] RIGBY and HOWARD : Torsion of the Testis, Lancet, Lond., 1907, i, p. 1415.

[22] SCUDDER, C. E. : Strangulation of the Testis by Torsion of the Cord. Ann. Surg., 1901, xxxiv, p. 234.

[23] FARR : Strangulation of the Undescended Testis. Ann. Surg., 1913, lviii, p. 838.

[24] LAUENSTEIN : Sammlung klin. Vortr., 1864, No. 94.

[25] KOCHER : Deutsch. Chir., 1887, p. 585.

[26] DALOUS and CONSTANTIN : Bistournage spontane-tuberculose interstitielle de l'epididyme. Ann. d. mal. d. org. genito-urin., Paris, 1904, xxii, p. 1255.

[27] VILLARD and SOULIGOUX : Congres francais de chir., 1906, xix, pp. 578–636.

[28] PUTZU : Clinica chir., Milan, 1912, xx, p. 1295.

[29] DAVIES-COLLEY : Brit. Med. Jour., 1892, i, p. 811.

[30] BRYANT : Med. Chir. Transac., Lond., 1892, lxxv, p. 247.

[31] THOREK : Interstate Medical Journal, xxvi, No. 3, 1919.

B. Tumors of the Testicle.   Benign and Malignant.

Scrotal elephantiasis is occasionally met with. (Fig. 62.)

Epididymal spermatic cysts are often observed. They may arise from remnants of the Wolffian bodies isolated from the excretory channels, or they may be due to the rupture of one of the epididymary or efferent canals. They may thus be either congenital or acquired. Such cysts often contain spermatozoa. They are benign tumors, which as far as we know, do not interfere with spermatogenesis or excretion even when large.

Cysts of the seminal glands are usually situated just above or below the epididymis. They are also called spermatic cysts because their contents usually enclose more or less spermatozoids. Such cysts are very frequently found during autopsies, and clinical cases giving symptoms are rare. According to Hochenegg's statistics, one man in every five will show a cystic condition of the testicle or epididymis. They may be divided into two classes: (1) supraepididymary cysts, *i.e.*, small cysts usually situated on the convex face of the epididymis and not giving any clinical symptoms; (2) large cysts, sub-epididymal in situation between the epididymis and testicle. These are the only ones which may have a clinical interest.

The first type occurs mostly in the middle-aged and elderly subject, and are usually multiple and contain serous fluid. Monod and Terrillon [1] think that these small cysts originate from the seminal elements of the testicle, or its adnexæ.

Large cysts have their walls composed of two layers, a fibrous layer and

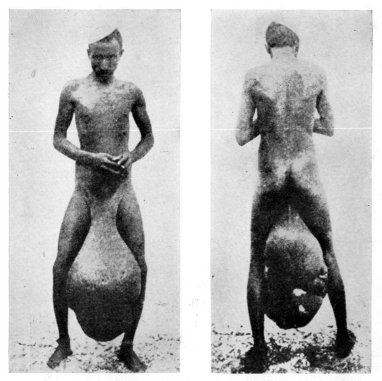

FIG. 62.—Elephantiasis of the scrotum. (After Murray.)
Left, anterior view. Right, posterior view.

an epithelial lining. The content is usually a serous fluid which contains spermatozoa. It is usually accepted that such cysts arise from debris of the Wolffian bodies. (Figs. 63–66.)

Primary tumors of the testicle proper are relatively rare. They may develop at the expense of the seminal cells or of the interstitial cells, or as intratesticular embryomata, etc. *Seminal epitheliomata* may arise from any layer of the evolving seminal cells. Malignant neoplasma of the testicle usually occur at the age of sexual activity, but more than forty cases have been observed in infants. Chevassu,[2] in his thesis in 1906

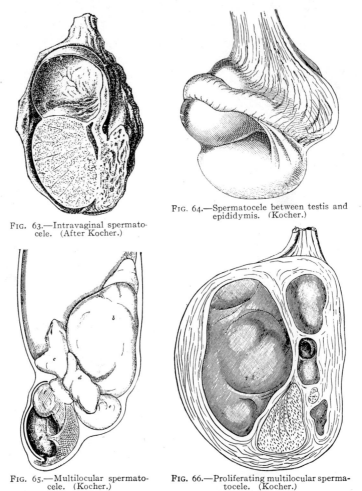

FIG. 63.—Intravaginal spermato-cele. (After Kocher.)

FIG. 64.—Spermatocele between testis and epididymis. (Kocher.)

FIG. 65.—Multilocular spermato-cele. (Kocher.)

FIG. 66.—Proliferating multilocular sperma-tocele. (Kocher.)

gives the following classification of testicular tumors based on the occurrence of tumors either in the special or incidental tissues of the testicle:

1. *Histoid tumors proper to the testicles:*

    (a) Neoplasms of the seminal epithelium.

    (b) Neoplasms of the interstitial cells.

2. *Common incidental testicular tumors*, *i.e.*, neoplasms of the connective, fibrous or loose tissue.

3. *Organic tumors* (embryomata) including tumors arising from embryonary rests, whether of testicular origin or not, but which are found in the testicle and develop within its domain.

Tanner [3] has quite recently published an important contribution to testicular tumors.

Tanner says that in tumors of the testicle not only are found the usual grounds for variability, but in addition we are dealing with a gland the function of which is peculiarly adapted to the production of germ cells. Thus the theoretical classification of tumors of these organs embodies the widest possible range of new pathological formations.

Tanner has made detailed histological studies of one hundred testicular tumors, and of these ninety-seven were malignant in type. From these studies Tanner suggests the following classification:

Tumors of the Testicle.

A. *Malignant:*
  (1) " Carcinomatous "—large cell, large nucleus type undoubtedly closely related to
  (2) " Mixed type:"
    (a) Tumors containing cartilage, cysts, glands, etc.
    (b) Ordinary glandular structure tumors.
    (c) Chorio-epithelioma.

B. *Benign:*
  (1) Dermoid.
  (2) Epithelial:
    (a) Adenoma of the seminal tubules as described by Pick and Chevassu.
  (3) Mesoblastic:
    (a) Interstitial cell tumors.
    (b) Fibroma.
    (c) Lipoma, myxoma.

Tanner finds that new testicular growths are only observed about once in every two thousand male hospital admissions. The disease is practically always unilateral, involving both sides only as a metastatic growth from

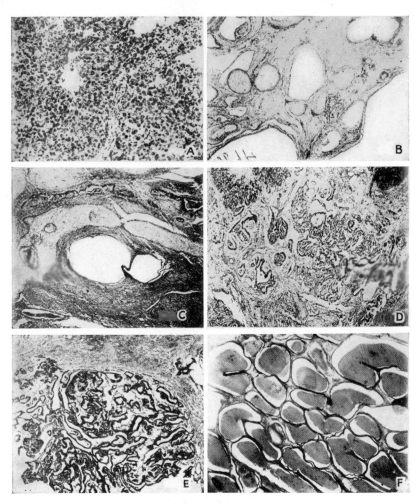

Fig. 67.—Tumors of the testicle. (Tanner.)

A, Case 9, typical large polyhedral shaped cells with deeply staining nuclei and pale cytoplasm, characteristic of the carcinomatous type of tumor. B, Case 1, cystic spaces and areas of cartilage in mixed type tumor. C, Case 12, cystic spaces and nests of squamous epithelium containing pearl formations, found in mixed type tumor. D, Case 63, peculiar gland-like structures. E, Case 65, still another type of gland-like formation in mixed type tumor. F, Case 80, low-power photomicrograph showing thyroid-like tissue. Other areas in same tumor also showed carcinomatous-like cells and still another area showed gland-like structures.

the skin, seminal vessels, etc. Both testicles are involved with about equal frequency. (Fig. 67.)

Such tumors are frequently the result of trauma.

Tumors of the testicle are most frequently observed between the ages of eighteen and fifty years, the period of greatest sexual activity.

Undescended testicles within the canal are more apt to become malignant than normally placed organs. Undescended testicles within the abdomen are relatively immune to malignant changes. The average mor-

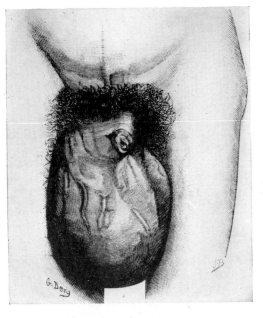

FIG. 68.—Large carcinoma of the right testicle
(After Monod and Terrillon.)

tality among patients attacked by malignant testicular tumor is about 80 per cent. The so-called mixed type of tumor gives a much higher mortality than the carcinomatous type. Tumors containing cartilage and squamous epithelium seem to have a decidedly unfavorable prognosis. The following illustrations depict some of the tumors occasionally met with. (Figs. 68 and 69.)

Radical operation is indicated in all cases of malignant testicular tumor in which the malignant process is strictly limited, that is where there are no metastases. However, occasionally the ordinary castration operation, even when supplemented by X-rays or radium, is often disappointing.

Tumors involving the sperm cells or interstitial cells may be directly concerned in the production of hypo- or hypersecretion of testicular hormone and thus be the direct cause of one of the dystrophias due to malfunctioning of this hormone.

In considering the radical operation for teratoma testis Hinman, Gibson and Kutzmann[8] give an analysis of seventy-nine cases, ten of which are personal. These authors believe that tumors of the testicle present two considerations not found to a like degree in tumors elsewhere. First, their complex and diverse pathology which has aroused so much difference of opinion as to its nature and, secondly, the embryological and anatomical peculiarities which render the surgical treatment of the condition in one way very easy and in another way very difficult. They consider the clinical recognition of testicular tumor as largely a matter of exclusion. The tumors present no pathognomonic signs or symptoms, and they believe that in view of the difficulties in diagnosis, the extreme malignancy of the growths and the simplicity of exploratory examination, the interest of the patient demands that every testicular enlargement which is in any way suspicious should be immediately inspected surgically, and when necessary its exact nature determined by microscopic study.

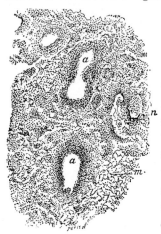

FIG. 69.—Lymphadenoma of the testicle. (After Cornil and Rámever.) Enlarged 40 times. *aa*, lumen of seminiferous tubules; *n*, tubular wall transformed into reticulated tissue; *m*, connective tissue transformed into reticulum.

For clinical purposes Hinman finds it convenient to divide testicular tumors into two large groups, which occur with about equal frequency, *seminoma* (Figs. 70, a, b, and c) and *teratoma* (Figs. 71, a, b, and c). In the seventy cases of radical operation the prognosis appeared about equally good for either type. The prognosis from the standpoint of pathology is indicated in Hinman's Table III. The extremely poor outlook for patients suffering from tumors of the testicle is well recognized. Orchidectomy, even with early diagnosis, has proved a dismal failure and

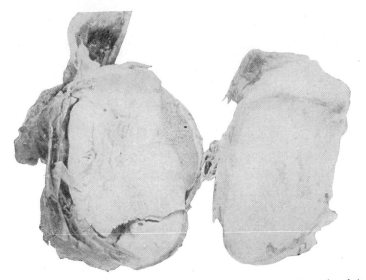

FIG. 70a.—Photograph of single cell type tumor, a seminoma. At the inner edge of the left half of the specimen is seen a small, compressed remnant of the testicle. Usually no normal testicular tissue can be found. The tumor measured 5 by 5.7 cm. (Hinman et al.)

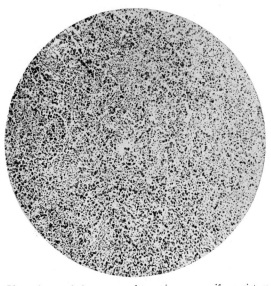

FIG. 70b.—Photomicrograph (low power) of a seminoma, a uniform picture of large, round, vesicular cells resembling the spermatoblasts. This is the type of tumor which probably has been so frequently wrongly diagnosed as sarcoma. (Hinman et al.)

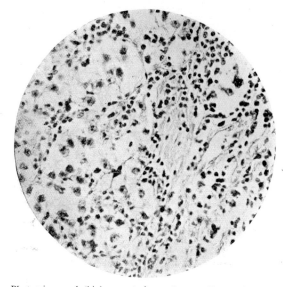

FIG. 70c.—Photomicrograph (high power) of a seminoma. The uniform round vesicular cell distributed in a lymphoid stroma is characteristic. The nucleus is large and shows fine stippling as seen in spermatoblasts and generally one or two large nucleoli. (Hinman et al.)

FIG. 71a.—Photograph of a mixed cell type of tumor, a teratoma. No normal testicular tissue is seen. Multiple dissimilar areas characteristic of different types of tissue, such as cartilage, gland, and single cell forms give a totally different picture from that of Figure 70a. The size of the tumor was 9 by 10 cm. (Hinman et al.)

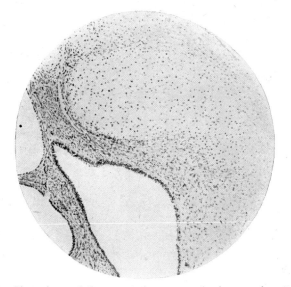

FIG. 71b.—Photomicrograph (low power) of a teratoma, showing area of cartilage and three cystic spaces, each lined with a different type of epithelium, cuboidal, short columnar, and high columnar. (Hinman et al.)

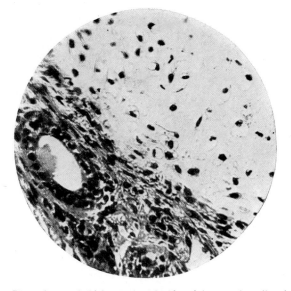

FIG. 71c.—Photomicrograph (high power) at the edge of the area of cartilage in Fig. 71b, but with a small epithelial lined cyst surrounded by connective tissue stroma invaded at portions of the outer rim of the cyst wall by malignant tumor cells. (Hinman et al.)

there is statistical evidence to prove the inadequacy of simple castration, as shown in Table II. A mortality after surgery of over 80 per cent. is appalling, and that castration must be supplemented by radium, X-ray or more radical surgery is apparent if any considerable improvement in treatment is to be gained.

The results of Barringer and Dean,[9] in a four years' systematic use of radium are far from encouraging (Cf. Table II, Hinman). The X-ray has also been used in the attack on these tumors. Orbaan's is the only systematic study available. He reports nine cases treated before and after castration. Eight of these showed clinical evidence of recurrence when X-ray treatment was instituted. Six cases have died and three are living 24, 25, and 30 months, respectively, after starting X-ray treatments, and the patient living 25 months still shows clinical evidence of metastases.

The results of findings in the seventy-nine cases of attempted and successful radical resection are indicated in the accompanying tables (Cf. Tables I, IV, and V, Hinman).

TABLE I.—ANALYSIS OF SEVENTY-NINE CASES OF RADICAL OPERATION WITH RESPECT TO LUMBAR METASTASES. (AFTER HINMAN)

	Group I-A — Lumbar glands palpable clinically before operation	Group I-B — Lumbar metastases so extensive as to be inoperable	Group II-A — Metastases not found in the lumbar glands that were removed	Group II-B — Metastatic glands found and completely removed	Group III-A — Incomplete data
Number of cases	9	13	25	26	6
Inoperable	8	13			
Radical removal	1	0	25	26	6
Surgical mortality	3	2	3	2	
Died of metastases	5	4	8	6	1
Lost after discharge	0	0	1	0	
Living with metastases	1	4	1	0	
Living and well			12 / 2 over 4 yrs.	17 / 4 over 4 yrs.	5
Incomplete data		3			
Accidentally killed					

Summary

Group I—
Operative mortality............ 22.7 per cent.
Morbidity to date.............. 75.0 per cent.
Probable morbidity............ 100.0 per cent.
Group II—
Operative mortality............ 9.2 per cent.
Morbidity to date............. 37.2 per cent.
Living 4 years or longer....... 6 cases
Living over 2 years........... 14 cases

Grand Summary

Operative deaths.................. 10 (12.6%)
Died of metastases................ 24
Living with metastases............ 6
Living and well................... 34
Killed or lost.................... 2
Incomplete data................... 3
                                   ——
Total............................. 79

TABLE II.—RESULTS FOLLOWING SIMPLE ORCHIDECTOMY. (AFTER HINMAN)

Author	Number of cases	Number lost from observation	Number of cases dead					With metastases clinically	Number of cases living							4 yr. cures
			Time not stated	Within 1 yr.	In 1 to 4 yrs.	After 4 yrs.	Total		Time not stated	Less than 1 yr.	1 to 3 yrs.	3 to 4 yrs.	Total	Longer than 4 yrs.	Total	
Chevassu......	100		15	38	27	1	81					4	4	15	19	19%
Chevassu......	S 47		7	8	23	1	31					4		12	16	34%
	T 50			28	11		47							3	3	6%
Kober.........	76		40	All died within 3 yrs.		1 (6yrs.)	41			18	6	2	26	8	34	13%
Nicholson.....	18			12			12		6 (1 to 5 yrs.)				6			
Howard........	57	21	27						6 (all less than 3 yrs.)			2	8	3		
Hinman........	24						20				1					
	S 9										1					
	T 9															
Coley.........	52 Orchidectomy and "Coley's serum"	14	18					9			3	3		3		
Barringer and Dean:																
Group II[1]...	8	2	3					8		2	3	1	3			
Group III[2]..	19	6	8					19		2			5			
Group IV[3]...	6	2	2							2						

S—Seminoma. T—Teratoma. [1]No Surgery. "Primary inoperable." [2]Castration plus radium—"recurrent." [3]Castration plus radium—"prophylactic."

TABLE III.—PROGNOSIS AS REGARDS DURATION AND TYPE OF TUMOR.   (AFTER HINMAN)

	Seminoma			Teratoma		
	Duration	Died	Living	Duration	Died	Living
Group I-A......	18 mos. 10 mos. Not stated	3 mos. 5 mos. 5 mos.				Not stated 2 mos.
Group I-B........	8 mos. Not stated 9 mos. 6 mos. 6 mos.	31 mos. 4 mos. 13 days*	18 days 15 days	6 mos. 7 yrs.		
Group II-A......	15 mos. 7 mos. 11 mos. 4 mos. 5 mos. 3 mos. 3 yrs. 16 mos. Not stated	5 yrs. 7 days* 7 mos. 2 mos.*	2 mos. 18 mos. 4 mos. 2 mos. 10 mos.	14 mos. 12 mos. Several yrs. Not stated Not stated 3-4 mos. 29 mos. 6 mos.	Not stated 9 mos.	28 mos. 28 mos. 12 mos. 22 mos. Lost track of 24 mos. 2 mos.
Group II-B......	5 mos. 30 mos. 36 mos. 12 mos. Not stated		34 mos. 4 yrs. 10 mos. 8 mos. 10 mos. 8 yrs.	12 mos. 10 mos. 8 mos. 4 mos. 9 mos.	8 mos. 9 mos. 4½ mos.	3 yrs. 31 mos.

TABLE III.—PROGNOSIS AS REGARDS DURATION AND TYPE OF TUMOR—Continued

	Seminoma			Teratoma		
	Duration	Died	Living	Duration	Died	Living
Group II–B (Continued)	Not stated 6 mos. 3 mos. 4 mos. 5 mos. Not stated**	8 mos.* 18 mos.	3½ mos. 30 mos. 8 yrs. 14 mos.	3 yrs. 1 mo. 7 yrs. 4 mos. 8 mos. 10 mos.	few hrs.*	7 mos. 21 mos. 4½ yrs. 2 mos. 1 mo.
Group III–A	Not stated		24 mos.			
Total		12 cases	17 cases		6 cases	16 cases
Total		29 cases			22 cases	

*Died of cause other than tumor.　**Reported as carcinoma.

SUMMARY

In 79 cases of radical operation for malignant tumor of the testicle, 29 are reported as seminomata, 22 as teratomata, and 28 are indefinite. Twelve cases of seminoma are dead and 16 living; 6 cases of teratoma are dead and 16 living. Omitting Group I, which was inoperable, and the 5 cases dying of causes other than tumor, supplies us with more exact comparative figures, thus, of 16 cases of seminoma 3 are dead, and 13 living (3 living and well over 4 years, and 2 living and well approximately 2 years or more). So far as this limited series permits of analysis, the prognosis for seminoma and teratoma is about the same. The reader will recall that Chevassu in 100 cases of simple castration found that teratoma gave a decidedly less favorable prognosis than seminoma.

TABLE IV.—SEVENTY-NINE CASES OF RADICAL OPERATION.

Time elapsed since operation	Group I-A — Lumbar glands palpable clinically before operation		Group I-B — Lumbar metastases so extensive as to be inoperable		Group II-A — No metastases found in lumbar glands removed		Group II-B — Metastatic glands found and completely removed		Group III-A — Incomplete data		Total	
	Dead	Living	Dead	Living	Dead	Living	Dead	Living	Dead	Living	Dead	Living
0–6 mos.	6[3]	1*	5[2]	3*	4[3]	3	4[2]	4			19	11
7–12 mos.	1				3	2,1*	4	3	1		9	6
13–18 mos.	1			1*	1		1	1			3	2
19–24 mos.					1	3		1		1	1	5
25–30 mos.						2		1				3
31–36 mos.			1					3			1	3
37–42 mos.												
43–48 mos.												
over 48 mos.					1	2		4			1	6
Not stated			(3)		1	(1)				4	1	4
Total	8	1	6 (3)	4	11	13 (1)	9	17	1	5	35**	40

SUMMARY

Thirty-four cases dead, 40 living; 6 of 40 cases living have metastases, leaving 34 cases living and well. Four cases (indicated by parentheses) not stated (killed or lost). Ten cases (indicated by co-efficients above—2,3) are included in the surgical mortality. Six cases (indicated by asterisks above) are living with metastases. It is to be noted that deaths after operation occurred almost always within the first year, and cases surviving this period in good health have a fair guarantee of cure. A point of prime importance in support of the radical operation as against simple castration is the fact that 4 cases having lumbar metastases have remained cured over 4 years since operation (2 of these are living and well 8 years after operation). (Hinman et al.)

**This figure includes 1 case accidentally killed, and the 10 cases of surgical mortality, leaving 24 dead from metastases.

TABLE V.—ANALYSIS OF CASES OF RADICAL OPERATION. (AFTER HINMAN et al.)

Group I.—Inoperable Cases

A—Cases with Metastatic Lumbar Nodes Palpable before Operation

Author	Date of operation	Age, years	Duration	Side	Clinical metastases	Operation and microscopical diagnosis	Died post-operative	Metastases	Living
1. Gregoire[2],[3],[4], Case 2	4-8-07	42	18 mos.	R	Abdominal masses palpable	Radical. Hard irregular mass on vena cava. Few glands removed for examination Diagnosis: seminoma	3 mos.		
2. Gregoire[2],[3],[4], Case 3	8-1-07	40	10 mos.		None at time of castration. Lumbar glands felt at time of radical	Castration 8-10-06 Radical 8-1-07. Hard diffuse mass upper limits of which could not be felt. Mass surrounded ureter. Operation confined to freeing this Diagnosis: seminoma	17 mos. after castration. 5 mos. after radical	Viscera and lumbar glands	
3. Fredet[2],[4]	4-24-09	27		L	Mass in left iliac fossa. Lumbar region negative cord infiltrated	Radical. Large adherent mass in left iliac fossa. Enlarged adherent glands about aorta. Left lumbar gland size of almond. Fragments removed for examination Diagnosis: seminoma	5 mos. †	Lumbar glands	
4. André	Not stated Reported 5-8-12	40	8 mos.	L	Lumbar glands and mass near hilus of kidney size of walnut felt	Radical. 1 gland lower pole of kidney, 3 in angle formed by aorta and renal vessels removed. Suspicious induration higher up which could not be removed			Lost from observation after discharge 2 weeks

5. Pillet.........	Not stated Reported 1913	37			Iliac and inguinal glands palpable	Radical with removal of all glands	1 yr. †	Lumbar glands
6. Georgesco and Savesco...... Case 2	Not stated Reported 1914	24	1 yr.		Lumbar glands palpable	Radical exploratory incision with removal of testicle and cord. Abdominal mass inextirpable	15 days ‡ Pneumonia	Lung, spleen, and lumbar glands
7. Descomps...... Case 5	Not stated Reported 1920	40		R	Metastases recognized 3 mo. after onset. Patient emaciated	Radical exploratory incision with incomplete removal of large lumbar masses	48 hrs. Shock	Lumbar glands
8. Descomps..... Case 6	Ibid	40		R	Metastases recognized at 4 mo. Patient emaciated	Radical exploratory incision with incomplete removal of large pre-aortic masses	48 hrs. Shock	Lumbar glands
9. Descomps...... Case 7	Ibid	40		L	Metastases recognized at 6 mo. Patient emaciated	Radical exploratory incision. Inextirpable masses about aorta. Partial removal	1 mo.	Lumbar glands

†No autopsy. ‡Iliac juxta- and pre-aortic glands enlarged and confluent mass size of fist, between kidney and aorta. Nodules in spleen and lung. 1 cancerous subclavicular gland.

1Cited by Mascarenhas.   2Cited by Delbet.   3Cited by Chevassu.   4Cited by Sébileau and Descomps.

TABLE V.—ANALYSIS OF CASES OF RADICAL OPERATION—Continued

Group I.—Inoperable Cases—Continued

B—Cases in Which Inoperable Lumbar Nodes Were Found after Retroperitoneal Exposure

Author	Date of operation	Age, years	Duration	Side	Clinical metastases	Operation and microscopical diagnosis	Died post-operative	Metastases	Living
1. Gregoire [1,2,3,4] Case I	4–20–05	33	8 mos.	R	None	Long inguinoscrotal incision extending to twelfth rib and then anteriorly along costal margin. Peritoneum stripped up to expose renal pedicle and abdominal vessels. Vena cava surrounded by mass of hard glands; I size of pigeon egg removed, others inoperable. Diagnosis: seminoma	31 mos.	Lumbar glands	
2. Mauclaire [2] Case 3	Not given Reported 1907					Radical operation. Retroperitoneal metastatic glands inextirpable			
3. Mauclaire [2] Case 4	Not given Reported 1907			L		Radical. Found inoperable retroperitoneal mass, so was content to explore region of renal pedicle		Local and lumbar metastases	
4. Barbier [1]	7–5–10	43		L	None	Radical. Large adherent gland mass about the aorta. Inoperable. Diagnosis: epithelioma	3 mos.	Yes	
5. Duval [1] Case I	4–12–10	29			None	Radical. One gland removed from large inoperable mass Diagnosis: seminoma	4 mos.		

	Date	Age	Duration	Side	Metastasis	Operation and diagnosis		Viscera and lumbar glands	
6. Duval[1] Case 2	11-8-10	37	5 yrs.	R	None	Radical. Large mass of metastatic glands in region of coeliac axis inoperable. 2 glands removed for study. Diagnosis: epithelioma	3 to 4 mos.		18 days post-operative. Metastases present
7. Picot[1, 4]	4-25-12	35	9 mos.	R	None	Radical. Enlarged glands extending up to renal pedicle and behind left renal vein, removed. Weight 52 grams. Other inextirpable masses on left. Diagnosis: seminoma			
8. Patel Case 1	Mar. 1913	18	6 mos.		None	Radical. Large inextirpable glandular metastases at bifurcation of vena cava. Diagnosis: teratoma			
9. Georgesco and Savesco Case 3		36	6 mos.		None	Radical. Inoperable mass found on aorta. Diagnosis: seminoma			15 days post-operative. Metastases present
10. Descomps Case 4	8-17-17	25	6 mos.	L	None	Radical. Inextirpable masses found on aorta. Diagnosis: seminoma	13 days Embolism		
11. Roberts	10-16-01	38	14 mos.		None	Castration July, 1900. Operation for local recurrence July, 1901. Oct. 16, 1901—long median abdominal incision. Unsuccessful attempt to remove enlarged lumbar glands transperitoneally. Diagnosis: embryonal carcinoma	6 wks. Peritonitis		

TABLE V.—ANALYSIS OF CASES OF RADICAL OPERATION —Continued

Group I.—Inoperable Cases—Continued

B—Cases in Which Inoperable Lumbar Nodes Were Found after Retroperitoneal Exposure

Author	Date of operation	Age, years	Duration	Side	Clinical metastases	Operation and microscopical diagnosis	Died post-operative	Metastases	Living
12. Hinman. Case 8†	1-6-21	34	7 mos.	L	None	Castration Dec. 1, 1920. Radical Jan. 6, 1921—Removal of cord and spermatic vessels. Gland size of olive removed from bifurcation of aorta, and several large glands removed along aorta above bifurcation. Mass size of hen's egg at renal pedicle not removed. Given repeated X-ray treatments over abdomen post-operative Diagnosis: seminoma			Living and well 18 mos. post-operative gained 30 pounds. No metastases palpable
13. Young*. Case 5	4-20-22	30	7 yrs.	R	None	Radical. Inoperable masses on aorta at level of renal pedicle Diagnosis: teratoma			2 mos. X-ray shows metastases to lung

SUMMARY OF A:

Operative deaths 3
Died of metastases 5
Living 1
　　　　　　　　　 —
Total 9

SUMMARY OF B:

Operative deaths 2
Died of metastases 4
Living with metastases 4
Incomplete data 3
　　　　　　　　　 —
Total 13

SUMMARY OF 22 CASES, GROUP I:

Operative mortality..... 22.7 per cent
Morbidity to date....... 75.0 per cent
Probable morbidity..... 100.0 per cent

†Previously reported.   *Personal communication.   ¹Cited by Mascarenhas.   ²Cited by Delbet.   ³Cited by Chevassu.   ⁴Cited by Sébileau and Descomps.

TABLE V.—ANALYSIS OF CASES OF RADICAL OPERATION—Continued

Group II.—Successful Resection of Primary Lymph Area

A—No Invasion of Lymph Glands

Author	Date of operation	Age, years	Duration	Side	Clinical metastases	Operation and microscopical diagnosis	Died post-operative	Metastases	Living post-operative	Metastases present
1. Mauclaire[2]... Case I	1905				None	Radical—no glands found			8 yrs.	Excised in scar 5 years and 8 years post-operative
2. Chevassu... Case 2	11-6-09	31	15 mos.	L	None	Radical—no glands found Diagnosis: seminoma	5 yrs. †	Lung		
3. Chevassu[1]... Case 3	10-31-11	28	7 mos.		None	Radical—removed 18 glands including 1 small one from iliac where it crosses ureter, 3 small pre-aortic, 1 small gland behind aorta on vertebral column, 1 gland beneath renal vessels and 3 glands in angle formed by aorta and iliac artery. Glands showed inflammatory reaction but no metastases	7 days Peritonitis ‡			
4. Morestin[2,4]... Case I	1910	50		L	None	Radical—no glands found (patient obese and alcoholic; anaesthetic poorly taken) Diagnosis: malignant tumor	48 hrs. Pneumonia †			

[1] Cited by Mascarenhas [2] Cited by Delbet. [3] Cited by Chevassu. [4] Cited by Sébileau and Descomps.

No metastases found. † No autopsy. ‡

Table V.—Analysis of Cases of Radical Operation—Continued

Group II.—Successful Resection of Primary Lymph Area

A—No Invasion of Lymph Glands

Author	Date of operation	Age, years	Duration	Side	Clinical metastases	Operation and microscopical diagnosis	Died post-operative	Metastases	Living post-operative	Metastases present
5. Morestin[1,4], Case 2	2–3–11	27	11 mos.	L	None	Radical—7 iliac glands removed. No lumbar glands found. 4–20–11 supraclavicular gland removed. Diagnosis: seminoma	7 mos. §	Left kidney and lumbar glands		
6. Jacob[1,4], Case 5	10–7–11	22	4 mos.	R	None	Radical—numerous glands removed from vena cava and 3 or 4 from iliac fossa. Diagnosis: seminoma			2 mos.	None
7. Gregoire, Case 5	1910	34	3 mos.	R	None	Radical—no glands found			10 yrs.	None
8. Gregoire, Case 6	5–10–15	46	5 mos.	L	None	Radical—removal of tumor and regional lymph glands. Diagnosis: seminoma	18 mos. †	Probably lung		
9. Duval[1], Case 3	2–20–11		3 mos.		None	Castration 2–14–11. Radical 2–20–11. 3 glands removed—1 on aorta at renal pedicle, and 1 at bifurcation of aorta. Diagnosis: epithelioma	9 mos.	Lumbar glands		

						Radical—no glands found				
10. Duval[1] Case 4	12-12-11	44	8 mos.	R	None	Radical—no glands found			18 days	None
11. Delbet	2-18-10	43	14 mos.	R	None	Castration 2-14-10. Radical 2-18-10. 1 gland adherent to vena cava removed. No other glands found Diagnosis: teratoma			28 mos.	None
12. Michon[2,4] Case 1	1-29-10	25	12 mos.	L	None	Radical—2 small glands removed from aorta Diagnosis: teratoma			28 mos.	None
13. Michel[4]	7-27-10	32	3 mos.		None	Radical—1 small gland in spermatic sheath removed Diagnosis: seminoma	2 mos. Pneumonia			
14. Pringle*	3-20-12	28	Sev. yrs.	L	None	Radical—lumbar iliac, and inguinal glands removed en masse Diagnosis: teratoma			2 yrs.	None
15. Lapointe and Alberstadt[4]	11-30-12	39	8 mos.	R	None	Castration 11-13-12. Radical 11-30-12. 2 small glands at iliac bifurcation; several glands where ureter crosses iliac, also on vena cava and aorta removed Diagnosis: epithelioma	6 mos. =	Liver, lung		
16. Georgesco and Savesco Case 1		35	3 yrs.		None	Radical—1 gland removed from iliac fossa and 1 from aorta to which it was adherent Diagnosis: seminoma			9 mos.	Symptoms of hydronephrosis

[1] Cited by Mascarenhas.
* Personal communication.
∞ Large lumbo-aortic masses with invasion of lower pole of left kidney.
[2] Cited by Delbet.
† Case previously reported.
[3] Cited by Chevassu.
[4] Cited by Sébileau and Descomps.
|| Metastases both lungs and liver.

TABLE V.—ANALYSIS OF CASES OF RADICAL OPERATION—Continued

Group II.—Successful Resection of Primary Lymph Area

A—No Invasion of Lymph Glands

Author	Date of operation	Age, years	Duration	Side	Clinical metastases	Operation and microscopical diagnosis	Died post-operative	Metastases	Living post-operative	Metastases present
17. Barringer* Case 1	Reported in 1921				None	Radical—2 enlarged glands found high up in spermatic chain, showing chronic interstitial and hyperplastic inflammation. Radium emanations given. Diagnosis: teratoma			22 mos.	None
18. Barringer* Case 2	Reported in 1921				None	Radical—no suspicious glands found, so radium not used. Diagnosis: teratoma (chorioma)		Lung		
19. Barringer* Case 3					None	Radical—no suspicious glands found, so radium not used. Diagnosis: teratoma			Lost track of	
20. Young* Case 1	11–24–14	36	18 mos.	R	None	Radical—glands not stated	2 yrs.	Lumbar glands		
21. Young* Case 3	4–17–19	29	3 to 4 mos.	L	None	Radical—no metastatic glands. Diagnosis: teratoma			2 yrs.	None

										Clinical evidence of visceral metastasis
22. Hinman† Case 2	12-13-17	33	29 mos.	R	None	Radical—1 macroscopic gland at point where ureter crosses iliac. Diagnosis: teratoma	9 mos.	Lungs and lumbar glands	8 mos.	Clinical evidence of visceral metastasis
23. Hinman Case 9	6-30-22	30	6 mos.	R	None	Radical—removal of iliac and pre-aortic glands with spermatic sheath up to renal pedicle. Diagnosis: teratoma				
24. Hinman (Hepler) Case 10	June, 1922	26	16 mos.	R	None	Radical—3 large glands removed from iliac vessels, and 1 from between aorta and vena cava 2 centimeters below renal pedicle. Diagnosis: seminoma			2 mos.	None
25. Lipschutz	12-31-20	45	Not stated. Sudden increase in size 6 days before	R	None	Radical—no glandular metastases found. Testis undescended inguinal. Given Coley's serum and radiotherapy postoperatively. Diagnosis: seminoma			10 mos.	None

SUMMARY OF A

Operative deaths.......... 3
Died of metastases.......... 8
Living.................. 13 (over 4 yrs., 2)
Lost after discharge........ 1
                          ———
Total................ 25

1 Cited by Mascarenhas.
* Personal communication.
2 Cited by Delbet.
† No autopsy.
3 Cited by Chevassu.
4 Cited by Sébileau and Descomps.
‡ No metastases found.

TABLE V.—ANALYSIS OF CASES OF RADICAL OPERATION—Continued

Group II.—*Successful Resection of Primary Lymph Area*

B—Metastatic Extension to Lymph Glands

Author	Date of operation	Age, years	Duration	Side	Clinical metastases	Operation and microscopical diagnosis	Died post-operative	Metastases	Living post-operative	Metastases present
1. Cuneo[1, 3]....... Case I	8–26–06	26	12 mos.	L	None	Castration 4–21–06. Radical 8–26–06. 1 lumbar gland showed metastases Diagnosis: teratoma			3 yrs.	None
2. Gregoire[4]...... Case 4......	4–10–08	21	10 mos.	R	None	Radical—6 glands removed: 4 from vena cava, one at bifurcation of aorta, and 1 on iliac vein where ureter crosses. Latter, only, showed metastases Diagnosis: teratoma	8 mos.	Lung; none clinically in lumbar glands		
3. Gosset[2, 4]......	2–6–09	32	5 mos.	L	None	Radical—removed 3 glands below hilus of kidney, 1 on ureter 5 cm. from renal pedicle, and 3 at bifurcation of exterior iliac. All lumbar glands showed metastases Diagnosis: seminoma			34 mos.	None
4. Chevassu*.... Case I	7–7–09	42	30 mos.	R	None	Radical—removed 3 glands on vena cava, 2 between vena cava and aorta and 1 iliac gland. Showed metastases Diagnosis: seminoma			4 yrs. 10 mos.	None

Name	Date	Age	Duration	Side	Scrotum	Operation and diagnosis	Metastasis	Interval	Period	Recurrence
5. Bland, Sutton	Sept. 1909	31	8 mos.	R	None	Radical—explored lumbar region removing glands which were palpable. Found 1 gland size of haricot bean on vena cava at level of third lumbar vertebra which was malignant Diagnosis: teratoma			2 yrs. 7 mos.	None
6. Vautrin	Apr. 1910	42	8 mos.		None	Radical—1 gland size of hazel nut on internal iliac, 1 below renal pedicle, 1 on aorta	Probably in spleen	1 mo.		
7. Michon, Case 2	2–25–11	31	3 yrs.	R	None	Radical—removed gland 25 cm. in diameter from anterior surface of vena cava which showed malignancy. 1 iliac gland removed showing only an inflammatory reaction Diagnosis: seminoma			8 mos.	None
8. Gayet	10–28–10	49	10 yrs. before pain, increase in size. 45 days before sudden increase	R	None, Scrotum ulcerated	Radical—removed large gland from iliac where ureter crosses (malignant), and chain of glands from vena cava and aorta Diagnosis: embryonal epithelioma	No lumbar gland metastases	25 days Pneumonia. Alcoholic nephritis †		
9. Howard*	1910	10	10 wks.	L	None	Radical—removed numerous glands along aorta	General, and in lumbar glands	1 yr.		

†No glandular metastases.
*Personal communication.

1Cited by Mascarenhas.
2Cited by Delbet.
3Cited by Chevassu.
4Cited by Sébileau and Descomps.

Table V.—Analysis of Cases of Radical Operation—Continued

Group II.—Successful Resection of Primary Lymph Area

B—Metastatic Extension to Lymph Glands

Author	Date of operation	Age, years	Duration	Side	Clinical metastases	Operation and microscopical diagnosis	Died post-operative	Metastases	Living post-operative	Metastases present
10. Davis.......	4–5–11	17	4 mos.	R	None	Radical—*en bloc* removal of testis (undescended inguinal) and gland-bearing area. I gland I cm. in diameter removed separarately at level of renal pedicle on vena cava showed metastases. Other glands not examined. Diagnosis: teratoma	9 mcs.	General abdominal and lumbar		
11. Maragliano[4]..	7–4–11	36	I yr.	R	None	Castration 6–27–11. Radical 7–4–11. Removed 2 glands in iliac fossa, one 4 cm. long, another midsacral I cm. long, another at aortic bifurcation 4½ cm. long, and I between aorta and vena cava 1½ cm. long. Latter showed metastasis. Diagnosis: seminoma			10 mos.	None
12. Descomps.... Case I	8–18–11	24		L		Radical—24 glands removed. Gland metastases present. Diagnosis: seminoma			8 yrs.	None

No. & Author	Date	Age	Duration	Side	Glands palpable	Operation / Diagnosis	Survival	Metastasis	Follow-up	Recurrence
13. Descomps.... Case 2	6-16-14	37		L		Radical—removed 64 glands (3 large). Gland metastases present. Diagnosis: seminoma	8 mos. Killed in accident	None		None
14. Descomps.... Case 3	1-15-20	40	6 mos.	L	None	Radical. (Duration of operation 1 hour.) 22 glands removed (3 spermatic, 9 iliac, 10 lumbar), all malignant with exception of 1 large lumbar node about which there is doubt. X-ray post-operative. Diagnosis: seminoma			3½ mos.	None
15. Lister........	1914	41		R	None	Radical—lumbar glands did not appear enlarged, but were sarcomatous on microscopic examination (inguinal cryptorchid). Diagnosis: sarcoma			3 wks.	None
16. Matas........	1-15-15	28	9 mos.	L	None	Castration 12-19-24. Radical 1-15-15. Malignant glands removed. Diagnosis: teratoma	4½ mos.	Lung		
17. Mauclaire.... Case 5	1922	48	3 yrs.	R	Palpable glands in groin. Skin adherent to tumor. Œdema of thigh and scrotum	Radical—including excision of inguino-crural glands and adherent scrotum. Glands removed from iliac vessels and vena cava. Diagnosis: teratoma (chorioma)			7 mos.	None. Œdema increased due to excision of lymphatics supposedly

⁴ Cited by Sébileau and Descomps.

TABLE V.—ANALYSIS OF CASES OF RADICAL OPERATION—Continued

Group II.—Successful Resection of Primary Lymph Area

B—Metastatic Extension to Lymph Glands

Author	Date of operation	Age, years	Duration	Side	Clinical metastases	Operation and microscopical diagnosis	Died post-operative	Metastases	Living post-operative	Metastases present
18. Young* Case 2	1-2-15	34	3 mos.	R	None	Dec., 1914, castration and removal of inguinal glands. Testis and glands showed sarcoma. 1-2-15 radical operation. Several glands removed, malignant Diagnosis: sarcoma, probably seminoma			2 yrs. 6 mos.	None
19. Young* Case 4	10-19-20	24	1 mo.	R	None	Radical—metastatic glands removed Diagnosis: teratoma			21 mos.	None
20. Hinman† (Eloesser) Case 1	11-20-14	30	4 mos.	R	None	Castration 10-27-14. Radical 11-20-14, performed because of recurrence in stump of cord. 1 small gland removed Diagnosis: seminoma			8 yrs.	None
21. Hinman† Case 3	1-29-18	30	7 yrs.	L	None	Radical—numerous small glands along iliac vessels and 1 large gland at renal pedicle removed in en bloc dissection. The latter was malignant Diagnosis: teratoma			4½ yrs.	None

22. Hinman† Case 4	7–27–18	36	4 mos.	R	None	Radical—large metastatic gland was found and removed which was very adherent to vena cava at level of lower pole of right kidney Diagnosis: teratoma	2 mos.	None
23. Hinman† Case 5	Aug. 1918	29	5 mos.	R	None	Radical—large gland removed from aorta and vena cava 5 cm. below renal pedicle Diagnosis: seminoma	18 mos.	Right kidney and lumbar glands
24. Hinman Case 7	1–5–21	24	18 mos.	L	None	12–27–20—Testis and epididymis removed, and through perineal incision 1 vesicle and vas were removed. Diagnosis TB clinically. 1–5–21— Radical—for teratoma testis. A chain of enlarged glands was found running along iliac vessels and up to renal pedicle. Large malignant gland removed at level of renal pedicle Diagnosis: teratoma	Few hrs.	Acute cardiac dilatation

*Personal communication   †Case previously reported.

Table V.—Analysis of Cases of Radical Operation—Continued

Group II.—Successful Resection of Primary Lymph Area

B—Metastatic Extension to Lymph Glands

Author	Date of operation	Age, years	Duration	Side	Clinical metastases	Operation and microscopical diagnosis	Died post-operative	Metastases	Living post-operative	Metastases present
25. Asteriades....	1921	35			None	Radical operation—metastatic gland size of millet seed removed where ureter crosses iliac. Diagnosis: carcinoma			14 mos.	None
26. Young* Case 6	10-16-22	33	10 mos.	L	None	Radical operation—unusually large lumbo-aortic glands removed just level of renal pedicle. Diagnosis: teratoma			Not stated	None

*Personal communication.

SUMMARY OF B

Operative deaths....................	2
Died of metastases..................	6
Living..............................	17 (over 4 yrs., 4)
Accidentally killed.................	1
	26

SUMMARY OF 51 CASES, GROUP II

Operative mortality.................	9.2 per cent
Morbidity to date...................	37.2 per cent
Living 4 years or longer............	6 cases
Living over 2 years.................	14 cases

TABLE V.—ANALYSIS OF CASES OF RADICAL OPERATION—Continued

Group III.—Incomplete Data and Mistaken Diagnosis

A—Data Insufficient for Analysis

Author	Date of operation	Age, years	Dura- tion	Side	Clinical metastases	Operation and microscopical diagnosis	Died post- operative	Metastases	Living post- oper- ative	Metastases present
1. Guyot	Not stat- ed. Re- ported 5-27-21					Radical operation follow- ed by radiotherapy			Yes	No
2. Patel. Case 2		16	5 mos.		None	Radical removal of tumor and regional lymphatics Diagnosis: sarcoma				
3. Mauclaire[2] Case 2	1907					Radical operation. Pa- tient very obese	9 mos.	Both humeri		
4. Pauchet.	1910	17	5 mos.		None	Radical operation with removal of glands which were not examined (lost)				
5. Marion. Case 2	1920	Young				Radical removal of en- larged lymph glands (ilio-lum.)				
6. Masini.	Not stat- ed. Re- ported 4-4-21					Radical operation Diagnosis: seminoma			2 yrs.	No

[2] Cited by Delbet.

Table V.—Analysis of Cases of Radical Operation—Continued
Group III.—Incomplete Data and Mistaken Diagnosis
B—Mistake in Diagnosis

Author	Date of operation	Age, years	Duration	Side	Clinical metastases	Operation and microscopical diagnosis	Died post-operative	Metastases	Living post-operative	Metastases present
1. Cuneo[1] Case 2	9-9-07	40	1 yr.	R	None	Radical operation—only 1 gland found at operation between aorta and vena cava Diagnosis: lues			5 yrs.	
2. Marion[1] Case 1	1910	37			None	Radical operation—no glands were found, and no attempt was made at lymphatic area Diagnosis: lues				
3. Mercade[1]	3-14-11	30	5 mos.		None	Radical operation—no glands found Diagnosis: lues			Yes	
4. Hinman† Case 6	8-7-20	46	3 mos.	R	None	Radical—numerous enlarged iliolumbar glands removed. On microscopic examination tumor proved to be massive. Tbc. epididymo-orchitis. (Fig. 2 a and b). Glands showed endothelial hyperplasia Diagnosis: tuberculosis			2 yrs.	

† Case previously reported.
[1] Cited by Mascarenhas.
[3] 4 cases of mistaken diagnosis not included.

SUMMARY OF 79 CASES

Operative deaths......... 10 (12.6 per cent.)
Died of metastases 24
Living with metastases ... 6
Living and well 34

Killed or lost............... 2
Incomplete data............. 3
                         —
Total........ 79[3]

Hinman believes that the present knowledge of the clinical course, diagnosis and prognosis of teratoma testis emphasizes the following points of treatment: An early and accurate diagnosis of every testicular enlargement is essential, and in every case of reasonable doubt there should be no hesitation in exposing the tumor to surgical inspection, and whenever necessary performing castration and subjecting the tissue to immediate microscopic examination. Once the diagnosis is established, one of two lines of procedure is indicated: either a palliative course of treatment by orchidectomy with radium or X-ray therapy, or an attack more commensurate with the extreme seriousness of the disease, by radical resection of the growth and its primary lymphatic area. The technical steps of radical operation for teratoma testis are shown in Figs. 72 and 73, (after Hinman et al).

Technic of Radical Operation for Teratoma Testis.

" The patient is better turned a little to the opposite side, with a small pad under the back. The cord is exposed through an inguinal incision and clamped so that subsequent pressure and manipulation in delivering the testicle will not spread cells into the blood stream. If upon delivery of the scrotal mass a solid testicular tumor is found castration should be completed by severing the cord below the clamp with cautery. The tumor mass is immediately sectioned by a pathologist or assistant in order to confirm the diagnosis. Too many radical resections of retroperitoneal glands for tuberculosis or syphilis have been performed (four are reported) to warrant the omission of this necessary diagnostic step. In case of malignacy the inguinal incision is extended to the twelfth rib, which it then parallels (Fig. 72a). Muscle and fascia are divided in the line of this skin incision down to the peritoneum. Beginning in the iliac fossa (Fig. 72d), the peritoneum is stripped back to and beyond the large abdominal vessels. The ureter and spermatic vessels with lymphatics strip up with the peritoneum but the lymph nodes remain upon, sometimes being quite adherent to, the vena cava and aorta. Theoretically the lymph area should be removed from above downward, but practically its clean and complete removal is more difficult in this way than by resection from below, for the reason that traction on the cord greatly facilitates following it and making a clean dissection. It is probable that the cleaner, more complete, removal permitted by dissecting from below upward offsets the theoretical

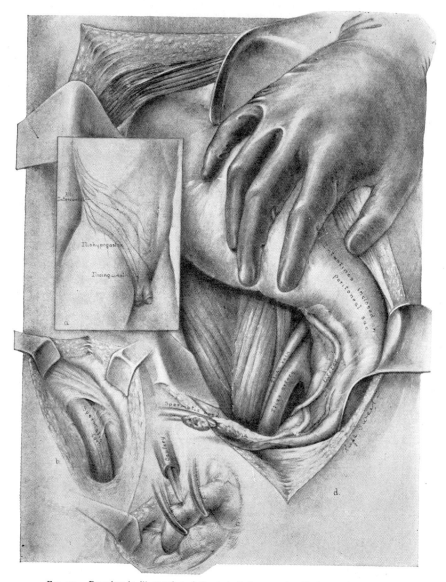

Fig. 72.—Drawing in illustration of the technical steps of radical resection of the primary lymph zone. *a* shows two types of incision. The one following the outer edge of the rectus for some distance and then curving out along the lower side of the twelfth rib gives a better exposure. *b* shows the initial inguinal incision exposing the cord which is clamped before delivering the tumor mass from the scrotum. *c*, cautery division of the cord after gross inspection has confirmed the diagnosis. *d* shows the method of stripping back of the peritoneum, beginning in the iliac fossa. The ureter and spermatic vessels strip up with the peritoneum. The vas deferens is seen crossing the ureter and is divided low down behind the bladder. (Hinman et al.)

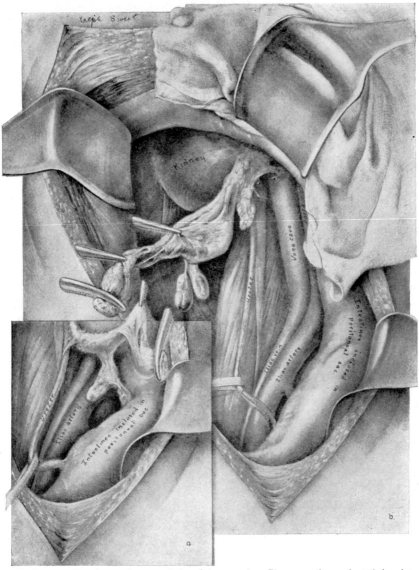

Fig. 73.—Drawing to show completion of the operation. The spermatic vessels at their point of junction with the abdominal vein and artery have been isolated, ligated and divided before resection is attempted, which may then be carried out from above downward or from below upward. (Hinman et al.)

advantage of peripheral attack. It would seem advisable, therefore, to combine the methods by first isolating, ligating and dividing the spermatic vessels at their points of union with vena cava, aorta, or renal vein and then proceeding with resection of the area from below upward. Occasionally the glands may be so matted about the inferior mesenteric artery that in order to effect a clean removal, the artery must be sacrificed near its origin. The practicability of this procedure seems feasible on the basis of a series of cats and dogs in which this artery was ligated and cut near its origin without apparently the least untoward effects. This procedure was necessary in one personal case (Hinman Case 7, Cf. Table V), but the patient died of acute cardiac dilatation a few hours after operation so that the efficacy of the collateral circulation in the human could not be determined.

" After completion of the resection, immediate exposure on the operating table of the retroperitoneal and iliac area to roentgen radiation is an added protection against recurrence because of possible isolated cells or metastatic areas left behind. The placement of rubber tubes for drainage of the serous discharge, with exit at the back or upper end of the wound, as after kidney operations, is advantageous, and these tubes may be used, or additional ones if desirable, to carry radium for radiation of the resected area for twelve to fourteen hours after operation."

These authors give the following summary and conclusions:

Summary

" 1. Testicular tumors affect all ages, but are most common between twenty and fifty. Seminoma rarely occurs in children, while teratoma is relatively common. Duration of these tumors is variable due to the frequency of periods of latency and quiescence in their development. The duration of the growth, or its clinical characteristics furnish no index as to whether or not metastases have occurred.

" 2. Diagnosis is chiefly a matter of exclusion. The growth may be mistaken for, or masked by, hydrocele. Four cases of radical operation have been performed by mistake on gummata and massive tuberculosis, a fact which emphasizes the importance of careful examination of the tumor before proceeding with the radical dissection.

" 3. The pathogenesis of testicular tumors has long been a subject for dispute, but for clinical purposes it is convenient to divide them into two groups which occur with about equal frequency; namely, the seminoma and teratoma. From the statistics on simple castration, teratoma gave a decidedly less favorable prognosis than seminoma. Analysis of cases of radical operation would seem to indicate an equally good prognosis for both groups.

" 4. Simple castration will cure 15 to 20 per cent. of malignant tumors of the testis. Obviously, the operation in order to effect a cure must antedate glandular or other metastases.

" 5. Realization of the inefficacy of simple castration has led to the development of the present radical operation which was made possible through exact knowledge of the primary lymph zones of the testicle, for which we are indebted primarily to Most (1899).[10] This zone occupies the retroperitoneal lumbar area along the aorta and vena cava. The first successful radical operation was performed by Cuneo[11] in France (1906), the patient remaining alive and well three years following the radical operation in which a metastatic lumbar gland was removed.

" 6. Analysis of seventy-nine cases of radical operation shows that nine cases had palpable metastases at the time of operation. That operation is contraindicated in this group is proved by the morbidity of 100 per cent. Thirteen cases revealed inoperable metastatic glands, not palpable clinically, at operation, so that a total of twenty-two out of seventy-nine cases proved to be primarily inoperable.

" 7. Another group of twenty-five cases showed, on subsequent microscopic study, no metastases in the glands removed. Eight of these cases, however, died later of metastases, showing that either the gland area was not completely removed or that metastases were overlooked microscopically in those glands that were removed. Of the twenty-five cases, twelve remain living and well. Even granting that simple castration would have cured all of these twelve cases, the findings showing that it could have cured none of the others, it would then have cured only about 16 per cent. of the entire seventy-nine cases.

" 8. In still another group of twenty-six cases the glands removed at operation showed metastases, and all twenty-six obviously would be doomed by simple castration. Our analysis shows that as a result of the radical operation, however, seventeen of these cases are living and well, four for over four years and eight for almost three years. It is reasonable to expect a fair proportion of the seventeen, who have not survived the four year time limit, to be cured, since recurrence generally occurs within the first year.

" 9. X-ray and radium seem to be valuable therapeutic and palliative adjuncts to the treatment of testicular tumors."

Conclusions

" 1. Seventy-nine cases of the radical operation for teratoma testis have been collected, either through personal communications, or from the literature. Ten of these comprise personal cases, five of which have been previously reported. It is believed that sufficient information is furnished by this material to permit of reliable analysis for comparison with the results following simple castration.

"2. Comparison of results of simple castration and radical operation shows, even at this early date for the latter, an improvement in the prognosis of at least 100 per cent., since about 15 per cent. of these cases are cured by simple castration, whereas at least 30 per cent. of the seventy-nine cases analyzed are found to have been cured by the radical operation."

Coley [12] believes that in the present state of uncertainty as regards classification it is wise to group all cases of malignant disease of the testis under the general heading of cancer of the testis, as is done by Chevassu,[13] subdividing the different varieties as far as our knowledge permits, into: (1) teratoma, to include the mixed type of tumor containing cartilage, cyst, glands; (2) embryonal carcinoma, to include the pure, solid tumor, which may or may not be of teratomatous origin, of the large-celled, large nucleus type; (3) the rapidly diminishing group of pure sarcoma.

In a former paper Coley [14] referred at some length to the opinions of various surgeons here and abroad regarding the end results following surgical treatment. Most of the authorities were uniformly pessimistic. He stated that there were no statistics, apparently, on which to base an opinion as to the end results following the combined operation of removal of the testis and the retroperitoneal glands by abdominal operation except those of Hinman [15] and Chevassu. The mortality of 11 per cent. in forty-four collected cases he considers sufficient to make one hesitate to adopt this operation until better end results have been obtained. Forty-one per cent. of these cases died at the end of one year. Hinman's statistics represent probably the most accurate estimate of the best end results that can be expected of modern surgery alone. Of twenty-four cases traced, of his series of thirty-two, twenty had died and four were living. While sufficient time has not elapsed to determine the number of permanent cures following radical operation, Hinman's statistics show beyond question, that the prognosis can be materially improved by the abdominal operation; but this can only be obtained at the expense of a mortality of 11 per cent. against a mortality of nil following the simple orchidectomy operation.

Coley is of the opinion that if we had no alternative we might be forced to admit that radical or combined operation should be the method of choice in malignant tumors of the testis; but in his opinion we have an alternative which should be seriously considered before resorting to such a serious procedure. Radium has come into much more general use and the methods of applying it have been greatly improved. So far there is no large series of cases in which radium has been used immediately after removal of the testis for malignant disease. In such a condition, immediate post-operative radium or X-ray treatment, he believes, will give better results than orchidectomy alone. It was hoped that by the use of large doses of radium it might be possible to treat successfully the recurrent abdominal cases, but Barringer's experience in nearly fifty cases of recurrent inoperable malignant tumors of the testis which have been treated by radium therapy, has demonstrated otherwise. It has been learned that by massive doses of radium, administered in the form of a radium pack, it is possible, in most cases, to produce very marked regression of a large retroperitoneal tumor and in a considerable number of cases cause its complete disappearance. Yet in practically all of the cases, with one exception, the disappearance or improvement has been only temporary. Therefore, as far as our present knowledge goes it must be admitted that we are unable to offer much hope of a cure if the disease has metastasized in the abdomen sufficiently to produce large and palpable tumors.

Coley's present series of cases show that even better results than those reported by the combined radical operation advocated by Hinman and Chevassu can be obtained by simple orchidectomy if the operation is immediately followed by the prolonged systemic toxin treatment, with or without radium. He believes that the best results are likely to follow the combined use of massive doses of radium over the abdomen and left supraclavicular glands, and prolonged toxin treatment. Another point worthy of special emphasis is, that these results have been obtained without any mortality.

Regarding the method of toxin treatment Coley says that this should not be employed at all unless the patient is willing to have it kept up for a considerable period of time, at least six months. It can be carried out at home by the family physician, and need not interfere with the patient's ordinary routine of living. The injection should be made deeply into the buttocks, beginning with a dose of one-half minim, diluted with a little freshly boiled water, and increasing daily by one-half minim up to the point of producing a slight reaction, temperature of 99 to 101 or 102 degrees. It should then be given only three times a week, increasing the dose only if necessary, to the point of a moderate reaction. At the end of three months it is safe to diminish the frequency of the injections to two a week, using doses just large enough to produce slight reactions. In all cases where it is possible either radium or deep X-ray therapy should be used in addition, covering the entire retroperitoneal glandular region on the side of the tumor. He considers it wise to repeat these treatments at the end of four to six months, and believes long-continued treatment very essential.

From his study this author arrived at the following conclusions:

" The number of permanent cures following surgical removal of the testicle for malignant disease is comparatively small, the proportion being not over 5 to 10 per cent. This number of cures, in our opinion, is not sufficiently increased by the radical operation of removal of the retroperitoneal glands by the abdominal route to warrant the very considerable risk of such an operation.

" Long continued systemic treatment with the mixed toxins of erysipelas and bacillus prodigiosus, combined with thorough radiation of the abdomen and supraclavicular glands by radium or X-rays, offers a far better hope of a permanent cure than any form of operative treatment alone.

" If one waits after operation until a recurrence has taken place, marked regression of these recurrent tumors, and in some cases complete disappearance, may be expected from radium treatment; but in the great majority of these cases, the regression or disappearance will prove only temporary and death from extension of the disease will occur.

"Since this paper was read, further evidence of the value of the mixed toxins as a prophylactic after operation has been presented by Brickner.[16] His report describes a man forty years of age, who was operated upon at the Mt. Sinai Hospital by Doctor Brickner on April 25, 1912. The tumor was of several weeks' duration, and was the size of a tangerine orange when removed. Three days later an orchidectomy was performed and the cord and testicle with its covering were removed *en masse*. Pathological examination by Dr. F. S. Mandelbaum: a perithelial sarcoma, chiefly of large round cells, with pronounced evidences of malignancy." The mixed toxins of erysipelas and bacillus prodigiosus were administered from April 30 to June 18, 1912 (twenty injections in all, the highest dose, 5 minims, producing a reaction of 100–1° F.). At the time of writing the patient was in perfect health with no sign of a recurrence, eleven years later.

" While in London in 1911, Doctor Coley saw in consultation a young man, seventeen years of age, suffering from a large sarcoma of the testis, for which he advised immediate orchidectomy, followed by toxin treatment. This was carried out but no further report of the case was had until May, 1923, when he was again in London and saw the surgeon who had performed the operation; he then learned that the patient was still in good condition, twelve years later. The diagnosis in this case was confirmed by microscopical examination.

" A personal communication just received from Dr. James T. Pilcher of Brooklyn, mentions the end result of a case of tumor of the testis operated upon by Doctor Pilcher in 1913; diagnosis by Doctor Murray of the Hoagland Laboratory of Long Island College Hospital: degenerate teratoma with both sarcomatous and carcinomatous degeneration; Doctor Lederer (Pathologist of the Jewish Hospital of Brooklyn) regarded it as a myxosarcoma of the testicle. This patient has remained in good health up to the present time, nine and one-half years later, without any prophylactic treatment following the operation."

The accompanying tables show Coley's tabulation of the operable and inoperable cases and the end results after operation followed by prophylactic toxins. (Tables I and II.)

TABLE I. (AFTER COLEY)

Table of Cases of Malignant Tumors of Testis Observed in Operable Stage. End Results after Operation Followed by Prophylactic Toxins.

No.	Name	Age	Date	Duration	Pathologic diagnosis	Trauma	Post-operative treatment	End result
1	P. G....	51	June, 1907, operation, Dec, 1908	6 months size of closed fist	Round-celled sarcoma by Doctors Mandelbaum, Welch, and Ewing	No	Toxins of erysipelas given immediately after operation, for 3-4 months by Dr. Lilienthal	Patient well March, 1923, 14 years
2	R.M.M.	32	Operation, Oct. 7, 1912 by Dr. C. C. Kimball	3 months	Large round-celled sarcoma	No	Toxins begun soon after operation and continued for several months	Patient well March, 1923, 11 years
3	T.H.M.	28	Operation, Dec. 2, 1910, Mayo Clinic	4 months	Sarcoma	Yes Tumor 4 weeks later	Toxins begun soon after operation and kept up nearly a year. Temperature reactions — 104°, highest dose — 42 minims	Patient well 8 years later. Died of influenza, Nov. 21, 1918
4	D. E. B.	37	Operation, June, 1908 by Dr. John B. Murphy	Few mos. rapid growth	Round-celled sarcoma undescended testis, diagnosis confirmed by Dr. Ewing	No	Toxins begun as soon as wound healed and kept up with intervals of rest for six months	Well for 3 years, then developed metastasis in abdomen. Died at the end of 3 years and 9 months
5	D. R....	44	Removal of right testis by Dr. J. A. Wyeth, 1899 1 year later recurrence in left testis	Few months	Round-celled sarcoma right testis. Patient refused to have left testis removed	No	Toxin treatment for 6 months carried out under Dr. Coley's direction	Patient personally examined 8 years later and well 15 years later when last heard from
6	J. P....	Adult	Removal Nov., 1910, Mayo Clinic	Few months	Sarcoma	?	Toxins begun soon after operation. Kept up 1 year	Well 7 years

No.	Initials	Age	Operation	Duration	Diagnosis	Recurrence	Treatment	Result
7	T.......	46	Feb. 23, 1906	3 months	Round-celled sarcoma	No	Toxins 1 month after operation. Recurrence in glands, inguinal and iliac, had taken place	Well 8 years later
8	G. J....	37	Dec. 10, 1910 (Coley), size of orange	7 months	Teratoma typical, Dr. Ewing	No	Toxins after operation	Well 3 years later
9	W.M.H.	26	Operation, Feb. 1, 1906	3 months	Round-celled sarcoma	Yes soon after	Toxins begun 1 month after operation and continued for several months	Well Dec. 22, 1922,17 years later
10	L. G. ..	24	Operation, Nov. 2, 1917	3 months	Large round-celled sarcoma. Report by M. Schofield, Pathologist to Royal Free Hospital, London, confirmed by Dr. Ewing (embryonal carcinoma)	Yes 4 months before	Toxins Feb. 3, 1918, 1 dose radium-pack given March 18, 2nd pack Sept. 18, toxins kept up nearly 1 year	Patient well Feb., 1923, 5 years
11	R. H...	20 mos.	1st operation April, 1917, 2nd operation, June, 1917, 3rd operation by Dr. Coley, Oct. 19, 1917	3 weeks	Sarcoma of testis, Dr. Ewing. (One of few cases Dr. Ewing has seen which he believes is a true sarcoma of testis)	Yes few months before	Toxins begun immediately after third operation (removal of very large, fungating tumor) toxins kept up 2½ years with intervals of rest	Patient in good health, March, 1923, 5½ years
12	S. S. S.	42	1st operation, 1902. Inoperable recurrence abdominal metastases, June, 1919	Recurred 1919, retroperitoneal tumor and large metastases in left supraclavicular pleura	Large round-celled sarcoma. Prof. of Pathology, Harvard Medical School	No	X-ray at Mayo Clinic, May, 1919, temporary relief. Tumor increased in size. Toxins begun July, 1919. Radium August, 1919. Treatment kept up 3 years	Patient well and free from all evidence of tumor, March, 1923, 3 years and 8 months

TABLE I. *Continued*

Table of Cases of Malignant Tumors of Testis Observed in Operable Stage. End Results after Operation Followed by Prophylactic Toxins.

No.	Name	Age	Date	Duration	Pathologic diagnosis	Trauma	Post-operative treatment	End results
13	J. D....	32	Operation, Dec., 1908 (Coley)	?	Carcinoma (Ewing)	No (?) Possible trauma from truss	No toxins. Only case in entire series well 4 years after operation alive	Well 4 years later
14	E. L. F.	42	Operation, Nov. 22, 1907, Dr. C. A. Porter, Boston	3 months	Round-celled sarcoma	No	Toxins begun 3 weeks after operation given by Dr. Faulkner under Dr. Coley's direction	Patient well 14 years. Then had recurrence in other testis, removed, diagnosis confirmed by mic. ex.
15			Recurrence in iliac and abdominal glands	Inoperable recurrence	Round-celled sarcoma		Toxins, apparent complete disappearance of tumor	Well 3 years, then died of recurrence
16	?	43	1st operation 1910, 2nd incomplete operation in August, 1910, by Dr. Percy Shields	Inoperable recurrence	Round-celled sarcoma	No	Toxins after second operation, glands disappeared, treatment continued for 1 year	Well 10 years later

Note:—In three cases the condition was inoperable metastatic recurrence and in two others the toxins were used after 2nd or 3rd operation for recurrence.

TABLE II. (COLEY)

Inoperable Cases Treated with Toxins by other Surgeons.

Name	Age	Date	Duration	Pathologic diagnosis	Trauma	Post-op. T.	End results
Case of Dr. Robbins. Reference, Hinman, Jour. A. M. A. Dec. 5, 1914	55	1st operation, Jan., 1909, 2nd operation, 15 days later, recurrence		Sarcoma	?	Toxins	Disappearance of tumor. Patient remained well for 4 years and then died of nephritis. No evidence of old trouble
Case of Dr. William Mabon, Manhattan State Hospital, personal communication		Testis removed in 1890, recurrence in tongue five years later		Testis, sarcoma, tongue, round-celled sarcoma, Dr. William H. Welch		Toxins	Well 15 years later
Case of Dr. Hertel of Copenhagen, reference, Hospitalstidents, April 7, 1909	29	3 recurrences, 3rd operation was Lennander's operation (incomplete)		Sarcoma		Toxins	Glands disappeared. Patient well 10 years

In view of the comparative benignancy of testicular tumors when properly treated, as pointed out by Hinman and Coley, the conservative procedure, I believe, would be to submit every testicular tumor to microscopic examination. If suspicious malignant elements are found, or a tendency to malignancy is suspected, in the very early stages orchidectomy should be done, supplemented, if need be, by röntgen or radium therapy or both. In a recent personal communication to the author Doctor Coley stated that he had not seen the latest contribution to the literature by Hinman et al, which is quoted above. The pessimistic attitude of Coley is based upon the high operative mortality in Hinman's first series. Hinman's latest conclusions, however, are very optimistic and forceful in urging radical removal of the testes and their lymph chains. It seems to the author that Hinman's dicta may be safely followed, provided no serious contraindications for the rather dangerous operative interference exist. Face to face with a destructive and progressive malady one has often to weigh carefully the *pros* and *cons* entering into the fabric of a given case. Hinman does not mention the use of prophylactic treatment following his radical operation, as advocated by Coley, but the author believes that on general principles and in view of the splendid results reported by Coley this should be tried. In other words, every possible chance should be given the patient from every source available in the armamentaria of the surgeon. In cases that have passed the stage of operability the use of Coley's treatment may still accomplish some good.

BIBLIOGRAPHY

[1] MONOD and TERRILLON : Maladies du Testicle. Paris, 1889.
[2] CHEVASSU : Thése, Paris, 1906.
[3] TANNER : Tumors of the testicle. Surg. Gynec. & Obst., 1922, xxxv, 565.
[4] COLEY : Ann. Surg., July, 1915, lxiv.
[5] EWING : Neoplastic Diseases, 1910.
[6] HINMAN : Surg. Gynec. & Obst., 1909, xxviii, 495.
[7] SCHULTZ and EISENDRATH : Arch. of Surg., 1921, ii, 495.
[8] HINMAN, GIBSON and KUTZMANN : Surg. Gyn. & Obstet., October, 1923, pp. 429–451.
[9] BARRINGER, B. S. and DEAN, A. L. : Journ. Am. Med. Assoc., 1921, lxxvii.
[10] MOST : Arch. f. Path. Anat. etc., Bull., 1898, xliv, 138–177. Arch. f. Anat. u. Entwickelungs gesch., 1899, p. 113.
[11] CUNEO, B. : Bull. et mein. Soc. Anat. de Par., 1901, lxxvi, 105.

[12] COLEY, WM. B.: Annals of Surgery, Sept., 1923, lxxvii, pp. 370–386.
[13] CHEVASSU: Revue d. chir., xli, 1910.
[14] COLEY, WM. B.: Annals of Surgery, 1915.
[15] HINMAN, FRANK: Journ. Am. Med. Asso., October 5, 1919 S. G. 106 November, 1922.
[15] BRICKNER: Am. Journal of Surgery, May, 1923.

C. Inflammatory Conditions of the Testes.

Many conditions arise which may cause an inflammatory condition in the testicle. Inflammation of the testicle or epididymis may show under either an acute or chronic form; it begins either in the parenchymatous or secretory part of the gland, or else in the excretory canal. If both testicle and epididymis are concurrently involved, the condition is called an *orchido-epididymitis;* if the testicle alone suffers, it is an *orchitis.*

Orchitis

Orchitis may result from traumatisms, infections or intoxications. From the pathogenetic viewpoint, therefore, there are three types of orchitis which are unequal as regards frequency; viz., *traumatic orchitis, infective orchitis* and *toxic orchitis.* In that condition which has been described by some authors as orchitis " by effort " there is always to be found some ulterior traumatic or infective condition (this latter usually being gonorrhea) which must be regarded as the underlying and predisposing cause; hence this type reduces to one of the three referred to.

Traumatic orchitis results from contusion or crushing, or other injury to the testicle by physical agents; also the injuries result following exposure to electricity, X-ray, etc., all of which are capable of starting an inflammatory process in the parenchymatous tissue of the testicle. Induration or sclerosis of the tissue is the most usual effect of a violent injury which causes inflammation and the final result may be *testicular atrophy.* This atrophy causes the functional loss of the organ; and, if the internal secretion fails, impotency as well as sterility, intervenes. There are numerous examples of traumatic atrophy of the testicle in the literature. Achard and Demanche [1] report the case of a man who, at the age of twenty-five years, received a violent kick in the testicles. The organs became swollen and by degrees suffered complete atrophy. From this time the man lost his vigor, his hair began to fall, his face became like that of an old woman; although sexual appetite persisted and the power of erection remained, there was no ejaculation. Thyroid dystrophia had followed the testicular dystrophia in this case, being the inverse of what happens in many myxedematous patients where testicular dystrophia follows that of the thyroid.

In certain cases of bilateral testicular atrophy, there is persistence of the functioning of the interstitial gland, *i.e.*, preservation of the secondary sexual characters and power of erection, but this is due no doubt to the fact that the interstitial glandular tissue has not been totally destroyed or degenerated. (Cf. Author's case in Chapter on Function of the Leydig Cells.)

Gallavardin and Rebattu [2] observed a patient, who at the age of eighteen years, when the genital functions could be normally exercised, suffered a violent traumatism of the genital region. Following this there was bilateral testicular atrophy with loss finally of sexual power and desire. At the age of twenty-three, the man presented an infantile aspect, with the voice and other characters of a eunuch. There was complete return of the prepuberty state, as well as definite psychical changes.

Light, heat, electricity, X-rays, and other physical and chemico-physical agents may act as traumatizing agents on the testicles. It has long been known that animals exposed in the scroto-funicular region to the action of X-rays become sterile, and many professional radiologists have become sterile from the constant exposure to the rays. Such glandular effects can be produced without any external manifestations of scrotal irritation and without involving the interstitial cells of the testicle, so that the sterility is not accompanied by impotency nor by the loss of secondary sexual characters. Bergonie and Tribondeau,[3] Simmonds [4] and Nogier and Regaud [5] have shown that the diminution or disappearance of spermatozoa following irradiation is not immediate but is slowly effected; and moreover that even after a period of absolute azoöspermia, spermatozoa may again appear in the seminal fluid.

The seminal cells are especially sensitive to the X-rays. The seminiferous tubules which have been most exposed to prolonged irradiations remain definitely atrophied, but others not so greatly injured appear to become rehabilitated, and after a few months again produce spermatozoa. Externally the testicle preserves its usual appearance, volume and consistency, but in some cases, in time, the testicle slowly diminishes in mass and softens, finally becoming only a small fibrous tissue mass, in which the seminiferous tubules have more or less completely disappeared, the lesions being proportional to the duration and intensity of irradiation of the gland.

Toxic Orchitis

Toxic inflammation of the testicle may clinically follow the treatment of hydrocele, etc., by chemical agents, especially iodine preparations, and have equally been produced experimentally in animals by the injection of other chemical substances.

Exogenous intoxications such as lead poisoning, alcohol poisoning, etc., may be reflected in the testicle. Alterations in the testicle due to toxic orchitis are characterized by arrest of spermatogenesis and by a shedding of the epithelium of the seminiferous tubules. There is an amount of support in literature that a toxic orchitis may follow hepatic insufficiency or other condition in which the organism fails to excrete poisonous metabolic products.

Infective Orchitis

Infection of one kind or another is the most prolific source of orchitis, and the immense majority of cases of orchitis and epididymo-orchitis belong to this class. Such an infection may be primary, the microbes reaching the testicle from the outside by an accidental or other injury; in such case, the etiology is somewhat of a traumatic orchitic nature, *a septic inoculation,* though the development is by the spreading of infection. But the infection more usually reaches the testicle through the general system and is then secondary. The microbic agents of infection may reach the testicle by the route of the excretory canal, by the blood vessels, by the lymph route, by the vaginal from the peritoneal cavity, or by the cellular tissue of the scrotum from the perineum.

The condition of orchitis is clinically seen following mumps, typhoid, tuberculosis, scarlatina, gonorrheal infections, etc., the blood route being the usual channel. In elephantiasis and malarial diseases, in which infective disease reaches and involves the testicle, the lymph channels are more usually the route of infection. Gonorrheal orchitis is much more frequently seen than any other infective type. Some authors, such as Monod and Terrillon,[6] think that generally the testicle may be exempt in gonorrheal inflammations which are confined to the epididymis. Many anatomico-pathological findings testify to the fact that after resection or ligature, or even extirpation of the deferent canal, the testicle may remain unaffected as regards its condition, yet there are undoubtedly cases where infection of the testicle and a subsequent atrophy of the organ followed the accession of microbes traveling by the excretory canals. When testicular lesions result from extension of gonorrheal epididymitis, such alterations, in the majority of cases, seem to be exclusively constituted by a diminished activity of spermatogenesis, or even a complete cessation of the spermato-genetic process. The testicle reaches a condition of functional rest. But such is not always the effect. Delbet and Chevassu[7] have shown that following obliteration of the excretory epididymal ducti in gonorrhea, the testicle can preserve its function and produce spermatozoa for many years following the obliteration.

Frank,[8] in 1907, showed that in three hundred and forty-four cases of bilateral epididymitis there was azoöspermia in three hundred and two. In such, however, there is no disturbance of erection nor of ejaculation. Atrophy of the testicle does not appear to have been ever reported as resulting from gonorrheal inflammation. Sebileau and Descomps[9] think that such atrophy exists, and they observed a case in which, following epididymal gonorrhea, the testicle was reduced to half its volume.

Of the non-gonococcic orchitis, the most important are those following mumps and variola; statistics vary, but generally the testicles are more or less involved in one-fifth or one-third of the cases. The orchitis is parenchymatous and is more frequent in cases of adults than in children, both in mumps and variola. In these diseases, the microbes seem to have a particular choice of location in the testicle apart from the epididymis. In mumps, the testicular involvement may be only temporary, but in the case of variola, the involvement may progress to a veritable testicular atrophy.

Tubercular and syphilitic infections of the testicle are of such a special type that they can merely be alluded to here as demanding special treatment owing to their complications. (Figs. 74–75.) (Cf. pp. 160–169.)

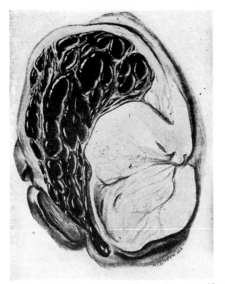

FIG. 74.—Gumma of the testis; hematocele. (Warren Museum, Harvard Medical School, No. 9688.) The body of the testis has been replaced by a large nodule of cheesy fibrous tissue. The tunica is filled with clotted blood. On the surface is a button-like necrotic area.

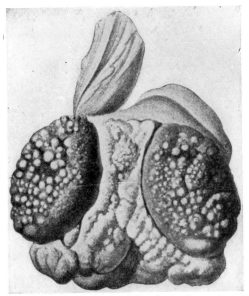

FIG. 75.—Tuberculosis of the testes and epididymis, the latter thoroughly infiltrated with caseous material. (Clinic of Hallé.)

BIBLIOGRAPHY

[1] ACHARD and DEMANCHE: Bull. et. mein. Soc. med. d. hop., Paris, 21, Dec., 1906.
[2] GALLAVARDIN and REBATTU: Lyon Med., 30 Jan., 1910.
[3] BERGONIE and TRIBONDEAU: C. R. Soc. de Biol., Paris, 1905, p. 154.
[4] SIMMONDS: Fortschr. a. d. geb. Roentgenstr., 12 Nov., 1909.
[5] NOGIER and REGAUD: C. R. Soc. de Biol., Paris, 20 Jan., 1911.
[6] MONOD and TERRILLON: Maladies du testicule, 1889.
[7] DELBET and CHEVASSU: Rev. de Chir., Paris, 1903.
[8] FRANK: Ann. d mal. d org. gen. urin., 1907.
[9] SEBILEAU and DESCOMPS: Maladies d org. gen. de l'homme. (In Delbet and Dentu Traste' de Chir., 1916, xxxii.)

D. DISEASES OF THE COVERINGS OF THE TESTICLE AND OF THE SPERMATIC CORD

As stated in the Chapter on Anatomy, the testicle and epididymis are covered by a membranous tissue, the tunica albuginea; the sides and anterior part of the testicle are also covered by a membrane which is a continuation of the peritoneal serous membrane, called the tunica vaginalis. Above the testicle and along the spermatic cord the coverings referred to are separated by loose connective tissue and fat. The spermatic cord contains the blood vessels and nerves supplying the testes, epididymis and vas deferens, the structures being held in loose connective tissue and surrounded by a fibrous sheath, the tunica communis, which is again separated from the dartos by connective tissue.

An *extravaginal hematoma* may arise from hemorrhage into the connective tissue between the coverings in the region of the spermatic cord or outside the tunica vaginalis. Such a lesion may be due to trauma or increased blood tension causing the rupture of a vessel. The symptoms of an extravaginal hematoma are the appearance of a tumor along the spermatic cord or near the testicle with pain along the course of the cord; if it extends into the inguinal canal it may be mistaken for a strangulated hernia, but the position of the testis, lying horizontally at the lower end of the tumor (due to depression of the upper pole by the tumor), as well as the impossibility of moving the testicle away from the tumor, differentiates the condition.

An *intravaginal hematoma* may also occur but is much rarer than the extravaginal hematoma. In the case of a blow on the testicle hemorrhage may occur within the tunica vaginalis giving origin to such a lesion. The testicle may be wholly lost in such a tumor, if extensive, and cannot be palpated as in the case of an extravaginal hematoma. There are usually some external evidences on the scrotum which serve to differentiate a *traumatic hematoma* from inflammatory conditions of the testicles.

Various other inflammatory and other pathological conditions of the coverings of the testis and cord may occur. These conditions may be either acute or chronic.

Among the *acute inflammatory* conditions are *acute serofibrinous periorchitis, purulent periorchitis,* and *acute hydrocele* of the spermatic cord.

Acute serofibrinous periorchitis usually follows injuries; in such case the tunica vaginalis contains cloudy serum and loose fibrinous clots; sometimes granulations develop on the surface of the membrane. The symptoms are redness and edema over the region of the testicle. The swelling is soft but extremely painful on pressure and is translucent on illumination and usually accompanied by some fever.

Purulent periorchitis may follow acute serous inflammation, or it may be due to infection introduced through a wound, as in the case of a puncture without proper aseptic precautions. The condition may also result from the spreading of an infective process originating in some neighboring region, such as the prostate. The symptoms are more intense than in serofibrinous periorchitis, and if pus perforates the tunica vaginalis and spreads to the surrounding tissues it may lead to extensive cellulitis.

Acute hydrocele of the spermatic cord or *acute perispermatitis* can only develop in case a part of the vaginal process remains impervious. It may follow a blow or fall, or it may develop secondary to an inflammation of the urethra, neck of the bladder, etc. The chief symptom is the sudden development of a tender elastic tumor in the course of the spermatic cord simulating a strangulated hernia, without the symptoms of ileus. But this tumor is always more movable than strangulated hernia;and it may be observed in children while strangulated hernia is rare in the child. Acute hydrocele of the cord may develop in the case of chronic inflammation.

Chronic inflammatory conditions of the coverings of the testicle and spermatic cord are: *Chronic serous periorchitis* or *hydrocele; hemorrhagic periorchitis* or *hematocele; proliferative periorchitis; adhesive periorchitis; hydrocele of the spermatic cord* or *serous perispermatitis; hematocele of the spermatic cord* or *hemorrhagic perispermatitis; multilocular hydrocele, diffuse hydrocele,* etc.

Hydrocele.—Chronic inflammation of the tunica vaginalis is a commonly met affection. The cause is often a traumatism, but this mode of origin varies much according to different observers. The condition is frequently observed in the first year of life, probably due to birth traumatism. Gonorrheal and other epididymites are frequently causes, the hydrocele sometimes developing during the acute inflammatory stage of the affection. Other causes may be retention cysts either in the testis or epididymis, or the presence of free bodies in the tunica vaginalis.

The serous fluid which collects in the tunica vaginalis may vary in quantity and has been observed to exceed more than twenty quarts; it may contain blood corpuscles, etc. In a hydrocele of long standing the tunica vaginalis may show more or less extensive inflammatory changes with calcifications, and the occurrence of adhesions between the testis and epi-

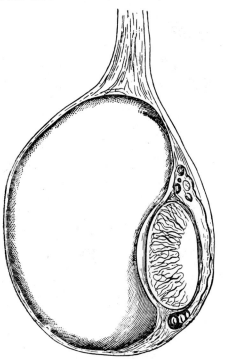

FIG. 76.—Sagittal section of an ordinary vaginal hydrocele, showing position of testis and epididymis in posterior position. (After Prof. Eberth.)

didymis, and such changes may affect the normal position of the testis. If there is much distention it usually takes place upward so that the position of the testicle is low. (Fig. 76.)

The development of hydrocele is usually painless and advice is sought by the patient either on account of its increasing size or its discomfort owing to the dragging on the inguinal canal and cord, especially when the patient has to be on his feet a long time. Translucency is one of the chief characteristics of serous hydrocele and this is easily observed by the usual methods of transillumination.

Hydrocele is occasionally complicated with hernia or it may be instrumental in producing a hernia by dragging the peritoneum into the inguinal canal and forming a pouch for the entrance of omentum or intestine. The hernial sac may be in contact through the upper end of the hydrocele so that the whole tumor may be mistaken for a hernia, as in a case reported

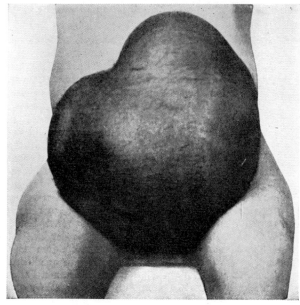

FIG. 77.—Hydrocele testis permagna.
Man aged 54 years; size over three human heads; weight 55½ pounds; duration 30 years. (Clinic of Hallé.) Cited by Professor Bramann and Professor Ramstedt.

by Bramann. As to what size a hydrocele may develop is shown in Fig. 77.

Another variety of hydrocele is that which reaches from the scrotum into the inguinal canal where it lies in contact with the second sac between the peritoneum and the transversalis fascia, either in the vicinity of the internal abdominal ring or in the iliac fossa. Such a tumor is called a *bilocular hydrocele*.

A *double hydrocele* is liable to interfere with the secretion of semen and thus produce sterility which, however, usually disappears after its cure.

Proliferative Periorchitis.—In this condition there is chronic inflammation of the tunica vaginalis marked by a new formation of connective tissue within the membrane and not upon its surface. The tunica albuginea is also thickened. Calcification of some portion of the tunica vaginalis may occur and the condition may sooner or later lead to loss of function of the testicle.

Adhesive Periorchitis.—Following chronic inflammations of the testicle fibrinous inflammations of the tunica vaginalis may occur, as a result of which membranous adhesions are set up between the opposing serous surfaces. Such adhesions are apt to interfere with testicular functioning.

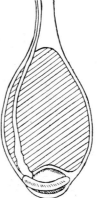

Hydrocele of Cord.—This occurs chiefly in children rather than in adults, developing in an unobliterated portion of the vaginal process and showing itself either within or outside the inguinal canal. It may coexist with hydrocele of the tunica vaginalis giving rise to the bilocular hydrocele already referred to. It is distinct from the testicle and if small can be easily moved about thus differentiating it from spermatocele which is never mobile upon the epididymis. It may be distinguished from a fluid collection in a hernial sac as the latter does not descend when the spermatic cord is dragged down.

Fig. 78. — Diffuse hematocele of the spermatic cord and testis. (After Kocher.) The vas deferens is seen to the left; the testis and epididymis being underneath.

Hematocele of Spermatic Cord.—This condition is usually preceded by hydrocele. An inflammatory process may be grafted upon a hematoma due to traumatism, and in this manner layers of fibrin and new connective tissue may be formed. The shape and position of this tumor are similar to hydrocele of the cord, but it is firmer and rarely translucent like the latter. (Fig. 78.)

Multilocular Hydrocele.—Either the tunica vaginalis or the partly obliterated vaginal process along the spermatic cord may be the seat of cystic dilatations, lying closely together or even communicating, and together forming a multilocular hydrocele. The cysts may originate in a variety of ways, frequently being the residue of Mueller's duct on the Wolffian body.

Tumors of the Membranous Coverings of the Testicle and Spermatic Cord.—Primary tumors of the membranous coverings of the testicle and cord are rare. Cystic tumors arising from embryonic rests have already been referred to. In addition to these, lipomata, fibromata, sarcomata and carcinomata may occur.

Varicocele.—This is the commonest tumor within the membranous coverings. It is an abnormal dilatation or elongation of the veins of the spermatic cord and corresponds to varicosity of the veins in the lower limbs. It may be uni- or bilateral, but is far more frequent on the left side. The condition is due to either increased blood pressure or to weakening of the venous walls. The changes are most marked in the veins nearest the testicle which often assumes an almost horizontal position. Atrophy of the testicle is liable to follow a well-marked varicocele. The tumor is more liable to occur in adults who are sexually active than in the very young or old. (See Special Chapter on Treatment for therapy of above described conditions.)

E. TUBERCULOSIS OF THE TESTICLE

Tuberculosis of the testes generally bears a distinct relation to the development of tuberculous foci in other parts of the body. It occurs at all ages between childhood and old age. A series of fifty-four post-mortems of tuberculous children showed an involvement of the kidneys in 51 per cent., of the bladder in 2 per cent. and of the genito-urinary organs in 2 per cent. of cases (Simmonds). Out of a series of five hundred cases of phthisis examined by autopsy, the genito-urinary tract was involved in 12.8 per cent. of cases (Reclus). Another series (Fowler and Goodloe) yielded 5.27 per cent. (of 531 cases) with testicular involvement.

The term testicle frequently is used without the proper differentiation between the body of the testicle and the epididymis, necessary in statistics and in differential diagnosis.

Long series of cases have been studied individually and comparatively by Barney, Dimitresco, Kocher, Koenig, and Keyes.

Etiology.—Tuberculous infection of the testicle occurs by way of the mucous membranes and through the blood- and lymph-vessels, the result of tubercular infection of the pulmonary and gastro-intestinal tracts. Primary infection of the testes, like similar manifestations of other remote organs, is considered not impossible, even though the avenue of ingress is not clear and pathologically indisputable cases are wanting. The sperma of a tuberculous individual may contain bacilli even when no pathological condition in the testes is distinguishable clinically (Jäckh). Bacilli may occur in the testes even when no active focus is located anywhere else and only a hereditary predisposition is proven (Koenig). Bacilli have been found in the testes at the time of birth and afterwards rendered active by trauma (Kocher).

In a vast majority of cases (average, 62 per cent.) tuberculosis of the testes is secondary to foci elsewhere in the system. Infection by coitus is denied (Kelley). Metastatic spread of an infection seems uncommon although undeniable. Infection into the testicle in many cases occurs from the prostate, where the disease long may remain without reaction (Lanceraux, Terrillon, Krziwicki); also, probably (Kelley) descending from the kidney or bladder. An ascending infection may be carried along the vas deferens (Cayla). The ascending spread of an infection from any focus in the genito-urinary apparatus is well recognized (Mark); but, again, cases show that a general infection of the entire tract from the bladder down, is not rare (Tuffier, Guyon).

Infection by virulent bacilli is possible whenever the condition of intervening tissues favors it. Experimental infection of a testicle always gives rise to a tuberculous process in the corresponding seminal vesicle and prostate, but does not usually develop in the opposite testicle. Injection of virulent bacilli in the aorta of rabbits was followed by various tuberculous manifestations, but only in two of twenty-eight cases did testicular tuberculosis occur without epididymal involvement.

Trauma is an important contributing cause and always should be inquired into. It is clinically evident, and very strongly emphasized by experiments in animals, that when a testicle, or any other part of the epididymis once has received a tuberculous invasion, a severe contusion (Simmonds) as well as any minor mechanical injury will facilitate the onset of an active process.

Bacteriological control is emphasized in all cases, but, as elsewhere, a negative finding is by no means conclusive. In all cases, especially doubtful ones, the bacteriological test should be respected at every stage of treatment.

Gonorrhœa and syphilis have been widely considered as inductive,

11

pathologically, to tuberculous processes in the testes. A mixed infection is rare, but there is no doubt that either of these chronic conditions contribute to open the way for a subsequent tuberculous infection. When a tuberculous subject contracts a gonorrhœal infection, even though the tuberculous process is localized elsewhere, the complication is very common, especially if prompt treatment is neglected.

Another contributing factor is frequent or continued congestion in the genito-urinary apparatus, (pathologic states; induced: sexual excesses).

Pathology.—The tail of the epididymis is the favorite site for the original infection, but occasionally the head may suffer first. The first tangible manifestation of an acute attack is the presence of one or more nodules in the region of the epididymis, or a gradual enlargement of the testicle. The tuberculous nodules at first are firm, with some vascular tendency of the tissue. One or more nodules also may occur on the body of the testicle. The bacterial processes are perivascular (Hutinel and Deschamps) in some cases; in other (Langhans) primary lesions were found in the epithelium of the vesicles. In the testes, the changes at first are characterized by a proliferation of epithelioid cells with large, distended-looking nuclei. The protoplasm of these cells shows spindle, or star-shaped formations. In the neighborhood of the connective tissue are found numerous lymph cells and some giant forms.

After some time the nodules soften, caseation sets in, and a fistula is formed, which continues to discharge for a while. Isolated cases are known where the disease terminated in the subacute state. In most cases, however, the infection spreads. Unless there are very active tuberculous lesions simultaneously occurring in other organs, the general health, and even strength, is fairly well sustained. There is little or no fever, and the pain varies. As the testicle becomes more and more involved, the process of caseation and abscess-formation continues rapidly—or, if the disease develops from the testicle itself, numerous miliary tubercles are formed, which develop into a progressive deterioration of the entire structure, terminating in a fungoid tumor. This clinical picture is true in at least 40–50 per cent. of the number of cases recorded. In some others, the process is spontaneously arrested within from one to five years after the onset, whether in the epididymis or in the testicle, and very occasionally we find an organic isolation of the area, with calcification of the tubercles; but the arrest commonly results in a subchronic condition, the nodules softening very slowly or remaining unchanged, the suppuration holding off, the general health continuing fair, unless an exacerbation occurs from some other, or new, focus.

No primary double testicular tuberculosis has ever been observed. A unilateral, or single, onset, is the rule. Whether treatment is instituted or not, a relapse on the opposite side occurs almost inevitably (80–90 per cent., Keyes) within a few years. (Figs. 79 and 80.) But few cases escape this rule (Marks). If the tuberculous process stops with operative treatment (removal of one or both testes), as it does in about 40 per cent. of cases, recovery may follow, or a non-active period of years ensue; if not, and the fistula continues to discharge, and a fungoid tumor containing masses of degenerated granular tissue and caseous accumulations, persists, an outbreak generally occurs in other organs, and the result is fatal.

Symptomatology.—Tuberculosis of the testes generally occurs in early life, from childhood to the age of fifty. Of forty-five cases recorded by Koenig, twenty-eight occurred between the ages of twenty and thirty-seven.

The disease is at first recognized by the formation of one or more hard nodules slightly or not at all sensitive, in the region of the epididymis or on the body of the testicle. The nodules may be the size of a pea or they may involve the larger part of the organ. In the acute type the patient complains of pain, quite severe, and all manifestations of a local inflammation. These inflammatory symptoms may disappear within a week or ten days, but usually they persist, but less acute in character. After the subacute stage, areas of fluctuation appear in the affected organ, followed soon by the appearance of abscesses, sinuses and fistulæ, which open and close from time to time.

Palpation in all types of the disease reveals the epididymis hard, nodular and not much sensitive, and distinctly separated from the testes, if the latter be uninvolved, by a groove which permits the two bodies to be distinctly identified. These nodules increase in size rapidly, and soften after some weeks, discharging their contents through a fistula. The onset

FIG. 79.—Tuberculosis of the testis. (After E. L. Keyes, Jr.) Right epididymectomy—left orchidectomy. On the right side the vas is manifestly enlarged; on the left it seems normal. The testis was removed because it was feared the blood supply had been cut off in removing the epididymis. Many small tubercles may be seen in the testis. Under ordinary circumstances, however, such a gland as this might be left in situ, with the expectation that it would heal.

may be acute, in which case probably a mixed infection (gonorrhœa, syphilis) is responsible. The gradual enlargement of the nodules and spread, or arrest, of the tuberculous process is slow. Hydrocele may be present. The loss of weight is slight, if any. The urine generally is

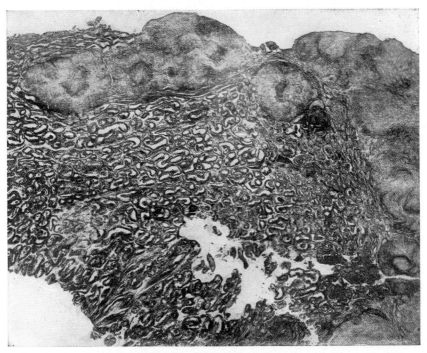

FIG. 80.—Invasion of the testis by tubercles. This specimen was taken from the gland pictured in Fig. 79. (After E. L. Keyes, Jr.)

normal. Pain is absent or slight at first, but distress increases until the subacute stage is reached, or operation brings relief. The urine is normal if the urinary apparatus is not implicated. If the vas is involved it will be found thickened perceptibly, hard and inflexible.

Diagnosis.—Differential Points: In testicular tuberculosis the epididymis is attacked before the testis. This is an important differential distinction, as regards syphilis, in which case the contrary obtains. From acute epididymitis tuberculosis differs by the absence of the acute exudate. Again, epididymitis is distinguished by acute pain, intense inflammation and swelling of the scrotum; these symptoms do not exist in tuberculous orchitis. Fever usually is absent in tuberculosis, but constitutes a typical attendant in epididymitis.

If the disease occurs, as it does in scarce instances, in the testis primarily, a series of examinations is necessary to establish its distinction from syphilis or sarcoma. A repetition of the Wasserman test will aid in the differentiation from syphilis. Sarcoma is characterized by the uniform enlargement and nodulation of the testicle and the relatively more active progress of the neoplasm.

Prognosis.—This depends upon the general condition of the patient and the degree of testicular involvement. When the resistance is good and the involvement unilateral and fairly limited, the prognosis is quite good. The tubercular process may spread to the prostate, seminal vesicles or opposite testis. In such cases the prognosis is, indeed, very bad. Ten per cent. of recorded cases, treated promptly and continuously watched, attained seemingly full recovery, even though some had much suppuration (Keyes). Active suppuration frequently results not only in temporary alleviation, but even in a cessation of symptoms for several years, perhaps for longer periods. Operation is beneficial, whether radical or partial. Death is not recorded in any case, from the immediate cause (Keyes, Koenig). The school of Bruns (Finkh, Dürr) advises against partial operation or palliatives. Early operation is strongly favored (Monod, Terrillon in order to prevent secondary or tertiary infections. Some spontaneous cures (less than 10 per cent.) are recorded. If the condition does not affect the urinary organs, complete recovery (freedom from symptoms during long periods) is almost certain, unless other foci open.

Treatment.—The varying development and clinical course of this disease, and the occasional possibility of spontaneous healing, have opened the way to a great diversity of opinion regarding the treatment. Most French investigators reject castration (Jullien, Deschamps, Reclus). The school of Bruns objects to anything but a radical operation and rejects a partial or one-sided removal. In forty-five cases (thirty-seven castrations, single and double), 75 per cent. yielded favorable results (Koenig). The radical operation, therefore, has gained considerable following.

Erasure of the affected area, with iodine treatment, results uniformly in a relapse.

Double orchidectomy is indicated for every severe case, because the unilateral operation generally is followed by involvement of other organs within two years.

Double or single epididymectomy, and in certain cases orchidectomy (Cf. Chapter on Treatment) has given very good results. After the removal of the affected epididymis, an infiltrated testicle often heals spontaneously. The critical phase of this operation is the treatment of the vas deferens, which is drawn downward at the point of incision in order that the removal may be as complete as possible. There is always danger of rupturing the vas high up, causing an infection of the peritoneum. The vas should be severed at the upper end of the incision and left protruding from the wound, to discharge any suppuration (Keyes). While, in cases of long standing, orchidectomy is unavoidable, acute tuberculous orchitis with the epididymis involved, should be submitted to a hygienic regimen until suppuration sets in, or the case becomes subacute. The suppuration should be treated by drainage except in aggravated cases where the radical operation alone can give relief. When a subacute stage is attained, a double epididymectomy is carried out, unless the presence of spermatozoa in the unaffected testis makes it desirable to attempt the preservation of the one organ.

Heliotherapy, occasionally, is indicated (Balduzzi). Many authors strongly recommend climatic and hygienic treatment. Suppurations, fistulization and sinus formation, should, of course, be subjected to surgical therapy. In every case of tuberculosis of the testes the constitutional diathesis must be treated according to indications and rational therapy instituted. Palliative measures are, unfortunately, only applicable to people of means, who are able to lead an out-of-door life or take a long sea voyage, and who can have constant medical supervision. Such measures may afford the caseation of the nodules if begun in the earliest stages of the tubercular involvement. The surgical treatment consists of *erasion, curettage; castration; epididymectomy.*

Erasion is applicable to cases where one or two nodules exist in the epididymis.

Castration, according to Jacobson, is indicated in the following conditions:

(a) When erasion has failed in lesions of the epididymis.

(b) When discharging fistulæ are present or are numerous.

(c) When, after erasion, persistent swelling of the testicle accompanied with night-sweats and loss of flesh is present.

(d) When *fungus testis* exists or when the body of the testicle is involved.

(e) In the presence of purulent hydrocele.

Castration is used in two different classes of cases:

Class A.—In primary tuberculosis, when the disease is limited to one testicle and has not extended too high along the cord, and when the bladder, prostate, and vesicles are not affected. In such a case a reasonable hope may be entertained that the disease may be permanently eradicated from the body. If the seminal vesicles are affected the indication for castration is not so clear, although, if the deposits are small and of recent date and the patient's general condition favors rapid healing, removing the testicle with its diseased nodules may retard the development of the tubercular foci located elsewhere.

Class B.—In cases where other organs of the body are tubercular and a cure is impossible, hygienic measures alone are the only treatment applicable. An exception should be made to this rule when the testicle is disorganized and the scrotum riddled with sinuses discharging pus. Here castration is indicated to relieve the patient from the drain of the exhausting discharges and from one source of his discomfort.

Molla calculates that the testis is spared in fully 80 per cent. of the cases of primary epididymitis. Radical treatment does not require more than removal of the epididymis and vas deferens, leaving intact the testis and all the vessels and nerves in the spermatic cord. The circulation of both blood and lymph is quite distinct in testis and epididymis. " With primary tuberculosis of the latter, partial operations intending to be conservative, conserve nothing but the tuberculosis. The function of the epididymis is lost by the infectious process and the partial operation as effectually as after radical epididymectomy, but the latter answers its purpose only when the vas deferens is removed in addition." Even when the seminal vesicles and the prostate are involved, these may heal after removal of the epididymis, just as the bladder heals after removal of the tuberculous kidney. In one case even the testis was invaded, but this was cauterized, and the man recovered completely under heliotherapy after removal of the epididymis and vas deferens. In three cases, erection and ejaculation proceeded apparently normally although the epididymis and vas deferens on both sides were removed.

BIBLIOGRAPHY

[1] BALDUZZI, A.: in Policlinico, Sez. Chir., xxviii, 1921, 417–431.

[2] BARNEY, J. D.: Tubercular Epididymitis; and results of seventy-one cases. Boston Med. and Surg. Jour., clxvi, 1921, 409–414.

[3] BARNEY, J. D.: Tubercular Epididymitis; an Analysis of one hundred and fifty-three cases. Amer. Jour. Urol., December, 1911.

[4] DIMITRESCO: De l'Epididymectomie paritelle ou totale dans le Tuberculeuse primitive du Testicule. These, Paris, 1897.

[5] EISENSTÄDT, J. S.: Tuberculosis of the testis in the child. Jour. A.M.A., lxxix, 1922, 2076–2079.

[6] JÄCKH, ALEX: Über den Bacillengehalt der Geschlechtsdrüsen und des Sperma tuberculöser Individuen. Virchow's Archiv., cxlii, 1895, 101–133.

[7] KEYES, E. L. JR.: Tuberculosis of the testicle; observations upon one hundred patients. Ann. Surg., xiv, 1907, 918–937, w. two plates.

[8] KOENIG, R.: Beitrag zum Studium der Hoden tuberkulose. Deutsche Zeitschr. F. klin. Chir., xlvii, 1897–98, 502–522.

[9] KRZYWICKI, C. V.: Twenty-nine Fälle von Urogenital-Tuberkulose-Ziegler's Beibräge, iii, 1888, 297.

[10] MARK, E. G.: Primary Tuberculosis in the body of the Testicle. Jour. of Urol., v, 1921, 171–176.

[11] RECLUS: in Duplay et Reclus, Traité de chirurgie, viii, 1892.

[12] ROUX: Excision de la vésicule seminale et du canal déférent. Congrés Franc. de Chir., 1891.

[13] SIMMONDS, J.: Tuberculosis of the male genital system. Beitr. Z. Klin. d. Tubuerkul., xxxiii, 1914.

[14] ULLMANN, K.: in Wien. Klin. Wochenschr., xxxiv, 1921, 559–561.

[15] MOLLA, RAFFAEL: Revista Espanola de Medicine y Cirugia, Barcelona., July, 1923, 365.

F. SYPHILIS OF THE TESTES

In earlier times, syphilitic orchitis was not recognized as a distinct luetic manifestation, although the frequency of symptoms must have been greater than now, owing to the relatively greater promptness of treatment in our day. The presence of a " swelling coming on without external injury," in uncomplicated lues, and which yielded readily to treatment (Bell) was pointed out long ago, but actual data on the frequency only occurred in later years, after syphilitic orchitis had been recognized as a tertiary manifestation.

The Bellevue Hospital autopsies of one hundred and seventy-one cases of late acquired syphilis revealed sixty-one instances of chronic interstitial syphilis (Symmers). Other studies (Warthin) showed the presence of Treponema pallidum in many congenital and early acquired cases without histological changes in the testes. The genitotrophic tendency of the Treponema has been demonstrated repeatedly in experiments on animals (Parodi, Noguchi). This tallies well with the microscopic analysis of human cases, by which the presence of the Treponema in histologically perfectly healthy testes, and in the seminal fluid, was ascertained (Finger and Landsteiner).

Several authors calculate that forty per cent. of all syphilitics earlier or later develop testicular symptoms.

Syphilitic epididymitis is scarce (Thompson, Dron). One series of two hundred and seventy-six cases of testicular involvement revealed six with epididymal affection, another gives a proportion of two thousand, three hundred to sixteen: an average of about 2 per cent.

Etiology and Pathology.—There is but one specific infection, already mentioned, to which all cases are referable.

In testicular syphilis two types are recognized: *Interstitial orchitis,* and *gumma.* The first occurs pathologically earlier than the second. Both forms now are clinically rare.

The *interstitial type,* frequently slight and unilateral in its onset, is characterized by a swelling of the organ. Some fluid may occur in the tunica vaginalis. Histologically, there is an infiltration of plasma cells and lymphocytes between the tubules. The fibroblasts of the stroma proliferate vigorously, the basement membrane is thickened. Spermatogenesis is decreased. Smaller areas of the testicle may be affected, or the condition may involve the entire organ. In advanced stages, fibroid changes occur. The active cellular infiltrations are the seat of treponematous infection.

The *gumma type* usually occurs unilaterally and is recognized as one or more fibroid nodules, which sometimes become multiple in the organ and may in time soften and discharge voluntarily through a fistula, with sinus formation. Some pain is present. Hydrocele is a frequent attendant phenomenon. The development is quite slow. The epididymis is rarely involved. Occasionally the gummata will coalesce into a smooth, indurated mass ("billiard-ball" testis). The clinical picture varies considerably with the variety of complications, and the extent of involvement differs much with the virulence of the individual case. Cellulitis of the surface of the scrotum is relatively common, occasionally edema sets in, with intense tenderness due to an association with lymphedema of the scrotal wall (pseudo-elephantiasis), referable to inguinal adenitis of specific origin. This condition may be referred directly to erosive chancres at the base of the scrotum. The tubules being buried in the gummatous masses, their destruction often is very extensive.

An *involvement of the epididymis* occurs rarely as an acute affection and is uncommon even in secondary syphilis. Palpation may reveal small nodules or a uniform gummatous enlargement, attended by hydrocele. The development is unilateral, scarcely ever double, the tunica vaginalis is thickened, and the histopathological elements are identical with those of the tubercular form. Syphiloderma also is an attendant condition. (Figs. 81 and 82.)

Diagnosis.—The condition often is so slight that it escapes observation except by autopsy. Palpation shows a hardness of the testis, with lack of sensation, except in later stages. From traumatic orchitis, syphilis is distinguished by the history, the presence or absence of tenderness, the rapidity or slowness of the swelling. In gonorrheal orchitis, which is rare, the epididymis usually is involved, or there is a history of urethritis. Tuberculosis has a far more rapid course, with fistula, and pain is pronounced.

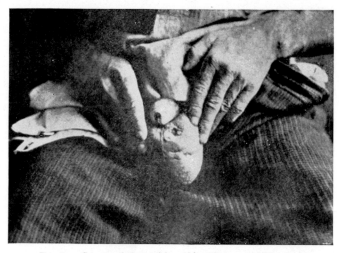

Fig. 81.—Gumma of the testicle. (After Herman and Klauder.)

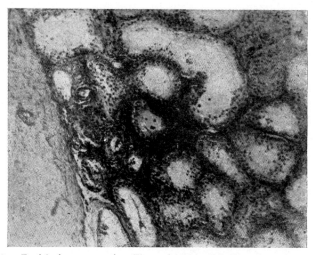

Fig. 82.—Testicle from a paretic. The testicle was clinically and grossly negative. The histological section shows rather extensive areas of fibrosis between tubules with round- and plasma-cell infiltration. The tubules show spermatogenic layers in good state, no atrophy; they were probably functionating. In the area of fibrosis there is present what is probably an obliterated tubule. (After Herman and Klauder.)

Bacteriological and clinical tests of course are indispensable in the differentiation.

Teratoma and sarcoma develop far more rapidly than either syphilis or tuberculosis and are attended with more pain, also remain unilateral relatively longer.

A biopsy, which would decide the diagnosis promptly in every case, is justified only in extreme cases and practically possible only when the destruction of internal parts of the organ is well advanced.

In the absence of deciding symptoms, a full history and clinical tests, the condition may be determined by a therapeutic test, *viz.*, a treatment for syphilis being instituted and the result watched; and unless the symptoms yield within a reasonable time (one to three weeks), extirpation is indicated.

The routine palpation should take cognizance of a possible involvement of the epididymis (Klauder), because the gummatous form of epididymo-orchitis may be mistaken for tuberculosis, teratoma, or even sarcoma. Gummatous epididymitis, rare as it is, appears first in the globus major and runs a course similar to typical gumma, but with a greater tendency to sclerosis and ultimate atrophy.

The distinction from gonorrhea often depends on the progressive clinical picture and the therapeutic results, than upon the history of the case.

White and Martin give the following table of diagnostic features of syphilitic orchitis, encephaloid cancer and tuberculous disease of the testis.

Syphilitic Orchitis	Encephaloid Carcinoma of Testicle	Tuberculous Orchitis
Syphilitic history.	No history of any special condition.	Tuberculous history.
Usually occurs at about twenty-five or thirty years of age.	Occurs at any age.	Not often seen after thirty.
Begins in the testicle.	Begins in the body of the organ.	Begins in the epididymis.
Is situated primarily in the connective tissue.	Begins by the deposit of small nodules in the seminiferous tubules.	Exists primarily in the tubules.
Tends to fibrous over-growth.	Tends to formation of patches of softened, white, p u l t a c e o u s material.	Tends to fatty, caseous, or purulent degenera-tion.

Syphilitic Orchitis	Encephaloid Carcinoma of Testicle	Tuberculous Orchitis
Slow in its progress.	Rapid in its course.	Slow in its progress.
Skin of the scrotum rarely involved.	Skin of the scrotum finally involved.	Skin involved only just before the formation of abscess.
Ulceration or suppuration rare.	Ulceration and fungus common.	Suppuration common.
Fistulæ rare.	Fistulæ common.	Fistulæ common.
A feeling of great weight, with only such pain as results from dragging on the cord.	Pain severe and lancinating in advanced stages.	Little pain.
Tumor very hard and uniform.	Soft and fluctuating.	At first hard, knotty, irregular.
Skin of scrotum purplish, but unaffected.	Network of large veins over surface of tumor.	Skin congested, but otherwise unaffected.
Testicle of moderate size; rarely attains twice its normal diameter.	Attains great size.	Of moderate size.
Painless on pressure.	Painless on pressure.	Often painful on pressure.
Both testicles often affected.	Generally only one testicle affected.	Often both testicles affected.
Fungus rare.	Fungus always present in advanced stages.	Fungus common.
No discharge or bleeding.	Bleeds freely; offensive discharge.	Less apt to bleed; discharge less offensive.
Lasts many years.	Rarely extends beyond twenty months.	Lasts several years.
Curable.	Usually fatal.	Generally incurable.
No involvement of inguinal glands, as a rule.	Inguinal, iliac, and lumbar glands and cord affected.	Usually no inflammation of glands.

Prognosis.—The prognosis is uniformly favorable as regards general health and life, even if total destruction of the organ takes place. The institution of a suitable therapy will result in a reduction and possibly a cessation of symptoms, occasionally in a surprisingly short time. The function of the testis, however, ceases or is irreparably reduced, in a very large proportion of cases, the permanent impairment depending on the extent of the lesions. There always is a pronounced atrophy, but when some portion of the glandular elements are preserved, the function may be retained proportionately.

Treatment.—Arsphenamine, mercury(mercury salicylate), and iodides (potassium iodide) should be used from the beginning and as large doses (increasing as the treatment proceeds) given as the individual conditions demand. If the organ is enlarged and very sensitive, a suspensory would best be used. In case of complications and severe pain, hospitalization is unavoidable.

Local treatment with the specific remedies elsewise used in syphilis must be instituted when the gummata become large and fistulous. Far progressed cases with extensive lesions and continued suppuration usually furnish indications for orchidectomy.

BIBLIOGRAPHY

[1] DRON, A.: De l'epididyme syphilitique, tumeur syphilitique de l'epididyme. Arch. gén. de Méd., ser. 6, ii, 1863, 513, 724.

[2] HERMAN, LEON, and KLAUDER, J. V.: Studies of the prenatal transmission of Syphilis: I. Syphilis of the testicle. Amer. Jour. of the Med. Sci., clix, 1920, 705–722.

[3] NOGUCHI: in Jour. Exper. Med., xv, 1912, p. 2.

[4] PARODI: in Centralbl. f. Bakteriol. u. Parasitenk. Orig., xliv, 1907, 428.

[5] RECLUS, P.: Syphilis du Testicule. Paris, 1882.

[6] SYMMERS, D.: Anatomic Lesions in late acquired Syphilis: a Study of three hundred and fourteen cases based on the analysis of 4,880 necropsies at Bellevue Hospital. Jour. Am. Med. Assoc., lxvi, 1916, 1457.

[7] THOMPSON, LOYD: Syphilis of the genital organs of the male and the urinary organs. iv: Scrotum, testicle, epididymis, spermatic cord, seminal vesicles. Amer. Jour. Syph., iv, 1920, 706–724.

[8] U. S. Surgeon-General. War Department Office. Studies of Syphilis, Washington, D. C., 1913.

[9] WARTHIN, A. S.: The new Pathology of Syphilis. Am. Jour. Syph., ii, 1918, 425.

[10] WILLIAMS, CAMPBELL: Syphilitic Testicle. In Clin. Jour., London, xxi, 1912, 56–60.

[11] WRIGHT, F. R.: Syphilitic epididymitis. Urol. and Cutan. Rev., xx, 1916, 661.

[12] WHITE and MARTIN: Genito-urinary and Venereal Diseases, 1907.

[13] ZIGLER, M.: Testicular Syphilis, with particular reference to Gumma. New York Med. Jour., civ, 1916. 998.

CHAPTER V

G. DYSTROPHIAS

a. Effects of Internal Secretion of the Testes upon Growth and Metabolism.

b. Effects of Castration; Eunuchism.

c. Eunuchoidism; Retarded Puberty and Infantilism.

d. Precocious Puberty.

e. Dwarfism and Giantism. (Its Relation to Gonadal and Other Endocrine Dysfunctions.)

f. Adiposity and the Endocrines.

g. Fröhlich's Disease.

a. EFFECTS OF INTERNAL SECRETION OF THE TESTES UPON GROWTH AND METABOLISM

Appearance of puberty in men is expressed by an increased vigor which affects both physical and psychical activity, and which indicates increased metabolic activity. Diminution of the functions of the genital hormone is accompanied by senile changes, the results being similar to those produced by castration. In the testes of old men, there is a marked diminution of interstitial cells, both as regards size and number. The profusion of pigmental matter in the substance of the cytoplasm suggests atrophy.

Weil[1] has investigated the question of bodily proportions and configurations with aberrations of sexuality as an expression of the internal secretions.

From the earliest times there have been attempts to connect the psychic condition of individuals with their outward form. Such can be gathered from the early Egyptian medical papyri as well as from the writings of Aristotle and the earlier Greek authors who formulated the humoral theory and connected phlegmatic and other temperamental dispositions with bodily expression. This may be considered as a kind of foreshadowing of the present day scientific tracing of human character to the normal or

176

abnormal functioning of the glands of internal secretion and their known effect on physical development.

The philosophic view, which considered the body and soul or mind as things apart and separate and independent of each other, is not supported by the endocrine doctrine which teaches that character and mentality are not merely influenced by, but are the accurate and actual expressions of our secretions. The endocrine viewpoint is very different from the older phrenological viewpoint which traced peculiar traits of mentality to localized areas in the skull and brain.

From our present-day knowledge we know that bodily shape and growth from birth onward are not unalterable. While heredity counts for much, especially in body length, yet there are other factors which determine proportions and development of bodily parts to each other. Such factors favoring the exaggeration or inhibition of the growth of certain parts or tissues depend upon the activity especially of the thyroid, thymus, pituitary and sexual glands of internal secretion. While the thyroid, thymus and pituitary secretions incite growth of bone tissue, this is inhibited by the sexual gland secretion, resulting in the fact that at the end of the stature-growth period, about the twenty-fifth year of life, a very definite equilibrium has been reached between the secretion of these glands with a very definite relation of the bodily skeletal parts to each other. There are two very special conditions established, *i.e.*, the relation between the proportions of the upper and lower body (measured from the head to the vertebral column and from this to the ground) and the proportion of the shoulder-width to the width of the hips. In a full grown normal man the first proportion is generally about 100 to 95, while in a normally grown woman it is about 100:90. The second proportion in the normal man is about 100:81, while in the woman it is about 100:97. These proportions depend especially upon the activity of the thyroid, but if this activity is disturbed or obstructed the proportion, both in man and woman, may be considerably altered. (See also Chapter dealing with the Skopze.)

A. Weil [2] has undertaken the study of these proportions in a number of persons whose sexual psychology he knew intimately, in order to ascertain if any parallel could be found between body proportions and sex gland abnormalities. Male homosexuals were especially selected for investigation and two hundred such were examined; but other abnormal sexual

12

conditions were also investigated and the experiments controlled by the measurements of normal heterosexual men.

As a result of his investigations, Weil found that 95 per cent. of all examined male homosexuals deviated in the proportion of the upper body length to the lower body length from the heterosexual average, the average proportion being 100:108. The findings are shown in the annexed

TABLE I

Lower length of skeleton in percentage of the upper length.	Percentage of heterosexual subjects.	Percentage of homosexual subjects.
87–90	11.2	
91–93	10.0	1.5
94–96	33.8	2.5
97–99	23.8	4.5
100–102	15.0	11.0
103–105	6.2	23.5
106–108	....	24.5
109–111	....	16.5
112–114	....	8.5
115–117	....	3.5
118–120	....	0.5
121–123	....	2.0
124–126	....	1.5

Table I, which shows without any equivocation the deviation of the homosexual from the heterosexual proportions.

In regard to the proportion of the shoulder-width to that of the hips, the results in heterosexuals and homosexuals are shown in Table II.

TABLE II

Shoulders: hip-width=100	Percentage of heterosexuals.	Percentage of homosexuals.
69–72	3.7	....
73–76	11.2	1.5
77–80	31.2	16.0
81–83	26.3	25.5
84–86	18.7	24.5
87–89	5.0	18.0
90–94	2.5	13.5
95–99	....	1.5

This table shows that in male homosexuals the proportion of shoulder-width to hip-width approximates the proportion found in normal women. Weil suggested that deviations in the measurements of the proportions referred to may be used as a basis in the differentiation of heterosexuality and homosexuality.

In a more recent paper Weil [3] gives the results of similar investigations made by him in psychosexual infantile subjects and in virile women.

In psychosexual infantilism Weil found that the average measurements of ten cases, as compared with similar measurements in a normal man, were as follows:

		Normal
Average Height	158.6 cm.	167. cm.
Upper Skeletal Length	77.4 cm.	85. cm.
Lower Skeletal Length	81.2 cm.	82. cm.
Shoulder-Width	35.8 cm.	39.3 cm.
Hip-Width	29.2 cm.	31.8 cm.

In the case of virile women the measurements were as follows (average of ten cases) :

		Normal Woman	Normal Man
Height	162.1 cm.	154 cm.	167. cm.
Upper Skeleton Length	79.3 cm.	79 cm.	85. cm.
Lower Skeleton Length	82.8 cm.	75 cm.	82. cm.
Shoulder-Width	36.1 cm.	35 cm.	39.3 cm.
Hip-Width	32.8 cm.	34 cm.	31.8 cm.

It will be observed that in the virile woman the body measurements approximate those of a normal man.

BIBLIOGRAPHY

[1] WEIL, A.: Arch. f. Entwicklungsmechanik, 1921.
[2] WEIL, A.: Zeitschr. f. Sexualwiss, viii, 1921.
[3] WEIL, A.: Fortschr. d. Med., June 7, 1922.

b. EFFECTS OF CASTRATION; EUNUCHISM

In order to study the *effects of castration* let it be said in the beginning that a great deal of work has been done by various observers, beginning with the lowest possible forms of life and gradually ascending to man. The living forms resorted to as experimental material were amphibiæ, arthropeds, worms, butterflies of all sorts, birds, trytons, mammals, and a host of others, with the final object of arriving at a definite conclusion and in this manner obtaining comparative results from the lowest possible forms of life to the human being. We shall first discuss the results obtained by depriving some of the domestic birds of their sex glands. The

most commendable work in this respect was done by Goodale[1] and
Pézard.[3] Pézard castrated three roosters of a mixed breed in which the
leghorn characteristics predominated. To this series he added three
Orpington roosters. These fowls were about three months old and the
external sex characters, such as comb, beard, wattles, spurs and plumage,
were not as yet devoloped. These birds were compared with normal fowl
and it was observed that the growth of the comb in the castrates differed
from that of the normal bird in which the comb grows more rapidly than
the rest of the body. In other words,
there results a discord between the
growth of the comb and the body.

Fig. 83.—The comb of a normal and castrated brown leghorn. *a*, full-grown rooster;
b and *c*, full-grown hens; *d*, full-grown male castrate. (After Goodale.)

Goodale has very carefully studied
these manifestations in the brown
leghorn. His observations were very
numerous and he found that the
comb and beard of castrates did not
remain of the same size as at the
time of operation, but that they
enlarged somewhat, *i.e.*, the comb
of the capon did not become feminine but remained infantile. To be more
specific the comb of the castrated bird does not even reach the size of the
normal female comb. (Fig. 83.) In contradistinction to the appendages
of the head, the growth of the spurs of the cock are not influenced by
castration. Both Pézard and Goodale made this observation in all the
fowls they have castrated, the spurs remaining the same as in the normal
bird. The plumage also is not influenced by castration. Goodale's and
Pézard's work proved conclusively that the plumage of the birds remained
unaffected by this procedure. Pézard emphasizes that the characteristic
feathers of the cock are frequently more abundantly developed in the capon,
and assume a more brilliant hue than is the case in the normal bird. In
this observation Pézard is supported by Goodale. These observers have
also established the fact that there are skeletal changes in castrated fowls.
That there is an increase in the weight of capons is a well known fact.
Pézard states that the periabdominal fat in castrated cocks averaged
somewhere between 90 and 150 gms., while in the normal fowl of the same
type it weighed between 10 and 60 gms.

Fichera and Massaglia (cited also elsewhere) found that in castrated cocks there is an increase in the size of the hypophysis.

Very interesting psychosexual changes are observed in castrated roosters. Usually a caponized rooster does not crow, has no spirit of combativeness with other roosters, pays no attention to hens and makes no attempt to trod them. In other words, the psycho-sexual characteristics of the normal male are here wanting. While Goodale observed some sort of crowing in capons and a weak manifestation of sexual instinct, Pézard insists that capons never crow, and if they ever emit a sound it resembles more a clucking such as is made by a hen. The capon is tame, shy and noncombative. Pézard has never observed a fight between a

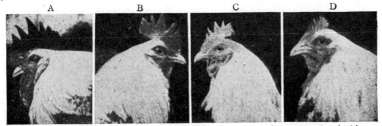

Fig. 84.—Regressive changes in the appendages of the head of a rooster that had been castrated at the age of one year. *a*, at the time of the operation; *b*, 26 days after operation; *c*, 36 days after operation; *d*, 3½ months after operation. (After Pézard.)

capon and a cock. Brought in contact with hens the latter approach him but the capon withdraws and pays no attention to his female admirers. He is "strictly neutral," as Pézard expresses it. The manifestations observed in the normal cock who seeks the hen in the most characteristic manner are totally absent in the capon.

The observers under discussion have taken cognizance of the fact that if only a small piece of testicular tissue be left behind during the process of castration the effects of the procedure as enumerated above are not evident, the secondary sex characters regressing in proportion to the amount of sexual gland tissue remaining.

In fowls that had reached maturity before being subjected to castration, a regression of comb and wattles was observed, but no change took place in the plumage. "If the castration is complete," says Pézard, "one observes the changes in the comb a few days after the operation. The comb, beard and wattles regress, the birds do not crow and soon lose their sexual instincts." (Fig. 84.)

It seems remarkable, indeed, that with the changes taking place in the caponized bird the plumage and spurs remain so resistant to the influence of castration. How-ever, this will be elucidated when we recite the changes taking place in castrated hens. For the purpose of this experiment Goodale castrated brown leghorn hens ranging in age between four weeks and four months. The results of such castra-tions were that the hens' plumage assumed the appear-ance of the feathers of the male, but resembled more the plumage of the capon than that of a normal cock. Simultaneously spurs also developed. The appearance of the castrated hen strongly resembled that of a castrated rooster. (Fig. 85.) This transforma-tion into male plumage Goodale has observed in a series of twenty-five cas-trated hens.

Fig. 85.—Castrated hen. Development of mascu-line plumage and spurs. (After Goodale, reproduced from colored plate.)

Pézard [4] was able to substantiate the findings of Goodale in this respect. His experimental birds developed spurs (Fig. 86), which grew with the same rapidity as in a normal rooster, having reached a length at the end of a year of about 2.5 cm. These castrated hens assumed the plumage of a full grown capon. (Fig. 87.)

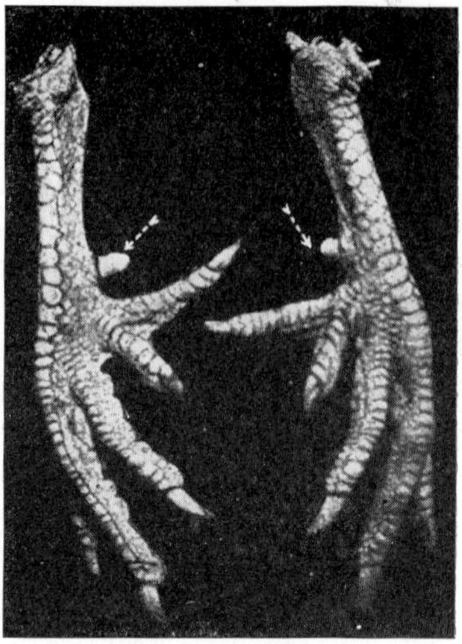

Both Goodale and Pézard empha-size that a castrated hen can only be distinguished from a normal rooster through the small comb and wattles. If one did not know that the hen in question had been castrated one could not tell by looking at the bird

Fig. 86.—Spurs developed in a hen that had been castrated six months before. Length of spurs 8 mm. At the end of a year the length of the spurs was 2.5 c.m. (After Pézard.)

whether it was a castrated hen or a castrated rooster. Also, that these castrated hens do not display any feminine sexual instincts. The observations
made by these investigators in the case of the rooster in reference to leaving behind a piece of the testis, hold true also in the hen where a fragment
of ovarian tissue is left behind after castration.

The effects of castration on the lower animals, particularly rats, has
been extensively studied by Steinach [6] who castrated male animals of this

FIG. 87.—Photograph of hen four months after castration, showing masculine plumage
and spurs. (After Pézard.)

species at the age of four to six weeks and carefully observed the manifestations following the ablation of the sex glands. The accompanying
picture of the normal sexual apparatus of the male rat will help to inter-
pret the description of the changes to follow. (Fig. 88.) The sexual
apparatus in rats, at the age at which Steinach experimented, is entirely
undeveloped. The seminal vesicles are about 3 or 4 mm. long and about
3 mm. wide; they contain nothing. Macroscopically nothing can be seen
that would indicate a prostate gland. The penis develops only when
maturity is reached. Up to that time it is short and thin. A glance at
the accompanying picture (Fig. 89) will show that the seminal vesicles
are normally developed; they are 40 mm. long and about 6 mm. wide and
are filled with a yellow seminal secretion. The prostate is a large lobulated
body, the penis is long and thick. In the castrated animal (Fig. 90)

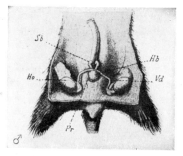

FIG. 88.—Normal male rat at the age of one month. *ho*, testicles; *pr*, prostate; *vd*, vas deferens; *sb*, seminal vesicles; *hb*, bladder. The seminal vesicles are very little developed, the prostate macroscopically barely visible. (After Steinach.)

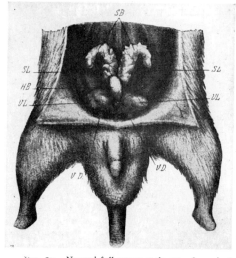

FIG. 89.—Normal full-grown male rat. *sb*, seminal vesicles; *vl*, anterior lobe of prostate; *sl*, seminal lobe of prostate; *vd*, vas deferens; *hb*, bladder. The testicles are not exposed. (After Lichtenstern. Quoted from Lipschütz.)

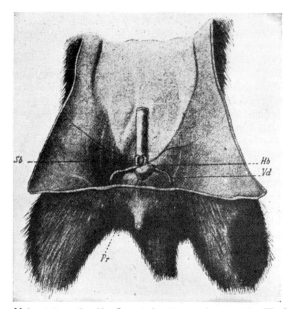

FIG. 90.—Male rat 8 months old. Castrated at the age of one month. We observe that both vasa deferentia are separated from the testes. Prostate and seminal vesicles remained undeveloped. (After Steinach.)

you will see that the seminal vesicles as well as the prostate have not progressed in development but show approximately the same picture as a normal animal at about the age of one month. In this process of retardation both the internal and external organs of generation of the male partake.

Only one conclusion can be drawn from these findings, and that is that castration of animals at an early age at once inhibits the progress of the development of the sexual apparatus. In other words, without testicles all the classical manifestations of a castrate become established. If castration is performed on an animal that has already reached sexual maturity a regression of the sexual apparatus becomes manifest. These manifestations have been described by Steinach [6] who found that one and a half years after castration the seminal vesicles had considerably regressed in size, and in this regression the prostate also shared.

Tandler and Keller [7] have studied the results of castration in mammals and have observed the same manifestations sometimes found in man after ablation of the sex glands; that is, an elongation of the shafts of the bones. The epiphyseal lines functionate longer, they remain open and supply the necessary elements for bone proliferation. This has been observed also in guinea pigs, dogs, sheep, cows, etc. Ablation of the sex glands has also shown, according to Fichera, Schönberg and Sakaguchi,[8] Thorek, and others that there is an increase in the weight and size of the hypophysis. The animals studied by various observers have been birds, rats, guinea pigs, buffalo, and other quadrupeds. This phase of the work will be considered further in the chapter on the interrelation of the sex glands and other endocrines, the results of investigations of the author.

Interesting observations have been made by Lipschütz [9] as to the relation of *body temperature and the testes*. Castration of females results in the reduction of the temperature in the animal. Implantation of testicular tissue into these female castrates reduces the temperature still further. The castration of males, however, does not change the body temperature. On implanting an ovary into such an animal the temperature will at once rise until it reaches the point of that of the female. Such observations demonstrate a higher rate of oxidation for the female than the male.

The hair in human castrates shows nothing of importance on the head, where it is abundant, but on the body it takes the disposition found on the female body. Lanugo hairs take the place of the mature hair on the face; the extremities and chest, as well as the axillæ with their characteristic disposition of hair in the mature male is usually absent in castrates, and on the mons veneris the disposition of the hair is of the type observed in the female. Observe the hair on the pubic region of a woman and compare these with the disposition of the hair of a castrate and you will find them analogous. (Figs. 91 and 92.) The latter shows the feminine configurations very distinctly. The skin of the castrate is pale, yellow and often wrinkled. The disposition of the fat is, according to Hirschfeld, and Tandler and Grosz, characteristic. There are, of course, some eunuchs who are emaciated. In this type the height and disproportion are more pronounced than in the obese type. The latter looks bloated. The principal areas of fat accumulation are the breasts, lower abdomen, hips, gluteal and trochanteric regions, mons veneris and upper eyelids.

The changes in the osseous system have already been alluded to. It may be added that the pelvis retains its juvenile form and approaches the female type, particularly in its transverse measurements. The upper and lower jaws are powerfully developed. The root of the nose is depressed and the superciliary ridges well marked. The neck of the eunuch remains feminine. The voice in early castrates retains its timbre of youth at about the age of puberty. The larynx remains small. The thyroid remains behind in development. The thyroid as well as the cricoid cartilages remain unossified and the *pomum Adami* is absent. The general musculature is weak.

The psychosexual conditions of individuals who have been castrated early in life clearly show an absence of sexual power. This may, however, occasionally be manifested to a very slight degree and that only exceptionally. Mentally, castrates are inferior to normal individuals, as has been ascertained in a number of cases.

Lichtenstern has recently reported the effects observed in castrates of various ages. One of his patients was twenty-eight and the other twenty-one years of age, and in them the manifestations of the ablation of the sex glands become evident, in one instance four months and in the

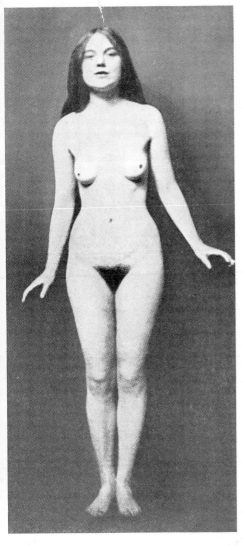

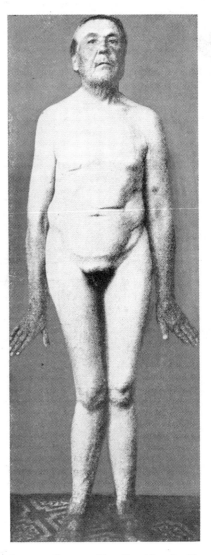

FIG. 91.—Note disposition of pubic hair in woman. (After Stratz.)

FIG. 92.—Castrate. Note disposition of pubic hair. (After Walter Koch.)

other in three weeks after the removal of the testicles. In all cases there was complete extinction of sex power and *libido*.

It has been observed that there is a marked diminution in the respiratory exchange in some animals following castration. Some observers maintain that this is due to a general indolence on the part of the animal. Van Noorden has pointed out that such results in the respiratory exchange should be considered as secondary or indirect and not as being due to the removal of the oxidizing agents. H. Wheelon [10] finds that such criticism is substantiated by the fact that there is a reduction in the irritability of the vasomotor apparatus and a decrease in the weight of the central nervous system as shown by Hatai [11] following the removal of the testes. Be this as it may, a number of investigators, particularly Murlin and Bailey, Pachter and others, have shown that castrated dogs do display a reduction in the respiratory metabolism for months following the operation. That there is a basal reduction in the production of carbon dioxid following castration, such reduction being greater in the liver than in the muscles, has been proven by Angolitti and Kajima. Löwy and Richter and others concluded, as a result of such findings, that the reduction of metabolism strongly points to being due to diminished oxidation and increased adiposity.

The effects of castration have been recently studied and published by Walter Koch [12] after a residence among the castrated sect of *Skopzies* of Roumania. Koch availed himself of the opportunity afforded by the German occupation of Roumania during the late war to study thirteen of these individuals in detail, and of these he gives excellent photographs in his monograph on the subject published in 1921.

The Skopzies are a religious sect living in Russia and Roumania, whose religion prescribes that male members be castrated. The Skopzies distinguish between the " great operation " in which both penis and testicles are removed, and the " little operation " where only the testicles are cut away. Although much has been written concerning this sect, yet little is really known about it.

In the individual cases studied by Koch he found the pale skin, abundant hair on the head, scanty beard, but few hairs on the body and in the axillæ, a female type of pubes, wrinkled face irrespective of age, small lymphatic apparatus in the throat, small thyroid and long extremities.

Koch described four types of Skopze: (1) The ordinary type with long extremities; (2) the type of gigantism; (3) the type with acromegaly, and (4) a type with hypophyseal adiposity. The type seems to depend upon the age at which the castration was carried out. This first type shows a normal sella turcica; in the second type the sella turcica seems to be enlarged; in the third type the sella is much larger and there are other abnormalities in the skull, especially rarefaction of the cranial bones.

Koch states that the Skopze originated from a sect of flagellants or quakers in the year 1757 in Russia, particularly in the region of St. Petersburg and Moscow and around the borders of the Black and Caspian Seas. The flagellants were given to vicious practices, and some of their fanatic members found the following passage in the Bible: " If thy right eye offend thee cut it out and cast it from thee," or " If thy right arm offend thee cut it off and cast it from thee." Arguing from analogy they concluded that the best way to rid themselves of sexual excesses was to follow the dictum of the Bible and cut off the offending members.

Andrei Sheliwanow is conceded to be the founder of the sect, which refers to him as the " Savior." They believe that Sheliwanow is still living and will sometime reign over Russia, and in that event the last judgment will be held, when everybody will be castrated.

Napoleon I is looked upon by these people as the Anti-Christ, who is supposed to be living today in Turkey as the devil's own, whence after being castrated and converted he will return. They also firmly believe that Christ was castrated, and consequently must be counted as one of their sect. To emphasize this contention they quote the Bible, I Corinthians, 7: " For I would that all men were even as I myself. . . . I say, therefore, to the unmarried and widows, it is good for them if they abide even as I."

Castration is practised in this sect on women as well as men. The operation was performed with red-hot irons, ligation with a heavy twine, ablation by a sharp instrument such as a kitchen knife, razor, scythe, hatchet, etc. Hemostasis was effected with alum or similar chemicals, and the wounds were dressed with various salves, wax dressings, etc. In order to avoid stricture of the urethra they introduced into it nails made of zinc and so gradually prevented the closure of the orifice remaining.

Maxim Gorky, the famous Russian author, describes in his memoirs (*Under Strange People,* translated by Scholz) the Skopzies in the following terms: "There arrived in Ssarapul on the Volga a remarkable passenger on board. A heavy-set man with withered, feminine, beardless face. His feminine appearance was accentuated by the long, warm kimono-like kaftan he wore and the fur cap with ear-laps which rendered him indistinguishable from a woman. . . . . Before Jakow (the fireman of the boat) reëntered the stoking room I asked him what kind of an individual this was. 'You can see at once, my dear friend,' he said

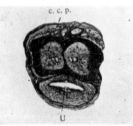

FIG. 93.—Transverse section of the stump of the penis of a eunuch 28 years of age. Magnified 3 times. *u,* lumen of urethra; *c. c. p.,* corpus cavernosum penis. The corpus cavernosum urethræ is of nearly normal development. The corpora cavernosa penis are remarkably regressed in size. (After Tandler and Grosz.)

solemnly, 'it is a Skopze from far-off Siberia! A very industrious fellow he is, lives after a plan . . . . I have hired myself out to him as a servant . . . . come with me, h'm? Come with me? He takes you also if I just say a word to him. . . . . They will cut off from you what you don't need and give you money. For them it is a great holiday when they can mutilate a man, but they reward him royally . . .' There the Skopze stood on board ship, with a white bundle under his arm, with eyes concentrated in a penetrating stare, as if in a semiconscious stupor, piercingly fastening his gaze on Jakow . . . ."

Tandler and Grosz [13] supply us with a picture of a transverse section of the stump of the penis of a eunuch twenty-eight years of age. (Fig. 93.) This individual lost his genitalia under the Skopzies. The penis, seminal vesicles and prostate are retarded in their development in the eunuch and castrate in the same manner as shown by Steinach in his experiments upon lower animals. Tandler and Grosz have made the interesting observations that the *corpus cavernosum urethræ* in the eunuch alluded to developed to a size corresponding to the age of the individual and that only the *corpora cavernosa penis* retrogressed in their development. In that penis stump microscopic examination of the *corpus cavernosum urethræ* shows that it is in structure nearly normal. On the other hand, in the *corpora cavernosa penis* the venous spaces have been so greatly reduced in size that only occasionally can one find an indication of the lumen of a vein and that all of the cavernous spaces have been supplanted by connective tissue.

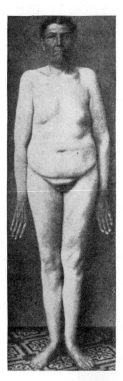

The prostate and seminal vesicles, as already stated, have been found to have much decreased in size. In the former there is a great deficiency of glandular tissue.

I wish to cite in this connection two typical cases from the series observed by Koch.[12] The first (Fig. 94), T. I. K., born at Cerno, Russia, was a bee-cultivator by occupation. Age fifty-one years; 174.5 cm. tall; weight 76 kilograms; temperature 36.7 C.; of giant-stature, well developed skeleton of somewhat feminine type, wide pelvis, slight lordosis, musculature well developed; fat deposit rich, particularly at the hips, lower abdomen and in the region of the breasts. The mammary glands

FIG. 94.—Skopzie No. iv. (After Walter Koch.) See text.

are of distinctly feminine, virginal type, with a distinctly glandular feeling. The anterior abdominal wall is pendulous, hanging apron-like over the mons veneris. The skull is round, the lower jaw strongly developed, the incisor teeth separated; abnormal position of other teeth; no wisdom teeth. The facial appearance is feminine; prominent malar bones of mongoloid type; no beard; low brow; long, blonde, soft wavy hair, long in the back, not cut. Eyebrows well developed, iris blue. In the genital region a complete absence of testes, scrotum and penis is observed. Of the latter only a stump remains. At the site of ablation a semilunar scar is observed under the root of the penis. The disposition of the sparse body hair is of distinctly feminine type. The thyroid gland cannot be palpated. The high-pitched voice remains that of the young boy. No albumin or sugar in the urine; reaction acid; specific gravity, 1.020.

Measurements of Body and Skull

Size	174.5	Length of foot	26.2
Stretching distance	183.5	Circumference of skull	53.0
Head and trunk measured while		Diameters: a. p.	18.8
sitting	85.5	b. p.	15.0
Circumference of chest	94.0	b. t.	13.2
Length of lower extremities	95.0	b. z.	14.0
Forearm and hand	50.0	m. o.	25.4
Middle finger	12.2	Length of ear	6.6
Little finger	9.4	Width of ear	3.3

Röntgen examination; base of skull traversed by X-ray obliquely: Slightly deepened, enlarged toward the sphenoidal fossa; apparent wide open sella turcica. Other sinuses well formed; large accessory sinuses. Delicate, somewhat pointed lower jaw; ossified hyoid bone; trace of ossification of the larynx. Macrodactyly, with special enlargement of the epiphyses; delicate structure of the bone of same. No visible epiphyseal lines.

When this individual was between eleven and twelve years of age he was castrated by his father, the scrotum, testes and penis being cut off with a knife. His father was castrated after his marriage. When the boy asked his father why he castrated him he received a thrashing. He has a brother who also is castrated, and a sister upon whom no operation has been performed. He has no sexual sensations. He also stated that the sect believes that Christ himself was, as he is, castrated, for it is so said in the Bible.

The second Skopze (Fig. 95), M. A., was born in Russia in the vicinity of Tula; is sixty-seven years of age, a cab-driver by occupation. Height 176.0 cm.; weight, with clothing, 77.0 kilograms; temperature 36.0 C. Acromegaly type; massive osseous development, somewhat flabby musculature and circumscribed voluminous panniculus adiposus, particularly on both sides over the pelvic crests, as well as in lower abdominal wall and chest, where one observes typically feminine breasts which give on palpation a sense of the presence of glandular tissue. Marked knockknees, particularly affecting the right lower extremity. Wide pelvis, which is not very conspicuous on account of the broad shoulders and marked adiposity. When the head is covered, the stature is that of a feminine figure with very long extremities. There is long, wavy hair on the head, which is cut slightly in the back. Marked sparseness of hair on the chin, but well developed eyebrows. The nose is plump, the jaw of moderate size and the ears are large. The face is greatly wrinkled and withered. There is no hair on the chest and the pubic hair has a typically f e m i n i n e distribution. There is complete absence of the penis and testicles; radiating scar on the scrotum underneath the root of the penis. There are

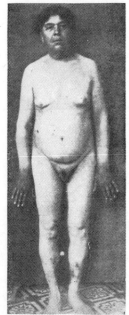

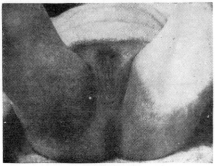

FIG. 95.—Skopzie. No. vii. (After Walter Koch.)
See text.

no hairs on the perineum. The thyroid is small and there is slight development of the lymphatic apparatus in the throat. Urinalysis dis-

13

closes an absence of albumin and sugar; reaction slightly acid; specific gravity 1.019. The face is strikingly feminine.

Measurements of Body and Skull

Height	176.0	Length of foot	27.4
Head and trunk measured while		Circumference of skull	56.0
sitting	84.5	Diameters: a. p.	18.5
Forearm and hand	50.0	b. p.	15.5
Middle finger	12.4	b. t.	13.3
Little finger	9.9	b. z.	14.2
		o. m.	25.7
		Length of ear	7.4
		Width of ear	3.3

Blood Examination: Polymorphonuclear neutrophiles 86
Lymphocytes 11
Mononuclears 2
Eosinophiles 1

Röntgen examination disclosed a remarkably enlarged sella turcica. Relatively small sphenoidal sinuses, prominent lower jaw, slight calcification of the os hyoid. Macrodactylism of the epiphyseal structures; calcification of the diaphyses of the bones of the middle of the hand and phalanges. Distinct epiphyseal lines in the ulna.

When between the ages of fourteen and fifteen this individual was castrated by his father. During the same year he moved to Bucharest. One of his nephews fifty-four years of age, a cultivator of bees by occupation, was also castrated, but one sister was not mutilated at all. The patient is rather talkative, emphasizing frequently his great belief in " the laws " of the sect, adding that it is conducive to longevity to live according to their laws, and pointing to the Epistle of John, Chapter XIX, which contains the fundamental laws of the sect.

Aside from the Skopzies there are other conditions under which men have lost their testicles. During warfare, as acts of revenge among savages and semi-civilized people as well as the " getting even " of jealous women with their lovers or untrue husbands; the removal of the testicles for the purpose of preparing children for choir service, accidental ablations, pathological conditions necessitating the removal of the diseased organs, all add their quota to the unpleasant after-effects of castration. In many countries where the master of the house is jealous of his numerous wives, and in order to protect them from sexual molestation by other men, he causes all male individuals to be castrated, creating them *eunuchs,* and then entrusts his women in their care. In Asia particularly, eunuchs are created in this manner.

While Mohammedans resorted to castration of young males for practical reasons, Christians castrated their young for *Church idealism.* The

FIG. 96.—Professor Alessandro Morechi. Castrated in his youth to retain beautiful voice.
(After Magnus Hirschfeld.)

well-known fact that the ablation of the sex glands does not permit of the full development of the voice has caused many parents to submit their sons to the operation of castration so that they may remain in the service of God by singing in various choirs.

Magnus Hirschfeld, in his *Naturgesetze der Liebe,* says: " In the Middle Ages the vocal accomplishments of Italian castrates were greatly extolled. Even throughout the entire Eighteenth Century more than two thousand children were castrated annually for that purpose in the states governed by the Church. ' La voix des castrates imite celle des cherubims au ciel ' was the sentiment of the day, and one could observe in the windows of almost every male nurse and barber in the city of Rome the following sign: ' Ici on chatre á bon marche,' or ' Qui si castrano ragazzi á buon mercato,' which, freely translated, means ' Here castrations are done cheap.' In 1827 Rossini wrote the opera *Aureliano in Palmyra* for the castrate Velutti, and it is said that Napoleon was moved to tears upon hearing the castrate Crescentini sing for him in *Romeo and Juliet*. I personally had the opportunity in Rome of being introduced to a number of castrated singers belonging to the famous choir of the Church of St. Peter. One of the most prominent ones was the noted singer of the Sistine Chapel choir, Professor Alessandro Morechi, whose picture I herewith reproduce (Fig. 96), which shows that this man, who has passed the fiftieth year of his life and was castrated in his youth, has the characteristic fat and smooth face of the castrate."

It has been stated above that during warfare acts of revenge are frequently perpetrated by ablation of the genitalia. The accompanying photograph shows such an unfortunate. (Fig. 97.) This case was reported by Magnus Hirschfeld, who has been enriching the literature on sexual matters for some time past.

This scientific observer concludes that castrates who lose their testes in warfare never again attain their former vigor. Scrutiny of the photograph of this former soldier will show the characteristic facies of the castrate and the classical manifestations as to the disposition of the hair and fat following the loss of the testes.

A case observed by the author may be interesting in this connection. It concerned a man thirty-one years of age, an actor, who developed a carcinoma of the penis. This he neglected until involvement of the inguinal glands and scrotum occurred, which necessitated ablation of the penis, scrotum, both spermatic cords, and dissection of the deep and superficial inguinal glands. The author was compelled to resort to this extensive operative procedure in order to be reasonably sure that an area free from carcinomatous dissemination was reached. The operation was performed in August, 1917. Under deep röntgen and radium therapy, plus skin grafts later in the treatment, the wound healed very kindly. The patient left the hospital after three months and did not communicate with the author until January 1, 1923, a period of about five and a half years. Unfortunately, he did not permit me to photograph him on his last appearance, but the following findings were noted upon physical examination:

His general appearance has become distinctly feminine; his face is that described by Hirschfeld. There was complete loss of mustache and hair

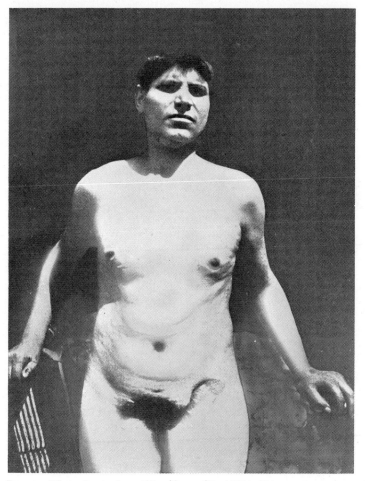

FIG. 97.—Effects of castration. (After Magnus Hirschfeld.) This man, twenty years of age, while an Italian soldier, during the Abyssinian war, together with numerous of his colleagues, had his genitals cut off. Gradually this fully developed man developed feminine characteristics. His voice became high-pitched, the outlines of his body assumed feminine form and his conduct was decidedly that of a woman. Observe the breasts approaching the female type.

of the bearded region, which is covered by a fine lanugo. There are accumulations of adiposity in the usual sites; namely, the nates, hips, mammary and trochanteric regions. A distinct change in the voice was observed—it is higher pitched than it was before the operation.

Being married and of markedly virile type prior to the onset of the disease he soon noted a gradual decline and finally a total loss of libidinous thoughts and desires. All characteristic evidences of a typical castrate are manifest in this individual. Sex gland implantation has been recommended by the author to improve his general condition and the patient is now seriously considering this therapy.

From a consideration of the experimental and clinical studies set forth above we are *forced to the conclusion that the incretory function of the testes is of vital importance for the well-being of the individual, that its correlation to other endocrines is of vast importance and that somatic and psychic changes are the rule following ablation of these important endocrine organs. It has been proven beyond the least shadow of a doubt that upon the internal secretion of the testes depends the development of the secondary sex characteristics, which may be, in the absence of such secretion, entirely wanting. Also that castration before the sex characters have developed may result in an indefinite type of individual of the so-called asexual form. Also, that the later in life the individual loses his supply of testicular hormone the less will the untoward manifestations be manifest upon his general physical make-up and secondary sex characters.*

BIBLIOGRAPHY

[1] GOODALE, H. D.: Gonadectomy in Relation to the Secondary Sexual Characters of some Domestic Birds. Carnegie Institute Publications, Washington, 1916.

[2] GOODALE, H. D.: Castration in relation to the Secondary Sex Characters of Brown Leghorns. American Naturalist, 1913.

[3] PÉZARD: Sur la détermination des caractéres sexuels secondaires chez les Gallinaces. Comptes rend de l'Acad. Sc. t. 153, 1911, p. 1027.

[4] PÉZARD: Le conditionment physiologique des caractéres sexuels secondaires chez les oiseaux. Edition du Bulletin Biologie de la France et de la Belgique, Paris, 1918.

[5] PÉZARD: Developpement experimental des ergots et croissance de la crete chez les femelles des Gallinacés. Comptes rend de l'Acad. Sc., Paris, t., 158, 1914, p. 513.

[6] STEINACH: Untersuchungen zur vergleichenden Physiologie der männlichen Geschlechtsorgane, insbesondere der akzessorischen Geschlechtsdrüsen. Pflüger's Archiv., B. 56, 1894.

[7] TANDLER and KELLER: Üeber den Einfluss der Kastration auf den Organismus, IV. Die Körperform der weiblichen Frühkastraten des Rindes. Archiv. f. Entwicklungsmechanik, B. 31, 1910.

[8] SCHÖNBERG and SAKAGUCHI: Der Einfluss der Kastration auf die Hypophyse des Rindes. Frankf. Zeitschrift für Pathologie, B. 20, 1917.

[9] LIPSCHÜTZ: Die Pubertätsdrüse, 1919. (Ernst Bircher. Berlin.)

[10] WHEELON and SHIPLEY: Amer. Jour. Physiol., 1918, xxix, 394.

[11] HATAI: The Effects of Castration, Spaying and Semispaying on the Central Nervous System and Hypophysis of the Albino rat; also The Effect of Semispaying of the Remaining Ovary. J. Exper. Zool., Phila.. 913, xv, 297-314.

[12] KOCH, WALTER: Ueber d. Russ. Rumänische Kastrationsekte, d. Spokzen, 1921.

[13] TANDLER and GROSZ: Ueber den Einfluss der Kastration auf den Organismus. Beschreibung eines Eunuchenskelets. Arch. f. Entm. Mech., B. 27, 1909.

c. EUNUCHOIDISM; RETARDED PUBERTY AND INFANTILISM; GENITO-GLANDULAR DYSTROPHIAS

Etiology.—Eunuchoidism is to be found developing on a congenital basis, the underlying factor being a lack of development of those elements that are responsible for the evolution of the normal psychic and somatic characters of the individual. *A eunuchoid* individual is, in other words, a eunuch in milder degree; an individual in whom the effects of castration are not so strikingly manifest as in the confirmed total castrate, the eunuch; the influence on the sex characteristics depending upon the presence and the degree of functioning capacity of the incretory elements of the testes. Outside of congenital factors any other agency that will cause an abolition of hormone function of the testes may result in eunuchoidism. Of these the most prominently found are various sources of injury to the testes as well as its suspending cord. The cord may be so influenced by compression or torsion as to cause serious damage to the testicular tissue (Cf. Author's observations on torsion of the spermatic cord in Chapter on Pathology of the Testicle); inflammatory processes; tumors or dysfunctions dependent upon a neurologic basis through the central or peripheral nervous systems. The degree of eunuchoidism depends upon the degree of arrest of hormone function and upon the age of the patient.

As stated in the opening remarks of this chapter, eunuchoids are eunuchs in a more or less milder form. The accompanying illustration after Tandler and Grosz, shows the skeleton of a normal individual and that of a eunuchoid, demonstrating the osseous changes that have taken place in a typical eunuchoid. (Fig. 98.) Tandler and Grosz have also supplied medical literature with illustrations showing the testes of the

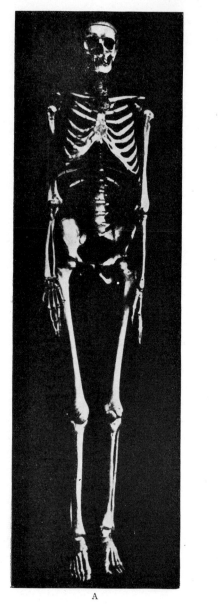
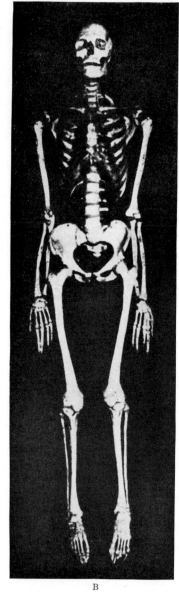

A   B

FIG. 98.—*a*, skeleton of normal man; *b*, skeleton of a eunuchoid. (After Tandler and Grosz.)

eunuchoid (Fig. 99), as well as the appearance of the prostate and seminal vesicles of an individual of the same type, twenty-eight years of age (Fig. 100). If one compares this illustration with that of a normal individual the great diminution in size of the prostate gland and seminal vesicles, as well as the vas deferens will at once be noted.

A mild form of eunuchoidism is known as *retarded puberty*. Similarly to precocious puberty, which will be discussed below, *retarded puberty* is explained by alteration in the normal development of the genital gland, or by any process which hinders its development, and consequently causes a deficiency or delay in the production of hormone at its normal time. Outside of maldevelopment of the testicle itself from any cause, the most usual etiologic factor is a lesion of the anterior lobe

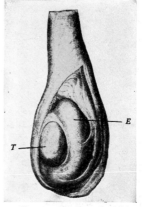

FIG. 99.—Testis and epididymis of a eunuchoid 28 years of age. Observe the relatively marked development of the epididymis *e* in contrast to the much under-developed testis *t*. (After Tandler and Grosz.)

of the hypophyseal gland, or through some biochemic influences retarded function of the Leydig cells. The usual sexual discrepancies noted in such cases are impotency, sterility, and deficiency of *libido*.

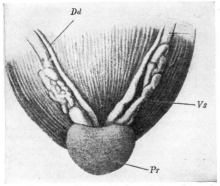

FIG. 100.—Prostate and seminal vesicles of eunuchoid aged 28 years. *pr*, prostate; *vs*, vesiculæ seminalis; *dd*, deferent duct. Parts much smaller than in normal individuals. (After Tandler and Grosz.)

In the true eunuch where the condition was produced before the onset of puberty, the s k e l e t a l configuration approaches the feminine type in many aspects. The bones are childlike, there is but little hair on the face, axillæ or pubic region, and such as occurs has a feminine distribution. The genitalia remain in an undeveloped childlike condition, and there is bodily distribution of fat as in the female.

Bassoe [1] mentions several instances of recorded *gigantism*, in all of which there was an infantile condition of the testes and absence of sexual attributes and functions. Bassoe saw one such case in which the man was

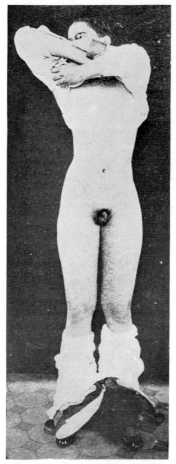

FIG. 101.—Genitoglandular dystrophy. (After Oscar de Sousa and Aloysio de Castro.)

7 feet 8-¾ inches tall and weighed 380 pounds, but was devoid of sexual feeling and never experienced erections. He was like an overgrown child and the penis and testes were small.

The question of mono- or pluri-glandular dystrophia, raised by the consideration of the pathogenesis of eunuchoidism, is one of the most important in modern medicine; it is the problem of the physiological significance of organs long ignored as well as the functional co-relations and their part in the economy under the direction of the internal secretions. We shall therefore devote a little further time to the consideration of this question.

Sousa and De Castro [2] have described many typical cases of genito-glandular dystrophia, most of which occurred in Brazil. Fig. 101 gives a good idea of such an individual. This man was forty-two years old. He has no trace of beard, only a fine down; complete absence of hair in the axillæ and pubes as well as the limbs. Fat well disposed in the mammary and abdominal regions. The penis is scarcely 3 cm. long and the testicles are only the size of almonds. He has only attempted to have sexual relations three times during his life. He does not care for women; shows mental deficiency. This man was later found to have a hypophyseal tumor with destruction of the posterior clinoid processes.

Although in genito-glandular dystrophia, the sex gland is that upon which the clinical character mainly depends, yet other internal secreting glands may be involved by association or secondarily, and thus various clinical types are manifested. The group of genito-glandular dystrophies may be classified as follows:

(a) Genito-glandular dystrophia of infantile type;
(b) Genito-glandular dystrophia of gerodermic type (senilism)·
(c) Genito-glandular dystrophia of eunuchoid type;
(d) Genito-glandular dystrophia of adipose-genital type;
(e) Associated types of genito-glandular dystrophia.

In the general characteristics of genito-glandular dystrophia, certain elements exist which are common to all types, and individualize the group, differentiating it from other dysendocrines. These are:

1. The condition of the sexual organs.
2. The state of the secondary sex characters.
3. The state of the metabolism.

The external organs are rudimentary, and internally there is reduction or absence of the tractus genitalis. The genital functions are suppressed or nearly so.

Of the sex characters, the most frequently noted is the absence of hair on the usual parts where it is abundant in normal males, also the skeletal development is frequently very marked.

Among the different disturbances in the metabolism due to genito-glandular dystrophia, experimental investigation has shown that lipoidemia must be included. Such an effect also follows röntgen raying of the genital region, and in the female ablation of the ovary.

Genito-glandular disturbance is also responsible for the aberrations of growth.

In the infantile type of genito-glandular dystrophia, the interstitial testicular gland is, according to Souques,[3] the main factor of the relations of infantilism with the internal secretion of the testicle. This author concludes: "Clinical and experimental reasons seem to me to establish the exclusive rôle of the interstitial gland of the testicle and to demonstrate that infantilism is always due to insufficiency of its internal secretion." While Souques admits infantilism of thyroidean and hypophyseal types, yet he asserts that "such primary lesions must be reflected in the testicle and alter its internal secretions."

Study of the literature justifies the inclusion of *infantilism* among the endocrine dystrophias contrary to the opinion of certain authors, such as Falta, who deny the intervention of the genital gland in the production of infantilism. These authors consider infantilism as due to arrest of development of the organism at a given period, from which time the sex gland is no longer developed, and the sex organs remain infantile. Such a conception seems to be entirely negatived by the clinical facts. According to the origin, there may be *general infantilism or testicular or ovarian infantilism.*

The gerodermic type of genito-glandular dystrophia has already been dealt with in connection with eunuchoïdism. This latter term appears to have been first applied to the condition by Griffith [4] in 1894, and in 1910 it was further vulgarized by Tandler and Grosz [5] who much extended the syndrome to its generally now accepted significance. There are four sub-types of this condition, according to Sterling; [6] (a) *total hyposexualism,* characterized by morphologic aplasia and absence of function; (b) functional dissociation, *i.e.,* functional deficiency without manifest aplasia; (c) *hypoplasia of the genital organs* and dissociation of the different funcitonal elements, and accompanied either by preservation of sexual instinct with sterility, preservation of genetic power without *libido,* or by impotency and sterility but with exaggerated *libido;* (d) *purely morphological dissociation,* small penis and well developed testicles, or vice versa.

Sterling and Sousa and De Castro have been able radiographically to demonstrate a bony intumescence in the centre of the palatal vault in genito-glandular dystrophias of the eunuchoid type, which, with other signs, they consider characteristic of this condition. There is no alteration in the sella turcica. In Fröhlich's infantilism, the condition is due to a functional insufficiency of the hypophysis which in turn interferes secondarily with the development of the testicles and brings about the resulting syndrome.

The best method of differentiating between Fröhlich's [7] syndrome and genito-glandular dystrophia of the eunuchoid type is to assure the presence or absence of a hypophysary tumor, or one in the zone of the hypophysis. Where there is such a lesion with the consequent testicular effects, the case may be called one of *hypophyseal eunuchoidism.*

Sousa and De Castro consider that the adiposity which is part of Fröhlich's syndrome arises from the secondary alterations in the sexual secretions and that this symptom of the syndrome is primarily genital or genito-hypophyseal.

Castex and Waldorf [8] have described these three principal types of eunuchoidism as follows:

(a) *Eunuchoidism feminism,* distinguished by feminism or infantilism, round face, feminine distribution of fat, hair on the pubic region having a feminine distribution, skeletal lines feminine.

(b) Rummo and Ferranini's [9] *type of genito-dystrophic gerodermia* was described by them in 1897, and is typified by senilism of the face and skin, with modifications of the skeleton and certain cutaneous disturbances. In this type, the skin is wrinkled, a beard is absent; according to Rummo " they are young and seem old," or " they are old and seem young." Their hair is thin and prematurely gray. The penis and testicles remain infantile. The genesial function may be modified considerably or entirely abolished, *i.e., impotentia cœundi et generandi* with absence of erotism.

A case has been reported by Ciauri [10] with severe testicular sclerotic atrophy and partial persistence of the interstitial cells. This author gives the pathogenesis of the condition as follows: Three endocrine glands are out of function—the genital, causing the special morphological changes; the hypophysis, inducing gigantic sclerosis through hypertrophy of the anterior lobe or hyperactivity of the posterior lobe; and the alterations attributable to the thyroid represented by the cutaneous and nutritional disturbances.

(c) The third type of eunuchoidism is *Falta's,* [11] *or the tardy type,* which appears after normal general and sexual development, which then begins to show regressive symptoms. The typical skeletal formations of the other eunuchoidal types are wanting in this type. This type arises in those who from any cause suffer testicular atrophy, with the accompanying retrogression of sexual characters. Such may be the result of traumatism, or it may be a sequel of infection (tuberculosis, syphilis, mumps), and later on assumes the character of pluriglandular dysendocrinism.

Castex and Waldorf themselves describe a case of premature senility, apparently of the second type, which they term *dystrophic geroderma,* in a man thirty-seven years of age (Fig. 102).

Figures 103, 104, 105, and 106 depict a case of genito-glandular dystrophia of gerodermic type observed by R. Ciauri. The author observed an individual, forty years of age who has the appearance of a man of sixty-five or seventy. Typical gerodermic manifestations were seen on the

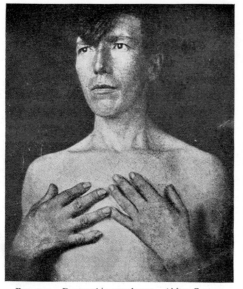

FIG. 102.—Dystrophic geroderma. (After Castex and Waldorf.)

entire integumental covering of the body. All the manifestations of senility were observed. This condition has set in suddenly in the last year. Prior to that he enjoyed the very best of health. In this case there was a marked diminution of sexual power and *libido* although not completely extinguished. No thyroid was palpable. Marked improvement was noted in this c a s e f r o m thyroid transplantation.

In the various types of *eunuchoidism*, the process is, therefore, always one of either failure to develop a normal testicle, or it is due to the breaking down of a perfectly normal testicle by some pathological or traumatic process.

Mariotti [12] also gives a good description of the first type of eunuchoid: In such the stature is almost always tall, never below the medium height, corresponding to the patient's age, with a special disproportion of the limbs, particularly of the lower limbs which are excessively long with respect to the skeleton of the trunk, tendency to fat about the nates, external regions of thighs and breasts, head small, hands long, generally graceful structure. The face shows a delicate pallor at times and is more or less feminine in aspect and in details of the texture of the hair, skin, etc. Intelligence is normal, but there is a characteristic psychism associated to puerilism or feminism; a greater or lesser failure of development of the genitalia with insufficiency of development of the secondary sexual characters.

The etiology of eunuchoidism is generally connected with inflammatory lesions of the sex gland during fetal life or early infancy, the effect of infective diseases which alter the interstitial or Leydig cells.

As stated, such eunuchoids are neither necessarily impotent or sterile. They may marry and beget children. Freiberg[13] described a specimen in the Pathological Institute of the Cincinnati General Hospital. The subject was a male of thirty years. He was married and had two healthy children. Necropsy report stated that he was of feminine type. The hair was coarse and thick, whiskers scant, hair of trunk had typical feminine distribution, thorax " chicken-breasted," hips flaring. Fig. 107 shows a section of this man's testis.

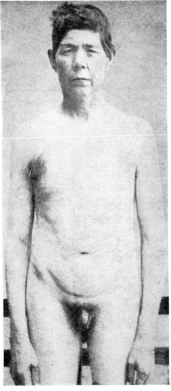

The histological picture shows an absolute lack of interstitial cells, whereas the seminiferous tubules are in good condi-

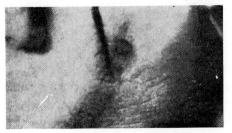

FIGS. 103 and 104.—Case of gerodermic dystrophy observed by R. Ciauri. Note dermal changes on face and general contour of body.

tion. Clinically, the man possessed *potentia generandi,* but lacked male sex characters, which would be strictly in accordance with the absence of interstitial cells.

The mild type of eunuchoidism may be due to a congenital failure in the proper development of the testicle.

Furno[14] has described five cases of eunuchoidism in three generations of one family. There is a type of *heredofamilial eunuchoidism* clearly distinguished from the types of direct transmission from father to son which are, according to Furno, only slight spurious forms of *hypogenitalism.*

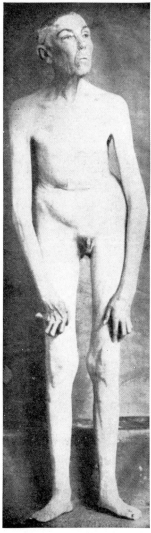

The heredofamilial form is a " dominant " character according to the Mendelian concept of heredity and usually mendelizes the female sex appearing to transmit this abnormality.

Furno c l a s s i f i e s eunuchoidism into four distinct types as follows: (a) pure eunuchoidism in which there is a deficiency or absence of genital glands; (b) *gerodermic eunuchoidism* in which the pathological hormonic influence of thyroid and hypophysis is a d d e d to congenital hypogenitalism; (c) *acromegalic eunuchoidism* in which the pathological hormonic influence of the hypophysis is added

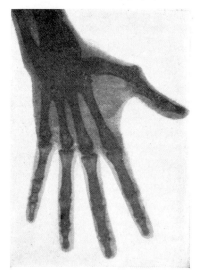

FIGS.—105 and 106.—Ciauri's case of gerodermic dystrophy with articular changes.

and complicates the congenital hypogenitalism; (d) *eunuchoid feminism* in which the congenital hypogenitalism is accompanied by a probable influence of heterosexual hormones.

Pure eunuchoidism is, therefore, according to Furno, a monoglandular syndrome; the other clinical varieties are pluriglandular. The gerodermic and acromegalic varieties of eunuchoidism and feminism are not such from birth, as is the case with pure eunuchoidism, but these types develop during the puberty period.

Libido may appear in eunuchoids as a product of the activity of the nervous and psychic centres, but it is late and does not last.

There is no constant finding in regard to vagotonia or sympathetico-tonia in eunuchs. Finally, Furno remarks that the grafting of cryptorchid testes rich in interstitial substance is the best treatment of eunuchoidism;

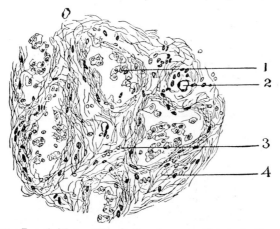

Fig. 107.—Eunuchoidism. (After Freiberg.) 1, atrophied gland cells; 2, vein; 3, nucleus of atrophied interstitial cell; 4, increased fibrous tissue.

opotherapy gives negative results. When the grafts survive, the morphology and the psyche improve to normal with the exception of generative power; and even if the graft is absorbed general improvement results.

Fig. 108 illustrates a case of congenital eunuchoidism reported by Magnus Hirschfeld. This individual was born in 1880 and consulted Hirschfeld during the past six years. He is the youngest of nine children. His six brothers and two sisters enjoy good health and are all married. The mother of this individual, to whom he is very much attached, is living at the age of seventy-two and enjoying the best of health. The father died at sixty-two as the result of arteriosclerosis. Both parents suffered from inguinal hernia. The patient was born when his mother was forty-four and his father forty-six years of age. There is nothing of

14

importance in the past history of the patient. His youth was uneventful and the same is true of his brothers. At the age of puberty the difference between his appearance and that of his brothers became manifest. At

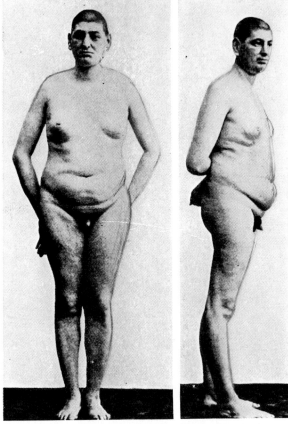

FIG. 108.—Eunuchoidismus. (After Magnus Hirschfeld.)

this period not a single sign of sexual maturity was evident. He consulted Hirschfeld when he was thirty years old and the following findings were noted: " At the site of the scrotum only a small corrugated cutaneous pouch is found, which is marked by a rather definite raphé. No contents are felt in this pouch. The inguinal canals are closed. Not a vestige of testes can be detected by rectal examination or otherwise. The prostate is found to be very small and barely palpable. The seminal vesicles cannot be detected. The penis is the size of that of a boy of four years. In the flaccid state it measures 2 cm. and when erect 5 cm. The patient is able to produce erection through masturbation, to which he has been addicted since he was twelve years of age, having acquired the habit through association with other boys. He has never had an ejaculation nor is there a secretion from the prostate. However, during masturbation he experiences marked pleasurable sensations which keep him chained to the practice of Onanism."

Hirschfeld also noted the following facts: " The patient is larger than his parents or other members of the family. He is able to extend his arms to a degree of 190 cm., which measurement exceeds the length of his body. The extremities are longer than the entire body. The circumference of the waist is 102 cm., and that of the shoulders is 182 cm., which corresponds to the average feminine measurements. The circumference of the head is 54 cm. The skin is perfectly free from hair, with the exception of the axillæ, and at the root of the penis, where a very sparse growth exists. Not the slightest suggestion of hair is to be observed on the chin. The hair of the head is very well developed, reaching well on to the forehead, which has rather deep furrows. The furrowing is also pronounced on the face, which gives the patient the appearance of advanced age. The ears are exceptionally large and projecting. The distribution of the fat is noteworthy. Marked accumulations of fat are to be found in the region of the breasts, which resemble those of a woman. On the lower portion of the abdomen, on the buttocks, the hips and the thighs there are marked deposits of fat. His face also is obese and the characteristic layers of fat observed in the upper eyelids are very marked in this case. The musculature is weak and flabby; as is the case in men who have no testes, this individual complains of lassitude, exhaustion and inability to exert himself. He blushes very easily and is hypersensitive to pain. He has the typical high-pitched voice. His larynx is barely palpable. His vocal cords are more than one-third shorter than those of a normal individual."

The remarkable thing that Hirschfeld points out in this case is that this man had perfectly normal sexual desire. The principal reason he consulted Hirschfeld was to ascertain whether he would advise his marrying. Hirschfeld advised against this step and informed the patient of the probable incurability of his condition, suggesting that it might be possible to improve his condition by a testicular transplant, but emphasizing the fact that it would be an experimental proposition pure and simple which offered some hope, as reported by various authors in similar cases.

Prompted by motives of patriotism this individual offered his services to his country, but was found incapable of performing the ordinary military duties because of general bodily incompetency.

With reference to his mental capabilities, he is industrious, a splendid independent merchant who takes excellent care of his mother. His intelligence is good and his memory excellent. He is much interested in politics and civic affairs and is much liked in the community where he resides. He suffers from occasional periods of depression.

In this connection among a number of cases observed by the author the following is instructive. It represents a type of eunuchoidism that is not as extreme as that of the last cited case, but has certain features that deserve emphasis and are rather interesting. This individual is an American by birth, merchant, a bachelor about forty-seven years of age. He had none of the diseases of childhood and experienced sexual awakening at the age of fourteen years or thereabouts. He has masturbated moderately since that time. He has two brothers and two sisters living. One brother died of appendicitis. One sister is a widow and has four children, the other sister is married and has ten children.

Physical examination revealed the general appearance of a eunuchoid. The measurements of the upper extremities exceed those of the entire length of the body as in the case of Hirschfeld cited above. The facial expression is typically eunuchoid. (Fig. 109.) One observes the marked furrowing of the forehead, and this condition extends over the face. There is no sign of hair in the region of the beard or mustache; the eyebrows also are sparse. The patient has been myopic since early childhood. The skin is pale and soft, the voice is high pitched. He is tall of stature with the characteristic elongation of the upper and lower extremities. His teeth are defective; the thyroid is only slightly palpable; no Adam's apple can be observed. There are no hairs on the body with the exception of a few in the axillæ and a few tufts on the pubis in distinctly feminine distribution. The fat deposit is characteristic. The breasts are of distinctly feminine type (Fig. 110); the waist line is that of a woman and there are accumulations of fat about the crests of the iliæ and buttocks.

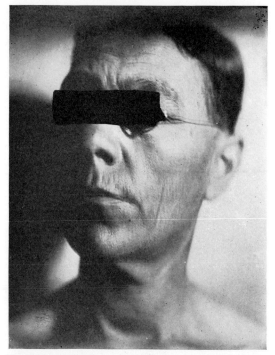

FIG. 109.—Eunuchoidism. (Author's case.) Observe characteristic appearance of face.

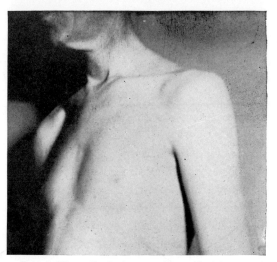

FIG. 110.—Eunuchoidism. (Author's case.) Observe feminine type of breasts.

The genitalia are very small. The penis measures one inch in the flaccid condition, two and a half inches when erect. The testicles are infantile, hard to the touch but in the normal position. The prostate is only slightly palpable; seminal vesicles are not to be felt. The patient has *libido*, experiences orgasm, but has no ejaculation.

Examination of the urine following intercourse shows total absence of spermatozoa. Physically he becomes easily exhausted. His superficial

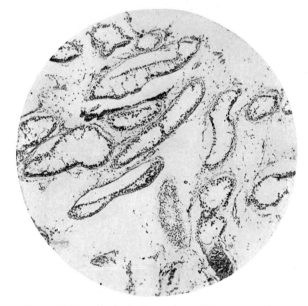

Fig. 111.—Eunuchoidism. (Author's observation.) Note absence of spermatogenesis and scantiness of interstitial tissue. Obj. 7.5; ocular 16; Leitz apochromatic. Hematoxylin and eosin. Magnified 90 diameters.

and deep reflexes are somewhat exaggerated. Hemoglobin is 70 per cent.; blood pressure, systolic 100, diastolic 60; pulse pressure 40. The heart and lungs are negative.

The patient was desirous of marrying and was sent to the author by his family physician for advice in this respect. He was told that a frank statement of his physical condition must be made to the girl he wished to marry to avoid marital disaster. Transplantation was suggested and this was carried out by the author's technic, the material used being the testes of a cynocephalus weighing about seventy-five pounds.

Post-operative Course.—Four days after the transplantation the patient reported violent erections. He remained at the hospital for two weeks, during which time these erections, accompanied by libidinous dreams, were frequently manifested and he evinced much gratification at this experience.

The preceding microphotograph from a similar one of the author's cases of eunuchoidism shows the picture usually encountered (Fig. 111). There is a total absence of spermatogenesis. The intertubular spaces are widened and the Leydig cells are very scanty.

TABLE OF DIFFERENTIAL DIAGNOSIS OF INFANTILISMS IN THE MALE, EUNUCHISMUS IN ITS DIFFERENT FORMS, AND EUNUCHOIDISMUS.
From B. Onuf.

Infantilismus. Of the Lorrain type in the male	Eunuchoidismus. Developmental or in other ways congenital.	Acquired: Eunuchismus.
	Pseudo-hermaphroditic; Monosexual.	
Beard and mustache absent or represented by a few hairs only at age of full maturity. Features delicate. Teeth appear late, are often eroded. Expression childlike.	At age of full maturity, or at any age, beard and mustache are entirely absent, or represented by a short lanugo. Face becomes prematurely senile, its skin being yellowish, kid-leather-like in consistency, atrophic, with radiate or vertical wrinkles of upper lip, as in women. Hair of scalp turns prematurely gray. In younger individuals, especially below 25, face may be ruddy, full, but showing sometimes already incipient wrinkling. Expression often effeminate.	
Voice thin and rough.	Thyroid cartilage not prominent. Voice of high pitch, subdued and gentle, more frequently strident, rasping, sometimes a pleasant tenor.	Voice high-pitched; that of child or boy.
Panniculus adiposus diminished.	Panniculus adiposus varying. Skin may and may not resemble the female in character.	Skin white and soft. Panniculus adiposus usually increased. Tendency to swag belly.
Musculature delicate.	Muscles are usually markedly flabby.	
Stature small, and delicate.	Stature sometimes undersized, but tall, slender types prevail.	Stature usually tall. Forms rounded. Limbs long with relative shortness of humerus. Hand slender.
	Hands apt to be of female type in shape. / Hands more frequently of male type of shape.	

The preceding table of differential diagnosis of infantilism in the male, auchism in its different forms, and eunuchoidism, as tabulated by B. Onuf, may be of assistance in the differential diagnosis of these conditions.

Treatment of Eunuchoidism, Retarded Puberty and some forms of Infantilism.

The eunuchoid is very much concerned about the small size of his penis,

his physical appearance, the manifestations of his sexual aberration, and frequently becomes morose and introspective.

Prognostically speaking, the earlier the condition is recognized the better is the outlook for some form of rectification and amelioration of some of the conditions. The size of the penis may be increased according to some authors by the various suction apparatuses (Fig. 112). Sex gland implantation is so far the most logical procedure in these conditions, many beneficial results having been observed by the author, particularly in the early cases. Good results have also been observed by other workers in this field.

Steinach states that Lichtenstern has observed that implantation of cryptorchid testicles into men having lesions of the testes seemed to cause a reappearance of the morphological, functional and psychic characteristics of the male sex. In one case of transplantation after four years of eunuchoidism there was a return of hair, musculature and virile potency; and in an infantile case masculine adult characters returned after transplantation.

FIG. 112.—Suction apparatus used for development of infantile penis.

BIBLIOGRAPHY

[1] BASSOE: Endocrinology and Metabolism, p. 811.
[2] SOUSA and DE CASTRO: Nouv. Iconog. de la Salpetriére, 1910, xxviii, 1 ; 390.
[3] SOUQUES: Presse med., Paris, 1912, p. 550.
[4] GRIFFITH: Amer. Jour. Anat., vi, No. 4.

[5] TANDLER and GROSZ: Die biologischen Grundlagen d. Sekundären Geschlechts-Charaktere, Berlin, 1913.

[6] STERLING: Zeitschr. f. d. gesamt. Neurol. u. Psychiat., 1913, xvi, 235.

[7] FRÖHLICH : Wien. Klin. Rundsch., 1901, Nos. 47 and 48.

[8] CASTEX and WALDORF : Revist. Assoc. med. Argentina, 1919, xxxi, 177.

[9] RUMMO and FERRANINI : Riforma med. Naples, 1897, iii, 340.

[10] CIAURI : Il senilismo, Rome, 1912.

[11] FALTA : Le Malattie d. Giandole Sanguigne, Milan, 1914.

[12] MARIOTTI : Riforma med., Naples, 1919, xxxv, 590.

[13] FREIBERG : Lancet-clin., 1916, cxvi, 325.

[14] FURNO : Rivist. di Patol. Nerv., 1922, xxvi, 245.

d. PRECOCIOUS PUBERTY

A premature, disproportionate and excessive development of the genitalia in childhood to the size of those of a full-grown man, and also an early development of the secondary sex characters, as well as certain unusual psychic features, are the distinguishing marks of precocious sexual development in the male. Generally speaking, it is the occurrence of puberty long before the usual normal time of its appearance.

White[1] described a boy who at the age of two years practiced masturbation with ejaculation of sperm.

According to statistics attested by Neurath,[2] there were eight cases in which symptoms of puberty appeared at the end of the first year of life and four within two years.

The psychic state in these precocious sexual development cases generally remains infantile. The mind corresponds to the real age, although premature awakening of the *vita sexualis* may give the character a peculiar turn. But there may be even lack of mental development in such cases.

The causative factor in premature puberty is some agency which brings about testicular hormonic action before the normal physiological time of onset. Such agency is generally a tumor acting directly on the testicle itself, or a tumor of some other internal secretory gland which indirectly influences testicular development and secretion. The hypophysis, adrenals, pineal or thyroid glands, seem to be those most particularly affecting the testicle.

Twenty-one cases, of which fourteen were in males, were collected by Neurath. Five of these showed neoplasms of the sexual organs; ten or eleven demonstrated neoplasms of the adrenals; three had tumors of the pineal gland, and in one hydrocephalus was found. In Sacchi's [3] case, a boy of nine had an enormous development of body, genitalia and beard. An alveolar carcinoma was removed from the left testicle, and most of the abnormalities disappeared in due course, with cessation of sexual impulses, emissions and erections.

Of ten cases compiled by Bulloch and Sequiera,[4] eight females and two males, eight showed an adrenal tumor. Tumors of the adrenals seem, according to Marburg,[5] to have a hastening influence on the development of secondary sexual characters, as well as on growth. Adrenal tumors are five times more frequent in female precocious sexual development cases than in males. On the other hand, nearly all cases where a pineal gland tumor has been found in a case of precocious sexual development, the subject was a male. Foa [6] observed that in young roosters after extirpation of the pineal gland, there was excessive development of the testes and of some secondary sex characters.

Horrax's [7] experiments on guinea pigs corroborated those of Foa.

It appears that in childhood the pineal gland normally exerts an inhibitory influence on development, that later this diminishes as the gland undergoes involution. Precocious puberty may then be associated with *hypopinealism* or any condition such as a tumor which interferes with the functioning of the gland.

Hoskins [8] thinks that the thyroid gland exerts an important influence upon the sex glands. In cases of Graves' disease, the sex functions are often affected and decreased; *libido* and *potentia cœundi* are said to accompany this disease. In districts where goitre is endemic, a large proportion of the females have scant menstruation as well as menstrual disorders, and among the males there is subnormal genital development. Thyroidectomy has been observed by many to result in depression of sex functions with atrophy of the gonads. It may be due indirectly to the effect on metabolism, as metabolism affects sex activity.

There are several observations in medical literature with regard to the intimate association of the hypophysis with the gonads. Administration of hypophyseal extract stimulates the gonads. Some of the most recent experimental work has been done by Houssay [9] of Buenos Aires, who found that *hypophysectomized dogs* that survived the operation showed genital arrest or retardation, and that atrophy of the gonads was usual when the whole gland, or the anterior lobe alone, was removed. Other investigators have incriminated the tissues in the immediate vicinity of the hypophysis.

According to Strauch [10] the endocrine glands in their interlocking and mutually affecting functions, are of the greatest importance for the normal growth of the body and for sexual maturity, among them especially, the genital glands, the adrenals, the pituitary body, the thyroid and the so-called " puberty glands," the thymus and the pineal, " their inextricable interaction in the main still defying analysis."

Strauch [10] reports the following case of precocious sexuality: " K. W., 11–1/2 years old, son of Ruthenian immigrants. The father is middlesized, of sturdy build, living at present out of Chicago; mother small. There were two other children with irrelevant histories. The patient was born at full term, weighed, allegedly, seven pounds. He first grew slowly, more rapidly at five years of age; he has always been mentally much below par and somewhat hard of hearing, according to his mother's statement. He learns poorly, has a very poor memory and is in the first grade of the public school where he has attended for three years. He has had measles, scarlatina, diphtheria and whooping cough. He often snores and sleeps with open mouth. He began to grow rapidly about one year prior to this report; no information can be obtained from the mother about the sexual development of her boy; neither does she remember when he began to walk and talk.

" Present Status.—The patient is of slender build, of blond type; height 1.51 m.; weight, eighty-five pounds, with waist and coat off. The lower half of the body, measured from the lower edge of the symphysis to the heel, is 75 cm. The musculature is flabby and poorly developed; head rachitic, tubera frontalia, and parietalia prominent; fronto-occipital circumference, 55 cm.; there are twenty-eight perfect teeth; no trace of caries; chest poorly developed; chicken-breast deformity; circumference in nipple-line during middle respiratory position, 67.5 cm. The lower part of the abdomen is somewhat pendant, the muscles of the abdominal wall flabby and poorly developed. There is a slight degree of genu valga and beginning pedes valgi. (Fig. 113.)

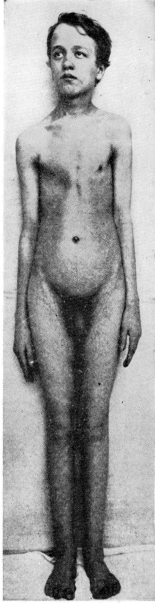

Fig. 113.—August Strauch's case of pubertas precox. This photograph was kindly given to the author by Dr. Strauch.

"Genitalia.—In comparison with the age of the boy his genital organs are striking in their degree of development; there are also some secondary sexual characteristics present. The penis is 10.6 cm. long, measured from the root at the symphysis to the end of the prepuce and 9 cm. in circumference in the non-erected state. The prepuce, reaches about 1 cm. beyond the glans. The testicles are of the size of those in the adult man, 3.5 cm. to 4 cm. long, the left larger than the right. There is an abundant growth of hair on the pubes, more than 5 cm. long; the upper border line is of feminine type; there is a conspicuous brown pigmentation of the median line from the mons veneris to the umbilicus. The scrotum is covered with a few hairs, 0.5 to 1 cm. long. In both axillæ there are patches of skin of 1.5 to 2.5 cm. diameters that are covered with a crop of blond hair about 1 cm. long. The boy has vigorous erections of the penis, as was witnessed in the hospital. The prostate gland is of the size of that of an adult. Massage of the prostate and seminal vesicles, performed once, did not yield sperma. The larynx is very prominent, the voice strikingly deep.

"The inner organs show no abnormal conditions; no tumor of the kidneys can be palpated, neither does röntgen-ray examination reveal any anomaly of these organs. The röntgenograms of the skull demonstrate a slightly enlarged sella turcica and a moderate increase in size of the skull.

Röntgenograms of the hand show no deviation from the ossification that corresponds to the actual age of the boy. The drums are only slightly retracted, the hearing little affected.

"Psychic Conditions and Habits.—The boy is very irritable; "nervous;" cries when his mouth is inspected. He is of a stubborn, disobedient, troublesome disposition and resentful toward other children, and has to be reprimanded for it in the hospital. At home he prefers to play with boys younger than himself and shuns boys of his size; there are evidences of sexual shame; he chews his nails habitually; these are much bitten off. There seems to be at present no particular propensity to the other sex. He cannot count to more than five; even then he must be helped. He cannot write his name unless a copy is placed before him; his handwriting is hardly readable; nor can he do sums; he says for instance, two and two are three, two and two are six; one and one are seven. He is not able to say his prayers without being helped by his mother; he does not know any verses or any song, although he has attended, as mentioned before, the public school for three years. In fact, he is too dull to answer simple questions that refer to his own person, and during examination he gives many evidences of a very poor memory even as to occurrences and experiences that would seem important to any normal boy."

Commenting on the case Strauch says: " Etiologically, the case may be classified as (primary) hypergenitalism without anatomicopathologic changes. The clinical examination excludes a tumor of the adrenals and there is no ground for suspecting a tumor of the pineal gland, corresponding cerebral symptoms being entirely wanting. Further, the *makrogenitosomia precox* due to hypopinealism occurs only through premature destruction of functionating pineal tissue, that is, before the seventh year of life, since at that time the involution normally commences.

" Against a hypophyseal affection (hyperpituitarism) militates the absence of such characteristic symptoms as were observed in the rare cases of acromegaly in adolescence and childhood. The slight enlargement of the sella turcica hardly has any bearing in our case, considering the hydrocephalic increase in size of the skull of the boy."

In a case reported by Luiser,[11] a boy 5–1/2 years old showed the sexual development of eighteen years. Autopsy showed a very large suprarenal tumor, and the thymus had apparently atrophied as in an adult.

Sacchi reported a case in a boy who, at the age of five years, showed great enlargement of the left testicle. At nine years of age his voice was like that of a man and there was marked development of the penis and pubic hair. On removal of the left testicle, which was the site of a testicular tumor, the sexual conditions returned to a state normal for a boy of his age.

In Stone's [12] case the boy of four years had a penis like that of a man and the pubes were covered with hair. There were constant erections and the testes and penis were able to discharge seminal fluid.

Lopez Albo [13] remarks that precocious genitalism of suprarenal, pineal or thyroidean origin, is to be explained by the reaction of the functionally altered gland of the gonads. There would follow an abnormally early activity of the interstitial genital gland, which, in its turn, governs the abnormal early growth of the body, the simultaneous development of the genital organs, and anticipation of sexual psychic maturity.

The condition of the skeleton in *pubertas precox* is the exact opposite of that of the eunuchoid. In the latter the incretory aberration so influences the osseous growth that the epiphyseal lines remain open for a long time; in the former the reverse is true, epiphyseal closure and ossification taking place at a much earlier date than is normally the case.

Hirschfeld recommends the following classification in *pubertas precox:*

   I. Genital precocity.

   II. Somatic precocity.

   III. Psychosexual precocity.

   IV. Psychic precocity.

Treatment of Pubertas Precox.—If adrenal or testicular tumor are discovered the indications for their removal are, of course, clear. Other concomitant endocrine conditions must be met with therapeutically according to conditions and indications in each case.

BIBLIOGRAPHY

[1] White: Medico-Chir., Transac., 1815.
[2] Neurath : Ergeb. d. inn. med. u. Kinderh., 1909, iv, 46.
[3] Sacchi: Riv. sper. di freniat., 1895, xxi.
[4] Bulloch and Sequiera : Trans. Path. Soc., London, 1905, lvi.

[5] MARBURG: Erbeg. d. inn. med. u. Kinderh., 1913, x, 146.

[6] FOA: Arch. Ital. de Biol., 1912, lvii, 233.

[7] HORRAX: Arch. inter. med., 1916, xvii, 607.

[8] HOSKINS: Endocrinology and Metabolism, 923.

[9] HOUSSAY: Revist. Asoc. méd. Argent., 1921, xxxiv, 1165.

[10] STRAUCH: Amer. Jour. Dis. of Child, 1918, xv, 132.

[11] LUISER: Cited in Endocrinology and Metabolism, 1922, ii, p. 505.

[12] STONE: Cited in Endocrinology and Metabolism, 1922, ii, p. 506.

[13] ALBO LOPEZ: Prog. de los Clin., 1919, vii, 167.

e. DWARFISM AND GIANTISM

(Its Relation to Gonadal and other Endocrine Dysfunctions)

A dwarf is a person of small size compared with the usual standard of the individual for the same age and race. Dwarfism may or may not be accompanied by malformity.

Dwarfs have been classified in different ways: V. Hansemann [1] classifies them as: (a) primordial or true dwarfs; (b) hypophyseal dwarfs; and (c) dwarfs of intermediate type.

The three foregoing types are *proportional* dwarfs, *i.e.*, the body parts bear the usual proportions to each other, there being only a general arrest of development uniformly distributed; but in the following there is *disproportion* between the various regions: (d) *achondroplastic dwarfs;* (e) *rachitic dwarfs;* (f) *cretins;* (g) *syphilitic dwarfs.*

The true dwarf (type a) is perfectly normal, physically and mentally; in every way normal but small.

Figs. 114 and 115 depict a true dwarf from Levi. [2] This dwarf, thirty-three years old, was 111 cms. high and weighed 25 kg. His father was also a dwarf. The dwarf was married and had children who were well formed and proportional. Most historical dwarfs are of this type.

The hypophyseal dwarf (type b) is normal at birth, but development is arrested later. There is persistence of epiphyseal lines and failure of genital development with psychic infantilism. The skin is usually senile. In this type autopsies have usually disclosed some lesion of the anterior lobe of the hypophysis.

The more usual classification of dwarfs is that which divides them into those of the *Paltauf, the Brissaud, or the Lorain type.*

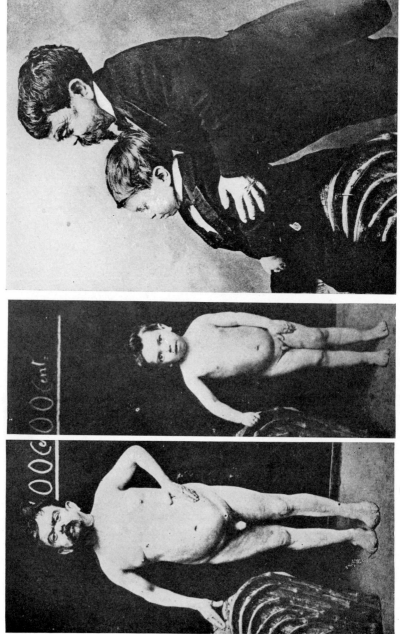

FIGS. 114 and 115.—Microsomia essentielle. Heredo-familiale. (After Ettore Levi.)

The Paltauf[3] type was first described by this author in 1891 and corresponds to the hypophyseal type of dwarf referred to above. The development at first is normal and it is only in early youth that the development becomes arrested. In this type the individuals are of normal

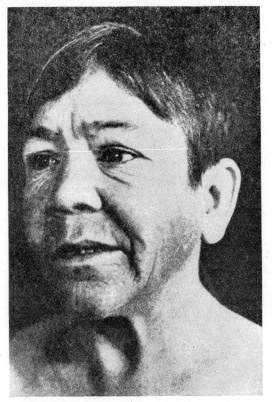

FIG. 116.—Paltauf type of dwarf with pituitary tumor. (After Walter M. Kraus.)

size at birth and at first develop normally. It is only later in early youth that their growth becomes arrested. The epiphyses remain open. Further growth is exceedingly slow, in all cases it being but rarely that the inhibition to growth is overcome at some later time. The development of the centres of ossification is but slight in almost all the cases. The development of the genitalia and of the secondary sexual characteristics are almost always arrested. Paltauf stated that the exact etiology of the condition was not known. They show a cretinoid appearance.

15

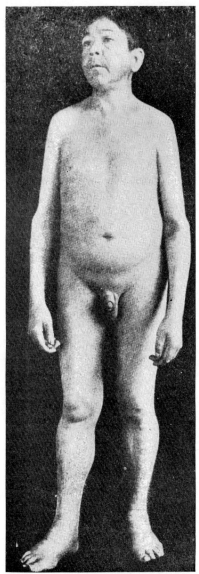

FIG. 117.—Paltauf type of dwarf with pituitary tumor. (After Walter M. Kraus.)

Kraus [4] reports a dwarf which furnishes a good example of this type; the height is about 40 inches, the face and general appearance is cretinoid; there is no appearance of feminism, but (Figs. 116 and 117) there is absence of hair on the entire body except on the head, brows and eyelids. In this case a hypophyseal tumor was found at autopsy.

In the Brissaud [5] type of dwarf which is also mainly of hypophyseal origin probably there is infantilism. The characteristics of infancy or childhood are especially retained. In this type the epiphyses are open and these dwarfs are obese, with childlike chubby faces.

Hewlett [6] reported the case of a man aged twenty-seven, height 4 feet 9–1/2 inches, which he considered showed many points in common with the Brissaud type. (Fig. 118.)

The history showed brain tumor; optic atrophy; retarded growth; sexual infantilism; obesity and diabetes insipidus. (Fig. 119.)

In the Lorain type dwarf the fusion of the epiphyses occurs at the normal time or prematurely and the arrest of development appears to occur much later than in the Brissaud type. According to Hewlett this type of dwarfism is rather unusual with pituitary disease, and obesity is much less usual as a characteristic. Frank L Hochwart [7] con-

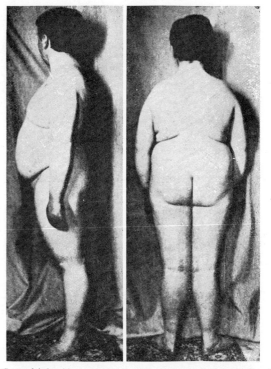

FIG. 118.—Case of infantilism associated with pituitary disease. (After A. W. Hewlett.) 1, lateral view of patient. Note obesity, lumbar lordosis, small hands and feet; 2, posterior view. Notice genu valgum and distribution of fat on body.

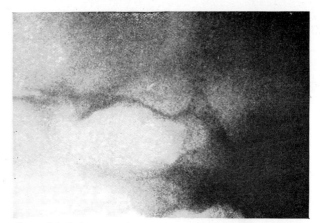

FIG. 119.—X-ray of skull of above patient. (After A. W. Hewlett.) Showing enlargement of sella turcica with wide entrance above. (Natural size.)

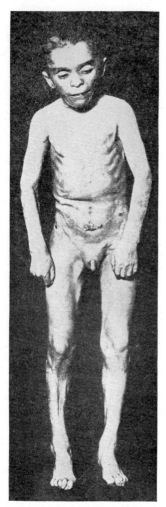

FIG. 120.—Infantilism in pituitary disease.   FIG. 121.—Pituitary tumor in dwarf.
Lorain type. (After A. W. Hewlett.)   (After Walter M. Kraus.)

FIG. 122.—Achondroplasia. (After Guiseppe Frachini and Mauro Zanasis.)

sidered that when pituitary disease occurs in early life obesity is more common than when it begins later, although the rule is subject to numerous exceptions.

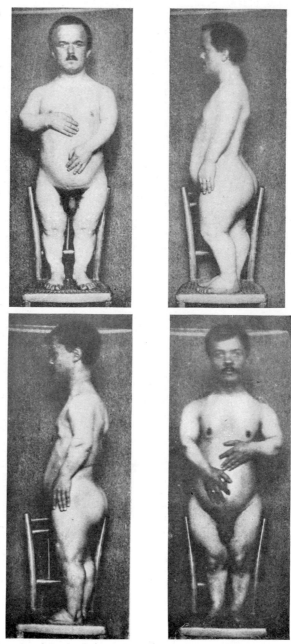

FIG. 123.—Achondroplasia. (After Guiseppe Frachini and Mauro Zanasis.)

Hewlett also reported a case which he considered of the Lorain type. (Fig. 120.) This man, aged fifty-two, was 5 feet, 2–1/2 inches high, showed

FIG. 124.—Gigantism. The Giant Hugo, acromegalic type. Height, 7 ft. 6 in.; age, 25; weight, 430 lbs. (Quoted by Bassoe after Launois and Ray.)

a small skeletal development with retarded sexuality. Radiograph of the skull showed a sella turcica rather larger than usual.

Erdheim's [8] dwarf was a man thirty-eight years old, 56 inches high, with open epiphyseal lines, cryptorchidism, small penis, absence of beard and

FIG. 125.—Gigantism   Ella Ewing, the Missouri giantess.   Height, 8 ft. 4 in.; age, 26; weight, 256 lbs.   (P. Bassoe.)

pubic and axillary hair.   The sella turcica was enlarged and contained a cystic tumor.

Sternberg's [9] dwarf was a male, aged seventeen years, and 92 cm. high.

Growth had been inhibited since one and a half years of age. There was deformity in this case due to Pott's disease. The body was infantile, the

FIG. 126.—Gigantism. Giant Wilkins and his brother. Height, 7 ft. 4 in.; age, 28; weight, 325 lbs. (P. Bassoe.)

genitalia small, no trace of beard, axillary or pubic hair. The hypophysis was apparently normal at autopsy but the testicles showed changes which the author considered due to defective development rather than to atrophy.

Sternberg considered that there were other endocrine causes besides hypophyseal deficiency involved in dwarfism.

In a case reported by Kraus (Fig. 121) the dwarf gave clinical evidence of involvement of the central nervous system and especially of pituitary insufficiency. There was evidence also of a deficiency of interstitial glandular secretion, undeveloped sex organs of secondary sex characters, and of infantile fat distribution. Some evidence of thyroid deficiency with a possibility of other glandular involvement. The syndrome was evidently polyglandular.

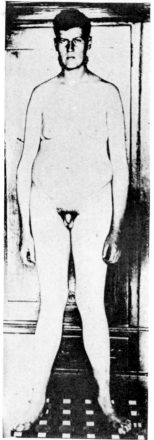

FIG. 127.—Gigantism, infantilism and feminism. (P. Bassoe.)

Kraus also mentions a female dwarf, aged twenty-five years, height 26 inches, otherwise apparently normal. This is a case of *primordial dwarfism* which belongs to the general group of ateliosis but differs from the Paltauf type. Falta [10] gives this definition of this primordial type: " The primordial dwarf is characterized by the fact that the dwarfing is present at birth, that excepting the smallness development goes on normally, that the genitals, bony ossification and intelligence are normal."

Dwarfism is often combined with rachitism, myxedema and imbecility. The most common type is that of *achondroplasia*. (Figs. 122 and 123.)

Gigantism appears to involve more than merely skeletal growth beyond the usual proportions in an individual of the same age and race; it includes, in addition to the excessive growth, some stigmata with which the abnormal growth is intimately connected.

Gigantism may be divided into three groups:

Gigantism associated with infantilism.

Gigantism associated with acromegaly.

Gigantism associated with infantilism and acromegaly.

The gonads are known to be intimately associated with growth, particularly of the osseous system. The effects of castration in over-development of the bones of the extremities has already been alluded to in the case of the Skopzie eunuch (Cf. Chapter on Effects of Castration). In the case reported by Sacchi a child of nine years reached the height of 143 cms. Changes in the bony skeleton are also characteristic of certain eunuchoids.

One of the most marked characteristics of gigantism is loss of sexual power and presence of infantile genitalia. When sexual power is not absent it is usually far below normal. Bassoe [11] described many cases of gigantism collected from literature and a case of his own combined with acromegaly. In most of these sexual deficiency was noted. (Figs 124 to 127.)

Bassoe's giant was 7 feet, 8–3/4 inches tall and weighed 380 pounds. He showed gigantism combined with feminism. He had no sexual feeling, never masturbated, never had any erections or sexual desires.

BIBLIOGRAPHY

[1] HANSEMANN, V.: Quoted by Bassoe, Endocrinology and Metabolism, 1922, ii, p. 843.
[2] LEVI: Nouv. Iconog. de la Salpetriére, 1910, Jour, xxiii.
[3] PALTAUF: Ueber den Zwergwuchs, Wein., 1891.
[4] KRAUS: Jour. Nerv. and Ment. Dis., 1917, xlv, 193.
[5] BRISSAUD: Nouv. Iconog. de la Salpetriére, 1907, xx.
[6] HEWLETT: Arch. Inter. Med., 1912, ix, 32.
[7] HOCHWART, FRANK L.: Wien. Med. Wchnschr., 1909, lix, 2127.
[8] ERDHEIM: Sitz. Ber. Akad. Wissensch. Wien., 1904, cxiii, 710.
[9] STERNBERG: Quoted by Bassoe, Endocrinology and Metabolism, 1922, ii, p. 847.
[10] FALTA: Die Erkrankungen der Blutdrüsen, 1914.
[11] BASSOE: Endocrinology and Metabolism, 1922, ii, p. 813.

f. ADIPOSITY AND THE ENDOCRINES

In the obese fat is accumulated in abnormal amounts, not alone in the subcutaneous tissues but also in other tissues and organs. This increased fat production seems to be the result of deficient oxidation of ingested fats, starches or proteins. Heredity is a predisposing factor, more than half the cases being traced to this cause; but any disturbing factor which lowers oxidation may be a cause. When fat accumulates independently of food and exercise the condition is spoken of as *constitutional obesity*. In endocrinology alimentary obesity is classed as exogenous, while constitutional obesity is endogenous in character.

The commonest type of obesity is *lipomatosis universalis.*

During recent years much attention has been devoted to the subject of the internal secretions and their connection with obesity, and several types of endogenous obesity have been described. Thus obesity may be due to thyroid dysfunctioning, to hypopituitarism, to hyperadrenalism, or to involvement of the sexual glands. One or more of these factors may be involved in any given case.

The dangers that may arise from excessive obesity, apart from the discomfort of the condition, are that it may cause fatty degeneration or infiltration of the heart which may result in cardiac and respiratory complications. (Thorek.[1]) Diabetes and gout are frequent in such cases, the liver may be enlarged and deranged. In some cases abdominal symptoms from abdominal fat deposits are marked. Certain types of hernia occur frequently. Fat embolism is apt to occur in the obese.

Kirchner [2] described these cases fully.

O'Malley [3] also draws attention to the influence of the endocrine secretions in determining the quantity and distribution of subcutaneous fat, and shows that there is a connection between the adiposity and sexual glandular disturbances.

O'Malley reports several cases of adiposity in females connected with disturbance in the endocrine secretions and more or less pronounced pseudo-hermaphroditism:

Case One.—Adiposity since birth; hypertrichosis of face and body with masculine distribution; external genitalia infantile. Author thinks there is a possible disturbance of the secretions of the gonad, hypophysis and suprarenals.

Case Two.—Somewhat similar but more marked facial hypertrichosis.

Case Three.—Contours of body and facies decidedly masculine; marked hypertrichosis; during depression her desires were homoxesual and during excitement heterosexual.

Case Four.—Similar with bisexuality.

Case Five.—Obesity, pseudo-hermaphroditism and homosexuality. Several cases of this type.

Case Seven.—Obesity very marked, hypertrichosis and homosexuality. (Figs. 128–131.)

The author considers that all the eleven cases of this type reported show an endocrinopathy. All conform to a certain individual type which

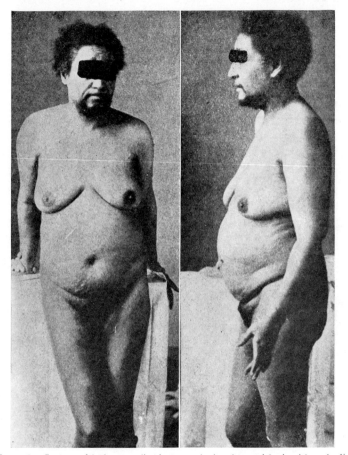

Fig. 128.—Contour of body masculine in type; obesity; hypertrichosis with male distribution. Gracile hand (Mona Lisa type), small and conical, fingers tapering. Joints very flexible with extreme hyperextension. Exophthalmus. (After Mary O'Malley.)

has long been recognized as a distinct group: outline of the body assumes a male habitus, voice is heavy and coarse, features atypical; the individual may be taken for either sex, depending upon drapery, but usually the hands are distinctly feminine and graceful. Hands of this type, O'Malley shows, are sometimes met in certain states of hypofunctioning of the hypophysis or other endocrine glands.

The genital anomalies are irregularities of menstruation and of the secondary sex characters. There is little coincidence of any somatic anomalies in the primary sex characters. The group as a whole shows clinical

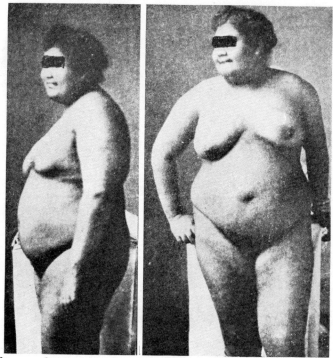

FIG. 129.—Observe obesity, hypertrichosis with male distribution. Face is heavy and masculine in type. Hands and feet delicately formed, fingers tapering. (After Mary O'Malley.)

evidence of pseudo-hermaphroditism of the external type manifested in the secondary sexual characters and in the mental processes.

O'Malley thinks that the direct action of the chemical products of the gonads through the nervous system influences the growth and metabolism of every tissue in the body, but how much the action is increased or inhibited by the chemical products of the other endocrine organs is unknown. That there is a direct relationship between the gonads and hypophysis is fairly well established. The changes in sexual characteristics and the adiposo-genitalis may be due to direct dysfunctioning of the gonads, or the dystrophia may be the effect of secondary action through the hypophysis.

Gottlieb [4] says that the association of dystrophia adiposo-genitalis with a particular lobe of the hypophysis is not justified, for it may arise from dysfunction of the anterior as well as from interference with the discharge of the secretion from the posterior lobe and stalk. Both hypo-

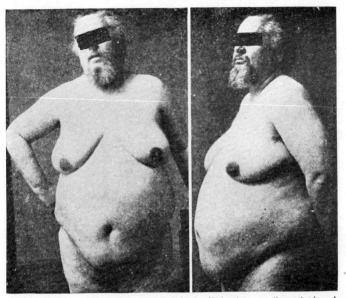

Fig. 130.—General appearance, pose and attitude, distinctly masculine; obesity; hypertrichosis with male distribution; hands and feet well formed and taper to a point. (After Mary O'Malley.)

and false secretion result in dystrophia adiposo-genitalis unless the false secretion arises from acidophilic changes in the anterior lobe, when acromegaly results. (Cf. Chapter on Fröhlich's Disease.)

Wheelon [5] points out that gonadectomy is frequently followed by an increased deposition of fat. This is also true in men of advanced age, and women after the suppression of the sexual activities. Such depositions of fat are peculiarly localized and to some extent characteristic in each sex. Castrated males, especially humans, are sometimes abnormally lean, but the obese type is frequently observed among eunuchs and Skopzies (Cf. Chapter on Eunuchoidism and Effects of Castration). In these cases the excessive fat deposition is noted in the mammæ, nates, ventral regions and hips. The true capon is excessively fat.

After briefly reviewing what is known of the interrelationship of the endocrine glands, White and Jelliffe [6] say: " Just as the complicated sensori-

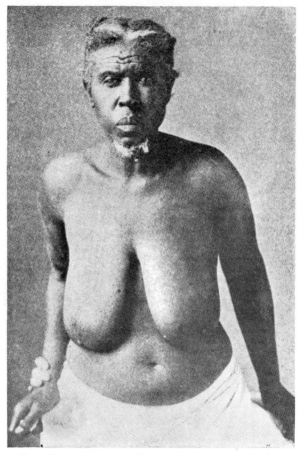

FIG. 131.—General appearance masculine; adiposity; hypertrichosis, male distribution; hands well formed, fingers long and slender. (After Mary O'Malley.)

motor integrations are effective in governing the muscular activities of the body, so the integration of the neuro-chemical regulators taking place at the physio-chemical level is effective in adjusting the metabolism of the body cells. Hormones are not the activators primarily; they are the servants of the vegetative nervous system. All of the endocrinopathies are really poly-glandular syndromes and are under psychical control."

The occurrence of adiposity in connection with bisexuality and homosexuality, also the well known fact that women become obese following the menopause, are facts that cannot be ignored as supporting a strong connection between obesity and the hormone secretion of the gonads.

BIBLIOGRAPHY

[1] THOREK: New York Med. Journal, cxvi, No. 10, p. 572, November 15, 1922.
[2] KIRCHNER: Jour. Missouri State Medical Assn., 1923, xx, 49.
[3] O'MALLEY: Jour. Nervous and Mental Dis., 1918, xlviii, 1.
[4] GOTTLIEB: Zeitschr. f. angeb, Anat., 1920, vii, 60.
[5] WHEELON: Endocrinology and Metabolism, 1922, ii, 463.
[6] WHITE and JELLIFFE: Diseases of the Nervous System, 1917.

g. FRÖHLICH'S DISEASE

(Dystrophia Adiposo Genitalis)

From the earliest times it has been known that eunuchs showed changes in skeletal development with fat distribution that differed from the normal. Reverdin [1] in 1883, associated a form of obesity with changes due to loss of thyroid functioning, and in 1901 Fröhlich [2] described a syndrome of obesity and genital hypoplasia associated with hypophyseal deficiency. This type of obesity had previously been known and regarded as cerebral adiposity, but no definite relation between the pituitary gland and adiposity had been established.

The outstanding significance of the Fröhlich syndrome is adiposity combined with a feminine type of fat distribution, and either non-development of the secondary sex characteristics (especially in the male) if the condition had occurred before puberty, or some loss of these characteristics if it occurred after puberty. Hence, in cases in which the disease begins in childhood the genital organs always remain infantile, the pubic and axillary hair never become more than very scanty, and in girls menstruation is never established. When the condition sets in after the establishment of puberty there is cessation of menstruation in women and impotence in men, with a gradual regression of the genital organs to the preadolescent state. (Fig. 132.) In adults there is a very decided diminution of the

16

body hair. The beard and mustache in males becomes thin and of slow growth, although the hair of the scalp does not seem to be affected. The skin is generally very dry and in males becomes of delicate texture, like that of a female. Metabolism is often disarranged.

Fröhlich described the case of a boy, aged fourteen years, who had

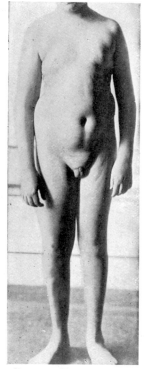

suffered from headache and vomiting for two years, and who showed a rapidly developing obesity combined with infantilism of the genitalia. The condition described was named by Bartels[3] *Dystrophia adiposo genitalis.*

In females the Fröhlich syndrome is characterized by excessive fat development below the waist, resulting in an abnormal figure; the body from the waist down is much enlarged in its normal proportion to the upper part.

Fröhlich ascribed the phenomena to hypopituitarism; but little attention was paid to this etiology until it received strong support from Cushing's experiments on dogs. Cushing[4] observed that puppies, deprived of all their pituitary glands, remained sexually infantile and that skeletal g r o w t h was much retarded. Similar experiments upon adult dogs produced adiposity and retrogressive sexual changes.

Fig. 132.—Dystrophia adiposo-genitalis. Patient aged 23 years. Note general infantile appearance of body; feminine disposition of fat (mammæ; hips); infantile genitalia. (Author's case.)

Cushing, in commenting upon his results, says that functional hyperplasia of the anterior lobe of the pituitary stimulates tissue growth, especially the skeletal; conversely, anterior lobe insufficiency should inhibit skeletal growth and sexual development.

Goetsch[5] found that by feeding pituitary extract to rats the period of sexual development was shortened by at least one-third and that the sexual instincts were awakened early.

The most striking symptoms in hypophyseal dystrophia, especially in males, are associated with a fairly definite type of fat distribution about the hips, upper thighs, lower abdomen and mons veneris. There is also a type in which the fat distribution is more general, involving the mammæ, shoulders, etc. This type presents a picture of obesity somewhat intermediate between thyroid deficiency and hypophyseal deficiency and which is probably due to functional hypoplasia of the sex glands secondary to hypopituitarism.

Hewlett,[6] in studying the types of infantilism arising from pituitary disease, divides them into two categories: First, those due to the mechanical effects of tumors, and, second, those due to altered internal secretion. To the first group may be referred patients showing persistent headache, vomiting and visual disturbances. To the second group may be referred sexual disturbances, obesity, stunted growth, and possibly diabetes insipidus, effects ascribed to altered or diminished secretion of the anterior lobe of the pituitary.

The male with *dystrophia adiposo genitalis* shows a disposition to sexual infantilism with absence of or delayed secondary sex characters, absence or deficiency of axillary and pubic hair and scant hair on the face. The tendency to reversal of sex type is more marked in the male than in the female; the skeleton assumes delicate feminine outlines, and a broad pelvis, narrow shoulders, and feminine distribution of pubic hair are the rule.

If the disease develops in adult life, in addition to the regressive changes in the sexual organs there is a corresponding diminution or loss of function with a tendency to revert to the characters of the opposite sex. The metabolic functions are below normal and the basal metabolism, as observed by Plummer, is from 16 to 18 per cent. below normal as a general rule, though it may reach as high as 25 per cent.

Many of the symptoms of *dystrophia adiposo genitalis* are apparently dependent upon the close interrelationship between the pituitary and other glands of internal secretion. This feature is of special importance in connection with the sex gland. Clinically and experimentally it has been demonstrated that deficiency of anterior lobe secretion of the pituitary produces hypoplasia of the sex gland and gives rise to the genital syndrome, while posterior lobe secretional deficiency lowers the carbohydrate metabolism.

These views have not, however, been allowed to go unchallenged. Gottlieb[7] says that the association of *dystrophia adiposo genitalis* with a particular lobe of the pituitary gland is not justified, since it may arise from dysfunction of the anterior as well as from interference with the discharge of the secretion from the posterior lobe and stalk. According to Gottlieb, both hypopituitarism and false secretion result in *dystrophia adiposo genitalis* unless the false secretions arise from acidophilic changes in the anterior lobe, when acromegaly results; besides, if the pituitary undergoes extensive changes in early childhood, dwarfism may result.

As a matter of fact, there is considerable doubt regarding the existence and functions of any internal secretion from the pituitary gland. Frank,[8] from a study of the literature, concluded in 1919 that pituitary extract had not been shown to stimulate the development of the female sex organs, and had very little, if any, effect upon those of the male. This view is, however, not tenable in the face of results of recent investigations. (Cf. Author's studies on Inter-Relation of the Endocrines.)

Sajous's [9] present *hypothesis* regarding pituitary activity is that the pituitary operates through the agency of a demonstrated nervous relationship by way of the splanchnics, such activity perhaps being possible because the posterior pituitary lobe is in reality the main ganglion of the sympathetic which controls and coördinates the thyroid, the adrenal and the thymus.

The dependence of the Fröhlich syndrome of *dystrophia adiposo genitalis* upon hypophyseal changes cannot be said to be proved. It is more probable that the sexual part in the syndrome depends upon failure of the secretion from the interstitial cells, although the exact factors responsible for such failure are not known, and further study in this connection is highly desirable.

The fat dystrophia in Fröhlich's syndrome may be affected by opotherapy, but the sexual deficiencies are not restored by such treatment. For such cases testicular transplantation would probably afford the most efficient treatment.

In 1911 Launois, Pinard and Gallais [10] reported a very interesting case of an adiposo-genital syndrome of *suprarenal* origin accompanied by hypertrichosis and sexual, nervous and mental disturbances. The patient was a girl aged nineteen years who had cessation of menstruation for more than a year. Examination showed a tumor in the left flank. Autopsy showed the hypophysis to be normal; the right suprarenal was normal but the left suprarenal was replaced by an enormous tumor, which (Fig. 133) weighed 2500 gr.

The authors in discussing this case refer to some others of a similar

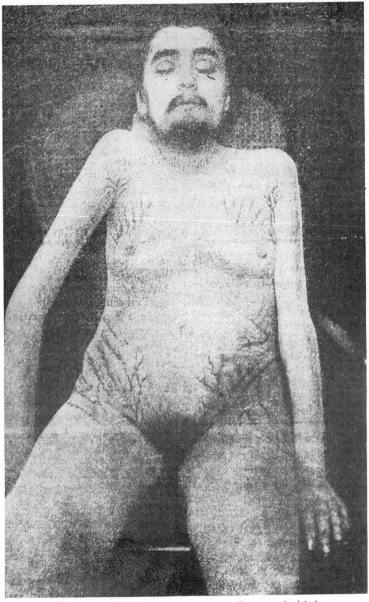

FIG. 133.—Dystrophia adiposo-genitalis. Syndrome of suprarenal origin in woman.
(After Launois, Pinard and Gallais.)

nature described in the literature. They contend that such lesions, when of embryonal origin, may be accompanied later by more or less pronounced hermaphrodism; in some cases sexual morphology may be normal but accompanied by more or less abundant hypertrichosis; in other cases there is precocious puberty accompanied by hypertrichosis and adiposity but without hermaphrodism; and there are cases in which the menses are disturbed, with exaggerated adiposity and abnormal occurrence and distribution of hair.

This type of suprarenal adiposity, without apparent connection with or involvement of the hypophysis, is unusual, and although strictly not a part of the Fröhlich syndrome, is placed here for the purpose of comparison in regard to the sexual effect of endocrine tumors.

BIBLIOGRAPHY

[1] REVERDIN : Rev. Méd. Suisse vorn., 1883, iii, 413.
[2] FRÖHLICH : Ein Fall von Tumor der Hypophysis Cerebri Ohne Akromegalie. Wien. Klin. Rundsch., 1901, xv, 883.
[3] BARTELS : Ueber die Beziehungen von Veränderungen der Hypophysengegend zur Misswachstum und Genitalstörungen (Dystrophia adiposogenitalis). Münch. med. Wchn., 1908, lv, 201.
[4] CUSHING : The Pituitary Body and its Disordres.
[5] GOETSCH : Johns Hopkins Hospital Bull., 1916, xxxvii, 29.
[6] HEWLETT : Arch. Intern. Med., 1912, ix, 32.
[7] GOTTLIEB : Zeitschr. f. angebor. Anat., 1920, vii, 60.
[8] FRANK : Jour. Amer. Med. Assn., 1919, lxxiii, 1764.
[9] SAJOUS : The Internal Secretions.
[10] LAUNOIS, PINARD and GALLAIS : Gar. d. hop., Paris, 1911, p. 649.

H. FUNCTIONAL VARIATIONS

a. HERMAPHRODITISM

By *hermaphrodism* or *hermaphroditism* is meant the union in the same individual of organs characteristic of both the male and female sexes. From the functional point of view, the sexual glands in the hermaphrodite reach maturity simultaneously, or approximately so. Autofecundation is possible, and such is seen in the vegetable kingdom where hermaphrodism is usual in certain species. In animal hermaphrodites, maturity of the male gonad generally, however, precedes that of the female gonad, and it is unusual for the testicle to secrete spermatozoa.

The study of hermaphrodism in man is bound up with the general question of embryology; it is generally admitted by embryologists that in the early stages of development, the human embryo is undifferentiated as regards sex, and that the determination of male, female, or mixed sex is a function of the development of the mesonephros and the Muellerian ducts.

In early fetal life, during mesonephritic development, the human organism is apparently undifferentiated as regards sex. At this time a cord-like ridge, which later gives origin to Mueller's duct, develops along the border of each mesonephros. On either side this lies internal to the Wolffian duct (primitive ureter) and terminates with the Wolffian duct into the urogenital canal. As the sexes differentiate, the fate of these structures is dictated by: (1) the development of the sex-gland (ovary or testis) which develops from the genital tubercle of the mesonephros, the latter in the male forming the epididymis and ducts, while in the female, it forms the paroophoron, etc. In the male, the Muellerian ducts become involuted, but in the female, they form the uterus, tubes and vagina. If in the male, Mueller's ducts persist, and to a greater or lesser degree produce the female genital organs, the condition of *hermaphrodism* arises. The cause of failure of involution of the ducts may be due to imperfect hormone action. *Bisexuality* in man up to comparatively recent times was based upon the general findings in the individual rather than upon histological evidence of the existence of independent tissues proper to the differentiated sexual organs. As a matter of fact, the existence of true bisexuality has been denied by many who believed that the coexistence of glandular functioning tissue of both sexes in the same individual was inadmissible, theoretically or practically.

Biedel and others assert that man is *bisexual,* and that every normal male and female retains cells of undifferentiated accessory sex organs of the opposite sex; *that there is no such thing as a pure male or female, but that each contains the elements of the other sex; that the secondary genital organs have a bisexual origin and, in the adult, show a certain degree of hermaphrodism.*

Falta thinks that the secondary sexual characters develop in a masculine or feminine direction according to whether the masculine or feminine internal secretory sexual glands predominate. The occurrence of heterologous sexual characters is explained by the supposition that the suppressed or dormant secretory portions of the sexual glands that belong to the other sex have obtained the upper hand.

Hermaphrodism may be *bilateral, unilateral* or *alternate.* In *true bilateral hermaphrodism,* there is a testicle and an ovary on each side instead of one, and the same kind of organ on each side; in *unilateral hermaphrodism* there is a testicle and an ovary on one side, and a testicle or an ovary on the other; in *alternate hermaphrodism* there is one testicle on one side and one ovary on the other.

Cases of all these types apparently have been described in medical literature, but owing to reluctance to admission of the existence of true hermaphrodism in man, or to the impossibility of submitting unquestionable histological proof of it, most cases are described in the literature as *pseudo-hermaphrodism* of either masculine or feminine type, and internal or external. These are cases in which an individual is apparently externally a male or female, but internally shows the existence of the genital organs of the other sex, or there may be external showings of partly developed organs pertaining to both sexes. An example of this kind is the case recently reported by Mackenzie [1] in which a man of thirty-eight years was found, on operation, to have two testes as well as a uterus and fallopian tube in the scrotum. This case is described as one of internal pseudo-hermaphrodism. There are nearly one thousand such cases recorded, the masculine type being easily predominant.

Tuffier and Lapointe [2] writing as late as 1911 on the question of hermaphrodism affirm that the coexistence of true ovary and testicle has never been demonstrated in man, and that embryology did not admit that the primary sex tubercle was capable of subdividing into two independent heterosexual glands. These authors denied the existence of true bilateral or true unilateral hermaphrodism as defined in the above classification, but on the other hand, they admitted that *alternate hermaphrodism* was possible. They did not admit that any case was known of an ovo-testis with the double function, and that where ovo-testes were demonstrated, the subjects were predominantly of one sex; true histologic bisexuality could only be admitted if it connoted functional bisexuality. These views are those of most of the important writers on this subject who regarded subjects with more or less development of both sexual gonads as pseudohermaphrodites, such pseudo-hermaphrodism being a purely local malformation of the genital organs.

Tandler and Grosz,[3] in 1913, divided hermaphrodism into *functional* and *morphologic*. The first did not exist in man. The morphologic was a malformation of the undetermined origin of the primary sex bud or tubercle.

On the other hand, Pick,[4] Venturi[5] and others, have championed the existence of true bisexuality. Venturi collected what he considered four cases of incontestible functional bisexuality in man, and twenty-two cases in animals, besides six probable cases in man and eight in animals. As examples, in Salen's[6] case, Pick was able to prove histologically that male and female gametes existed in the same gland; in Sinigaglia's[7] case the histological examination showed an ovo-testis with adult functioning ovarian tissue and fetal testicular tissue. This hermaphrodite was aged twenty-eight years and married. The external genital organs showed no malformation, but the right testicle was ectopic in the inguinal ring, the left testicle being in place but very small. The liquid ejaculated by this individual contained spermatozoa. The right, which was ectopic, was the ovo-testis.

The difficulty in most cases of alleged functional bisexuality has been to furnish a complete histological examination of the glands on both sides. In most cases part only of the glandular system was removed during an operation for hernia, etc., and the finding of an ovo-testis was accidental; or the individual was young and the glands not developed. In the cases published there has been a failure either to furnish complete histological proof of the bisexuality; or the bisexuality was found in the newborn or infants; or else the histological findings were open to doubtful interpretation.

A case has, however, been recently published by Brian, Lagoutte and Lacassagne[8] which is not open to such criticisms. The patient was an adult and the sexual organs had reached their maximum of development. The totality of the internal genital organs (glands and efferent ducts) on both sides were studied, whereas in most of the previously described cases this examination was confined to a single gland removed in the course of a local operation. Finally, the histological examination was made completely and the tissues were immediately fixed after their ablation and a large number of sections studied. This case in its completeness is almost unique. Summarized, this case is as follows:

Individual of twenty-eight years who had always passed as a male. The genital region showed the aspect of absolute hypospadia with bilateral cryptorchidism. (Fig. 134.)

On operation it was found that there was a uterus of about the usual size, found in a nullipara and two normal tubes; besides, there were complete spermatic cords which were examined from their origin to termination and showed the usual histologic structure of that organ. (Figs. 135 and 136.)

On each side there was a mixed sex gland, each containing an ovarian and a testicular part in different proportions. The left gland, by its situation in the pelvis, by its relations with the uterus and tube, and its external aspect, was an ovary. Internally, it

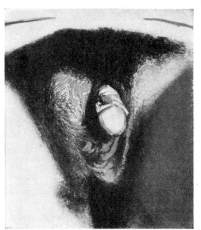

FIG. 134.—Hermaphrodism bilateral. Appearance of external genitalia. (Brian, Lagoutte and Lacassagne.)

was bipartate in structure, one part ovarian in full functioning, the other part testicular, but the seminiferous cells in which were limited to spermatogonia.

The right gland by its situation in the inguinal ring, by its vaginal envelope previously attacked by hydrocele, by its form and relations with the epididymis and deferent canal, was to be considered as an ectopic testicle. But internally also, it had a testicular and an ovarian portion. The testicular tissue had the seminiferous cells developed as far as the spermatocytes. The ovarian tissue contained follicles. This gland was in reality an ovo-testis predominantly testicular. (Fig. 137.) This individual may, therefore, be classed as a bilateral true hermaphrodite with bisexual glands functioning.

The fact that the individual lives still explains the reason why fuller details with regard to prostate, etc., cannot be given by the authors. The histological complete examination could only be made on the organs removed by operation. Three types of tubular structure were found. They are herewith reproduced. (Figs. 138 and 139.)

As already stated, many writers doubt the existence of true hermaphrodism as most of the examples given in literature lack complete histo-

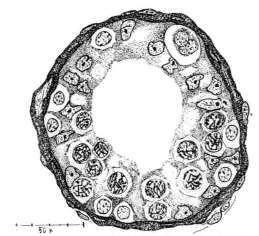

Fig. 135.—Seminiferous tube of a portion of the left testicle. Type 1.
(Brian, Lagoutte and Lacassagne.)

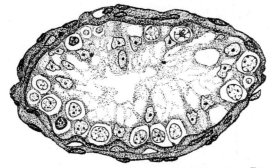

Fig. 136.—Seminiferous tube of a portion of the left testicle. Type 2.
(Brian, Lagoutte and Lacassagne.)

logical details. The above case is therefore important as the histological results are given by the author in the greatest detail and leave no reasonable doubt with regard to the identification of true bilateral ovarian and testicular tissue in the same individual. (Figs. 140 and 141.)

It is possible and even probable that if the opportunity for complete histological and other examinations were available, cases of true functional human bisexuality would be found more numerous than is believed. Undoubtedly histological study of the totality of the sexual glands is

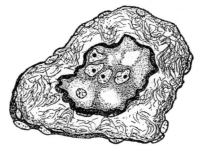

FIG. 137.—Seminiferous tube of a portion of the left testicle. Type 3.
(Brian, Lagoutte and Lacassagne.)

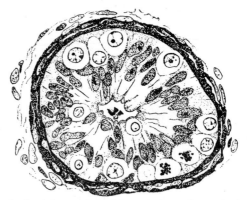

FIG. 138.—Seminiferous tubule of the testicular portion on the right side.
(Brian, Lagoutte and Lacassagne.)

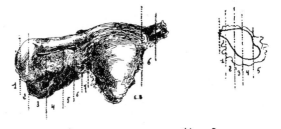

Série A   Série B

FIG. 139.—Outline of fragments taken from gross specimens for microscopic examination. *a*, left gland; *b*, right gland. (Brian, Lagoutte and Lacassagne.)

necessary to establish bisexuality in a case which must otherwise be described as pseudo-hermaphrodism. But it is clear from what is now known that an organ considered as an ovary may be a true ovo-testis and contain a testicular part within it; and an organ classed as a testicle can similarly enclose ovarian functioning tissue. Knud Sand's experimental autotransplantations of testicular tissue in ovaries, and ovarian tissue in testicles, prove without question that in such cases pure hermaphroditic effects, both physical and psychical, can be produced. Alexander Lipschütz has recently contributed valuable information on experimental hermaphrodism in guinea-pigs.

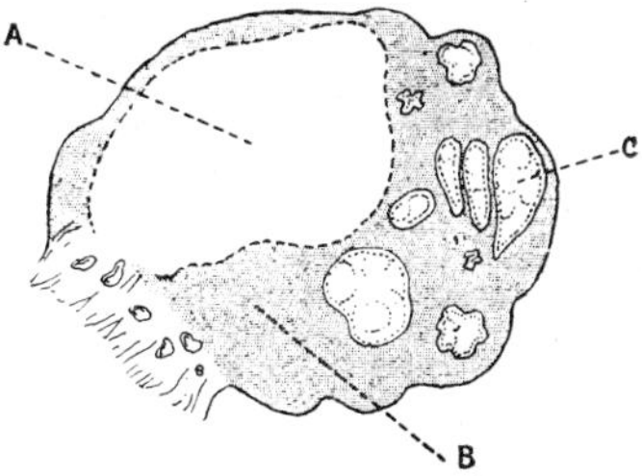

It is obviously clear that only in extremely few clinical cases can such a complete castration be made as would permit complete histological proofs to be forthcoming, and many cases where the sexuality is really mixed must remain classed as unisexual.

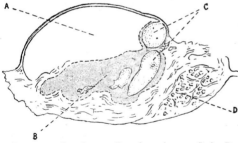

Fig. 140.—Outline of total section of fragment 5, Series A, magnified 3½ times. *a*, testicular portion; *b*, ovarian portion; *c*, corpus luteum in involution. (Brian, Lagoutte and Lacassagne.)

The point in which we are most interested in connection with hermaphrodism is, however, that sex, and sex manifestations are matters of the functional secretions of certain cellular tissues rather than the anatomical or morphological distribution or arrangement of organs. It has been shown that both female and male gonads may coexist in the same individual and function without prejudice to each other. Hence practically every type of hermaphrodism is possible, and, from what is known, fairly frequent.

Fig. 141.—Complete outline of specimen 4, Series B, enlarged 3½ times. *a*, testicular portion; *b*, ovarian portion; *c*, follicular cavities; *d*, head of the epididymis. (Brian, Lagoutte and Lacassagne.)

It is noteworthy that in experimental work done by Steinach he was never successful in implanting the testes into a normal female animal. On the other hand, in animals that were castrated the transplanted testes thrived and showed a marked proliferation of the interstitial cells. The studies and experimental researches of Sand have resulted in the obtaining of *ovariotestes*. He obtained his results by the implantation of infantile ovaries in the testicle of guinea-pigs between five and twelve weeks of age. He was able to show that both glands developed. In other words, ovulation and spermatogenesis continued. The remarkable part of his work was that hermaphrodites that showed characteristics of both sexes were produced in the animals experimented upon. In one of Sand's experiments an infantile male rat had two ovaries implanted into his testes. After four months the penis of this animal was about 0.6 cm. long; that is somewhat smaller than the penis of the control animals; both seminal vesicles were developed and contained secretion. In these animals the papillæ of the nipples of the breasts were large, well developed and pigmented with wide areolæ, and secreted upon pressure normal milk. In other words, both sexual characteristics, male and female, were to be observed in these instances.

Steinach and Holzknecht were able to destroy experimentally the generative part of the ovary. They used the X-ray. Very young guinea pigs were exposed for from two to four weeks with from 11 to 12 Holzknecht units, projected to the animal through the back without the use of the filter. After from three to four weeks the hairs began to fall out sparsely, and after eight weeks certain secondary sexual characteristics of the female became manifest.

In 40 per cent. of the cases the animals subjected to this treatment showed a marked development of the nipples of the breasts, like in pregnancy, to such a degree that the glands secreted milk for a period of two or three weeks.

Microscopic examination of the ovaries showed total atrophy of the follicles, and the entire stroma of the ovary was in great process of proliferation, and teeming with so-called puberty gland cells. (Figs. 142 and 143.)

Kiernan, of Chicago, has emphasized the theory of bisexuality. The point of view that originally all living animals were bisexual and gradually developed a monosexual individuality is sustained today by some of the most serious workers in this field. Semon's theory that bisexual elements are continued in the same individual throughout life has found a great many supporters. In other words, through certain influences which will be dwelt upon later, an accentuation of one or the other sexual life may be manifest. In Fig. 144, we observe a true hermaphrodite. This was a patient of the late Prof. Carl Beck of New York, who during an opera-

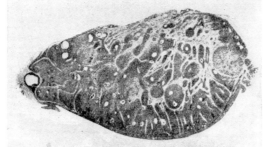

FIG. 142.—*a*, section from an ovary of a guinea pig 4½ months old treated with X-ray. (Steinach.)

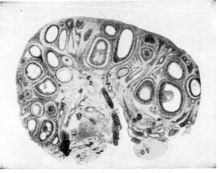

FIG. 143.—*b*, ovary of a sister of the guinea pig depicted above, not subjected to the action of the X-ray. (Steinach.)

FIG. 144.—Case of hermaphroditismus verus reported by the late Prof. Carl Beck, of New York.

tion discovered the existence of both sets of sex glands, male and female, (*hermaphroditismus verus*). Fig. 145 shows a rare case of true hermaphroditism described by Walter Simon in volume 172 of Virchow's Archives. In this case the patient was twenty years old. He grew up as a boy and felt masculine in every shape and form until at a later period the breasts swelled and a monthly menstrual discharge made its appearance. From the vagina a whitish mucus was discharged from time to time, accompanied simultaneously by erections and libidinous sensations

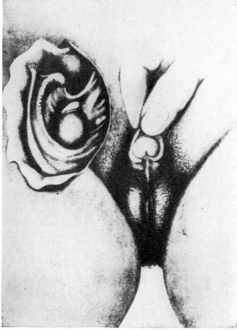

FIG. 145.—Hermaphroditismus verus, sexus intermis. Described by Walter Simon and quoted by Magnus Hirschfeld.

that concentrated principally on females. The form of the body and expression of the face were accentuatedly feminine. The shoulders made an exception to this for they were of masculine character. In the right inguinal region a hernia-like tumor was found which was disclosed upon opening to be an *ovariotestes, epididymis, parovarium, spermatic cord,* and *Fallopian* tube. Microscopic examination of the specimens disclosed distinctly the presence of sexual glands of both sexes.

In Fig. 146 we find depicted a dissected specimen in the possession of Dr. Magnus Hirschfeld, which was taken from the body of a child five years of age who was looked upon as a boy for the reason that the projection in the clitoridian area was thought to be a penis and the two adjacent labia gave the semblance of a scrotum. After the death of the child Hirschfeld discovered the presence of a uterus, tubes and ovaries. The microscopic examination showed the structure of ovaries without the

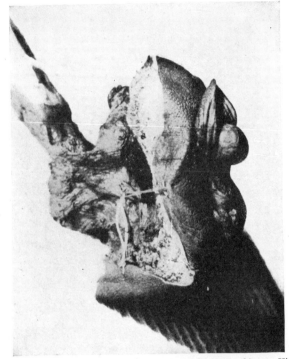

Fig. 146.—Pseudo-hermaphroditismus femininus (error in sexu). (Magnus Hirschfeld.)

presence of testicular tissue. This is a well illustrated instance of a pseudo-hermaphroditismus.

Figs. 147 and 148 depict another typical case of pseudo-hermaphroditismus. The patient is that of Dr. G. Merzbach. The patient was a soldier who died during the Boer War and the photograph was taken on the battlefield of Transvaal, the cause of death being a gunshot wound through the head. A study of these two photographs will show the marked development of the breasts, penis and other factors that permit

17

a clear classification in the same class as the preceding case; namely, pseudo-hermaphroditismus.

The following case may also prove of interest in this connection: Fig. 149 depicts a masculine pseudo-hermaphrodite presented to us by Dr. Magnus Hirschfeld. This refers to one named " Friederike S. " She was brought up as a girl. Throughout her lifetime she donned masculine attire only three times. The breasts were absent and the pelvis almost

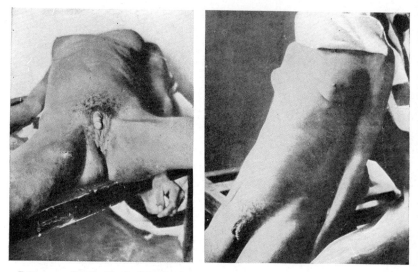

FIGS. 147, 148.—Dr. Merzbach's case of pseudo-hermaphroditismus. Soldier dead of gunshot wounds. Note remarkable development of penis and breasts.

masculine. Her genitals showed the genital ridge, a penis, under which was discernible a vaginal or, perhaps, scrotal slit. Both of these were surrounded by the labia majora and minora. The masculine type predominated.

According to Virchow, Neugebauer, and others there is a class of individuals who are sexless, *homines neutrius generis*. Virchow says, " There truly exists an individual of positively neutral kind. We may try as much as we like, but we cannot with absolute surety tell whether we are dealing in a given case with a man or a woman." A study of the literature, while confusing in its classification, will nevertheless permit in most cases classifying the individual by subjecting him or her, as the case may be, to a painstaking physical examination with a consideration of all facts at hand. Stieve in his latest communication classifies hermaphrodites into *complete* and *incomplete*.

Fig. 150 shows Salen's case of bisexual gland containing ovarian tissue, testicular portions, seminal canal, vesicles and corpora lutea. In Fig. 151,

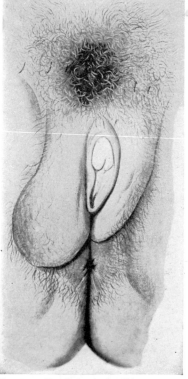

we see an ovo-testis of a homosexual goat. In this instance the testicular tissue has the appearance of a cryptorchitic testicle, much developed interstitial tissue and atrophic follicles.

As far back as 1885 Reuter described ovo-testes in animals, but the first description of human ovo-testes was given by Salen in 1899.

Hirschfield, after a résumé of the literature, would prefer to classify hermaphrodites in the following manner:

    I. Hermaphroditismus genitalis.

    II. Hermaphroditismus somaticus (Androgynie).

    III. Hermaphroditismus psychicus (Transvestitismus).

    IV. Hermaphroditismus psychosexualis (Homosexuality or Metatropismus).

FIG. 149.—Pseudo-hermaphroditismus, masculinus. (Magnus Hirschfeld.)

Also, should a more descriptive subdivision of genital hermaphroditismus become necessary, the following subdivisions may become practical (Hirschfeld):[9]

    I. Hermaphroditismus masculinus (masculine sexual gland with feminine adnexa).

    II. Hermaphroditismus femininus (feminine sexual glands with masculine adnexa).

III. Hermaphroditismus neutralis (rudimentary sexual glands which are neither masculine nor feminine).

IV. Hermaphroditismus dualis (sexual glands which are in part masculine and in part feminine—*ovariotestes*).

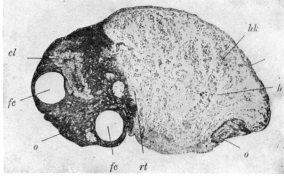

FIG. 150.—Salen's case of human bisexual sex gland. Magnified 1:4. *o*, portion of ovary; *h*, portion of testicle; *fc*, follicles; *cl*, corpus luteum; *hk*, seminal canals.

From the practical point of view it is necessary for the scientific observer to have a thorough knowledge of these conditions. From the

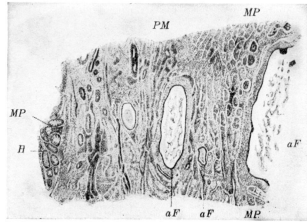

FIG. 151.—Section of an ovotestis of a homosexual goat. *h*, testicular tissue of the composition of a cryptorchid testicle; *mp*, masculine puberty gland; *af*, atrophic follicles. (Steinach.)

point of therapy, with the present status of our knowledge of advanced surgery and the advances made in neurologic technic, coupled with what is known today on sex gland implantation, some cases of this type may be benefited to no small degree. In some countries, notably in Germany, individuals in whom there is a preponderance of male characteristics frequently obtain permission from the authorities, or such permission is obtained by others, for them to bring that individual, by all means known, to the sex stage which she or he mainly represents. An appropriate cognomen is then assigned to the individual in question and proper attire legally permitted. In this country no such provisions exist and the author feels that in some cases a great deal of good may be accomplished by proper individualization of the cases presented and aid rendered to them to make their psychic and social condition as bearable and pleasant as possible, and train them in normal useful channels of activity. Coöperation between the legal minds, humanitarians and the medical profession is essential to bring amelioration, and often hold out the possibilty of some form of cure for this class of patients who not infrequently drift into a state of hopelessness with a tendency to self-destruction and utter dejection. Education of physicians, lawyers, judges, public welfare workers and teachers will, in time, it is hoped, bring about in at least some of these unfortunates a tolerable existence as free from humiliation and miscarried justice as possible.

BIBLIOGRAPHY

[1] MACKENZIE: Surgery, Gynec. and Obstet., 1922, xxxiv, 51.
[2] TUFFIER and LAPOINTE: Rev. de gynec., Paris, 1911, xvi, 209.
[3] TANDLER and GROSZ: Die biolog. Grundl d. sekund. Geschlechts charactere, Berlin, 1913.
[4] PICK: Arch. f. mikros. Anat., 1914, lxxxiv, 119.
[5] VENTURI: La Clin. Veterin., Milan, 1916, 543.
[6] SALEN: Verhandl. d. deut. path. Geselles., Berl., 1899, p. 241.
[7] SINIGAGLIA: Clin. Chirurg., Milan, 1914, No. 7.
[8] BRIAN, LAGOUTTE and LACASSAGNE: Gynec. et Obstet., Paris, 1920, i, 155; 273.
[9] HIRSCHFELD, MAGNUS: Sexual pathologie, Weber, Bonn, 1919.

b. HOMOSEXUALITY

It has already been stated that the human embryo is undifferentiated in regard to sex; it is potentially male or female. In the light of modern research, hermaphroditism and homosexuality are closely allied and must be considered not as abnormal but rather as *sex-intergrades,* natural variations resulting from some disturbance of the chromosome complex.

Homosexuality may be divided into two types: the *subjective* and the *passive*. Ferenczi[1] considered that the subjective male homosexual and the objective female homosexual were sexual intermediate states. They are biological anomalies of development which are often coupled with unmistakably physical signs, *viz.*, they show secondary sexual characteristics opposed to the individual's apparent primary sex.

This view, however, has not been universally held. By some, homosexuality has been considered as an acquired disposition having at least in part a psychic and environmental basis.

Walther[2] considered that although the sex of an individual is determined from the anatomical character of the sex gland, yet the development of the psycho-sexual centre is given an extremely wide scope, through education, example and suggestion, so that as a rule the psycho-sexual sensations of atypical persons are largely dependent upon their early environment.

Obendorf[3] also thinks that those who are prematurely fixed or arrested in the evolution of their sexual disposition are exposed to the danger that a strong flood of *libido* which finds no outlet may, through failure in social life, in strong outbursts of sexual needs or through disappointment in the opposite sex, be driven to *sexual inversion*. The symptom-complex common to all sexual perversions, including homosexuality, according to Adler,[4] consists in:

(1) Every perversion is the expression of a more or less widened distance between male and female.

(2) *Perversion* denotes a more or less deep-reaching revolt against participation in the normal sexual act and becomes evident as a systematized or unconscious artifice for the establishment of the pervert's own feelings or personality.

(3) Deprecation of the normally anticipated partner is always present. Therefore odiousness and conquest are feelings necessary to the pervert.

(4) Perversive tendencies in men show themselves as compensatory efforts for the exaltation of a feeling of inferiority against over-estimated power of woman; and similarly in the case of female perverts.

(5) Perversion usually grows out of a spiritual life, exhilaration, supersensitiveness and over-reached ambition. Lack of deeper companionship

and reciprocal kindness are present to a greater degree that is usually supposed.

Hirschfeld [5] denies Kraepelin's explanation that homosexuality is due to an acquired appetite, and thinks, on the contrary, that it is always congenital and an intermediate form from the normal, i.e., a sex intergrade.

Lazzeroni,[6] from a clinical study of homosexuals, remarks that if not all individuals who have a preponderatingly or exclusively feminine rôle are inverts, the majority of inverts have a rôle preponderatingly as exclusively feminine. And if such inverts have sons these latter are for the most part also inverts.

The congenital or *heredity aspect* of homosexuality naturally leads up to the present-day view that homosexuality is a condition dependent upon an anatomical basis, an alteration in the histological disposition of the sex glands, and a consequent disturbance in the sexual hormone production. This view is due especially to the work of Steinach.[7]

In pursuing his investigations on the secretions of the interstitial cells of the testicle Steinach reached certain conclusions of importance in regard to the human aspect of homosexuality. By experimental research in homosexual males Steinach believes to have succeeded in microscopically proving a deviation from the normal puberty gland. Irrespective of age the testicles of the homosexuals showed a restricted number of seminiferous tubules with the presence of large cells having abundant protoplasm, a clear nucleus and some chromatin resembling corpus luteum cells.

Steinach was also satisfied that homosexuality is not an inherited or acquired mental disease or perversion, but rather a constitutional condition of bisexual character caused by the existence of a hermaphroditic puberty gland. In such a puberty gland the male puberty cells predominate over the female puberty cells and at first there develops a male sex character with all its male marks. If later for any reason the male cells are temporarily stunted and their secretive function ceases the female cells become more active. (Figs. 152–155.)

Thus in established homosexuality there was found, in the sense of Steinach, an anatomical or biological basis for the condition; but in addition to this there is the further proof afforded by the work of both Steinach and Knud Sand [9] in experimentally producing bisexuality by the implan-

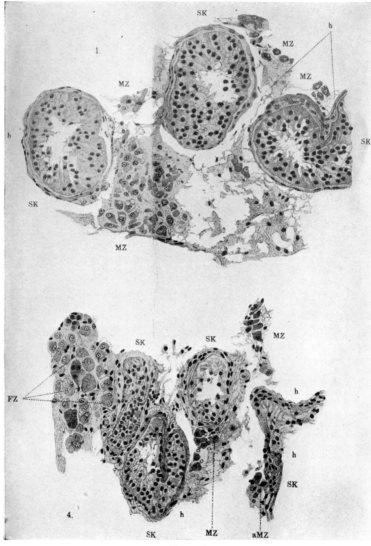

FIG. 152.

FIGS. 152 and 153.—Fig. 1. Section through a cryptorchitic testicle. To be used for comparison with following illustrations. Stained with hematoxylin and eosin. (Zeiss Komp. —Ok. 6 Apochrom. 8 mm. Tub. 145 mm.) *sk*, section through seminal canal which in comparison with seminiferous tubules of normal testicle is much smaller; the individual canals much separated from one another, their walls shrunken. Contents: Spermatogonia, as well as Sertoli cells. Completely atrophic. *h*, irregular humpy outline of shrunken walls of the seminal canal; *mz*, much proliferation of small groups of masculine puberty gland cells. In shape and size, as well as in staining characteristics and granulation, they are uniformly typical of the puberty gland of the normal testicle. The object of the picture is to depict the fact that the stunting of the development, or retrogressive process, leads in cases of cryptorchidism to atrophy of the puberty gland, but that the puberty gland of the cryptorchitic testicle is composed all the way through of typical masculine cells.

Fig. 2. Section through the testicle of a homosexual man 32 years of age, stained with hematoxylin and eosin. (Zeiss Komp. —Ok. Apochrom. 8 mm. Tub. 145 mm.) *sk*, two seminal canals widely separated from one another; their walls are indented, irregular, and form projections or humps along their course; *h*, contents: Degeneration or retrogression. (Degenerated spermatogonia, among which are visible cells without nuclei and large crypts in the structure; absence of spermatids and spermatozoa.) In some cases the spermatogonia are well preserved. In some places of the section degeneration is even more marked. *mz*, groups of masculine puberty gland cells. (Leydig cells of typical form, size and structure.) *amz*, atrophic puberty gland cells; *fz*, group of "F" cells. (Large cells rich in protoplasm, exceeding in size typical Leydig cells; markedly granular elements with large nuclei, poor in chromatin.)

Fig. 3. Three "F" cells from the *fz* group of Fig. 2 enlarged. (Zeiss Komp. —Ok. 18. Apochrom. 8 mm. Tub. 145 mm.) One of the cells has two nuclei in this enlargement. The marked granulations are distinctly visible.

Fig. 4. Section of a testis of a homosexual man 45 years of age, stained with hematoxylin and eosin. (Zeiss Komp. —Ok. 6. Apochrom. 8 mm. Tub. 145 mm.) *sk*, seminal canals remarkably diminished in size, shrunken and completely atrophied, the walls markedly uneven, indented and humpy; *h*, contents of seminal canals entirely atrophic. This includes the Sertoli cells also. This degeneration is marked throughout the section of the seminal gland. *mz*, groups of masculine puberty gland cells. (Typical Leydig cells correspond entirely with the Leydig cells of the normal or cryptorchitic testicle.) *amz*, atrophic puberty gland cells; *fz*, group of "F" cells. (Large partly binuclear and strongly or markedly granular elements.) -

Fig. 5. Section through a corpus luteum of a woman. This illustration is for purposes of comparison. Stained with hematoxylin and eosin. (Zeiss Komp. —Ok. 6. Apochrom. 8 mm. Tub. 145 mm.) Lutein cells taken from a somewhat loose portion of the corpus luteum.

Fig. 6. Three lutein cells of the specimen of Fig. 5 enlarged. To be used for comparison with Fig. 3. (Zeiss Komp. —Ok. 18. Apochrom. 8 mm. Tub. 145 mm.)

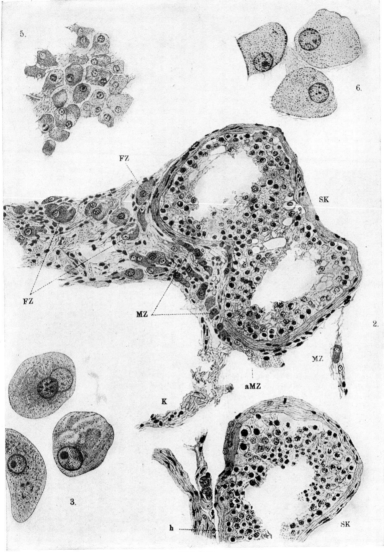

FIG. 153.

tation of heterogeneous gonad tissue in castrated individuals of the opposite sex. By abdominal transplantation of ovarian tissue in male castrated animals Steinach observed regression of the secondary male sexual charac-

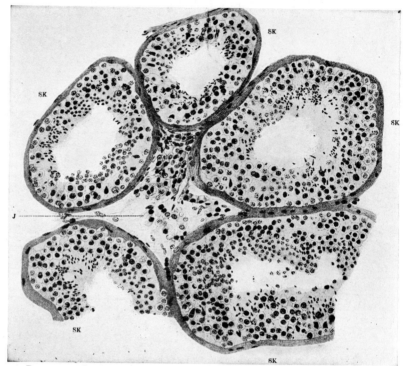

FIG. 154.—(After Steinach.) Fig. 1. Section through a testicle of a normal sexually mature man. This section is for comparative purposes. Bichlorid-iron-hematoxylin staining. (Zeiss Komp. —Ok. 6. Apochrom. 8 mm. Tub. 145 mm.) *sk*, transverse section through the seminal canal of normal size. The walls are either smooth or slightly wavy. Contents: Sertoli cells; spermatogonia and spermatids of normal structure. The sex gland in full spermatogenesis; the seminal canals of the normal testes abut one another closely and give comparatively small space to the interstitium. I. Interstitium with the elements of the male puberty gland. (Leydig cells of various forms and in all stages of development.)

teristics and development of female secondary characters; Sand by transplantation of testicular tissue in the ovaries of females produced hermaphrodites. There was no antagonism between the secretions of the gonads.

Steinach, in conjunction with his assistant, Lichtenstern,[10] believes to have succeeded in curing homosexual impulses in human beings. The sexual glands of the homosexual patient were removed and the sexual gland of

Fig. 155.—Fig. 1. Section of a testicle of a homosexual man, 37 years of age. Obtained by extirpating a very small piece for microscopic examination. Mallory staining. (Zeiss Komp. —Ok. 6. Apochrom. 8 mm. Tub. 145 mm.) *sk*, seminal canals widely separated from one another, shrunken. (Seminal cells markedly degenerated. Spermatids and spermatozoa entirely absent.) *h*, the humpy, zigzag contour of the shrunken wall of the seminal glands is markedly accentuated by the blue stain of connective tissue; *amz*, atrophic masculine puberty gland cells; *mz*, normal masculine puberty gland cells; *fz*, group of "F" cells. (Large markedly granular elements, with highly stained nuclei; the largest binuclear; the protoplasm of the adjoining one somewhat clefted.)

Fig. 2. Section through a testicle of a homosexual man, 23 years of age. Hematoxylin and eosin staining. (Zeiss Komp. —Ok. 6. Apochrom. 8 mm. Tub. 145 mm.) *sk*, seminal canals markedly shrunken, diminished in size, separated from one another. Contents degenerated and mainly very much atrophied; *b*, blood vessels; *mz*, groups of masculine puberty gland cells. (Typical Leydig cells of normal structure.) *fz*, "F" cells with two nuclei.

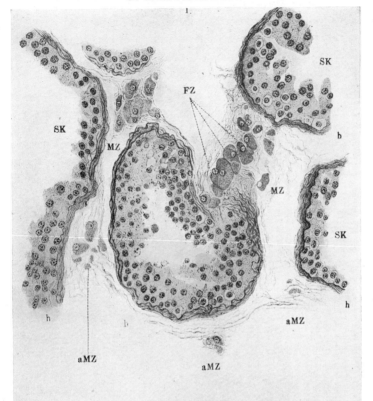

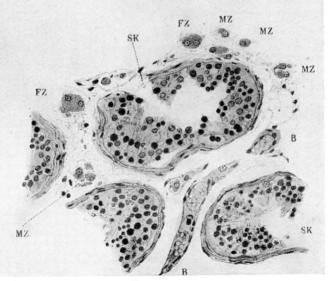

Fig. 155.

a healthy and normal man was implanted in the abdominal muscle of the homosexual patient. The feminine characteristics of his body development disappeared and male characteristics took their place. A complete change took place also in the realm of sex impulse and this continued permanently.

Pfeiffer [11] obtained similar success.

The excellent results obtained by Steinach and Lichtenstern and Pfeiffer from testicle transplantation in homosexuality have not, however, been confirmed by other operators. Stabel,[12] in six cases of homosexuality in which he transplanted a testicle, never saw any good from the operation. Kreuter [13] also very recently reported a case where he transplanted a half testicle from a confirmed homosexual into a man who two years before had been bilaterally castrated. The graft took and the man has continued to experience erections and *libido,* but there has not been the slightest indication of any homosexual tendency such as might have been expected from Lichtenstern's findings. The author examined a number of testes of homosexuals microscopically, and could not in this series of cases find the peculiar cells described by Steinach.

Recently Mühsam [14] removed the testes of homosexuals and had them examined histologically by Benda and v. Hansemann, but these observers also could not find the characteristic F and M cells described by Steinach.

BIBLIOGRAPHY

[1] FERENCZI: Zeitschr. f. Aerzt., Phychoanal., i.
[2] WALTHER: Bull. et Mém. Soc. de Chir., Paris, 1916, xlii, 382.
[3] OBENDORF: Medical Record, N. Y., 1919, xcvi, 840.
[4] ADLER: Alienist and Neurol., 1917, xxxviii, 268.
[5] HIRSCHFELD: Muench. med. Wchnschr.
[6] LAZZERONI: Revist. sper. di freniat., 1919, xliii, 564.
[7] STEINACH: K. Acad. d. Wissensch., Vienna, 1919, Nos. 36, 38, 39.
[8] STEINACH: Arch. f. Entwickel. Mech., 1920, xlvi, Heft. 1.
[9] KNUD SAND: Arch. f. d. ges. Physiol., 1918, clxxiii, 1.
[10] STEINACH and LICHTENSTERN: Muench. med. Wchnschr., 1918, No. 6, p. 145.
[11] PFEIFFER: Deut. med. Wchnschr., 1922, xlviii, 660.
[12] STABEL: Deut. med. Wchnschr., 1921, xlvii, 1248.
[13] KREUTER: Zentralbl. f. Chir., 1922, xlix, 538.
[14] MÜHSAM: Archiv. f. Frauenkunde, ix, Heft 3, 170.

CHAPTER VI

EXPERIMENTAL TESTICULAR TRANSPLANTATIONS IN ANIMALS

RESULTS OF SUCH TRANSPLANTATIONS

THE early experimental work of Berthold [1] of Göttingen in 1849, who transplanted the testicles of fowls into their abdominal cavities, has already been referred to in this work elsewhere.

The next important work in this connection was done by Mantegazza [2] in 1860. Mantegazza's first work was on frogs; he grafted the testicles beneath the skin of the abdominal wall, where they apparently became necrosed, although he states that he found living spermatozoa in the tissue after seventy days. Mantegazza's attempts at testicular transplantation in mammals (rabbits) failed.

In 1895, Lode [3] found that testicles transplanted subcutaneously retained their vitality and functioned actively, continuing to produce spermatozoa; he thought that, at least in fowls, a special nerve supply for the testes did not exist.

Goebell,[4] three years after Lode's experiments, found that when entire testicles of young guinea pigs were transplanted in the abdominal cavity they degenerated; but he had greater success with small fragments of the testicle. The central part of the graft degenerated, but the peripheral part became vascularized and continued to live for a considerable time.

Ribbert's [5] experimental investigations with fragments of testicular tissue, showed that sometimes the epithelial elements of the graft were destroyed, not by degeneration, but by a process of regression to a non-differentiated embryonic condition. The connective tissue elements, however, showed more advanced development. Ribbert found that in the rabbit total transplants of the testicle died; he considered that the reason for this was that the testicle, being a gland of external secretion, suffered involution when deprived of means of excretion; furthermore, on account of failure of nutrition.

Herlitzka [6] disagreed with Ribbert. Herlitzka, in a number of testicular transplants in male and female animals of the same species, found also that they died by degeneration, but he thought that this effect was due to absence of nervous trophic stimulus. He observed that other epithelial cells can be transplanted with success, but as in the case of the thyroid, the stimulus was derived from the blood stream. As the testicular stimulant was nervous, Ribbert's theory of malnutrition did not hold, as in Herlitzka's experimental work both peripheral and central vascularization of the transplanted testicles was greater than normal.

Herlitzka found progressive degeneration of the glandular tissue of the testicle and an abundant infiltration of migratory cells followed by neoformations of connective tissue until the glandular tissue proper of the testicle was replaced. The testicle, however, preserved its general morphological appearance and was well vascularized throughout.

Foges'[7] experiments on fowls demonstrated for him that transplanted testicles retained their power to produce spermatozoa, but such testicles failed to maintain the secondary sex characters. The influence of the isolated testicle to maintain sexual characters had generally been previously affirmed by Wagner,[8] Nussbaum, Sellheim,[9] and others.

Foá,[10] in 1901, repeated Mantegazza's experiments under strict surgical conditions. His work was on dogs, transplanting the testicle into the abdominal cavity. He found that the testicle, whether embryonary or adult, did not take in grafts, whether it was transplanted in its entirety in the abdominal cavity or in fragments in the tissue of another testicle; and that the results were *equally negative in autoplastic,* and in *homoplastic* grafts. He attributed the failure mainly to lack of vascularization and nerve connections. The author recently repeated Foá's experiments on a series of dogs and found that the conclusions reached by Foá were those obtained by the author. Obolensky,[11] as far back as 1876, had observed that following section of the spermatic nerve, there was fatty degeneration and atrophy of the testicle. Foá further believes that operative trauma had a good deal to do with the degeneration of transplanted testicles. Harms[12] observed in the frog that there was a hypertrophy of the remnants of testicles of partly castrated animals following testicular transplantation in the lymph glands.

In carrying out transplantations, either for experimental purposes or therapeutic purposes, we should be acquainted with three terms adopted in the literature to denote the type of transplantation practiced in a given instance.

1. By *autotransplantation* we understand the implantation of a given tissue in a certain portion of the body taken from the same animal.

2. *Homiotransplantation* or, as some prefer to call it, *homotransplantation,* signifies the implantation of tissue into the body of an animal from another animal of the same species.

3. In *heterotransplantation* we implant the tissue from the body of an animal of a different species.

The experimental animal investigations of Bouin and Ancel,[13] as well as Eugene Steinach, have already been dealt with in detail elsewhere in this treatise, their work being mainly concerned with the rôle of the interstitial cells of the testicles.

In the interval between the foregoing and the more recent experimental work, Meyns [14] showed that in the frog, testicles transplanted into the lymph channels lived, and Guthrie [15] found that an autotransplant into the shoulder of a fowl grew and became vascularized after four months. He confirmed Lode's observation of preserved anatomical structure, including masses of spermatozoa, in testicles grafted subcutaneously in abnormal situations. Cevolotto [16] found a degeneration of the highly differentiated testicular tissue cells and an increase in the Sertoli cells in fragments of testicles transplanted subcutaneously in rabbits.

The recent work which has raised the question of testicular transplantation from a mere experimental to a practical surgical plane, is due to Steinach, Knud Sand, and Voronoff and Retterer.

Steinach, besides having done pioneer work of great magnitude, transplanted ovaries into young male castrated animals. He demonstrated that the mammary glands of these animals hypertrophied and secreted milk, and that such animals looked like, acted as, and were considered as females. On examining the subsequently removed ovarian tissue, Steinach [17] found that the *corpora lutea* had lost all trace of true luteic structure, and consisted only of a mixed growth of degenerated follicles and thecal or interstitial cells. The ovum-producing activity of the transplanted ovary was no longer utilized, but was supplanted by the increased production of interstitial cells. Steinach accounted for the production of female sex characters in the males in which the ovarian tissue had been transplanted as thus ultimately due to the interstitial cells, which was on an exact par with his findings in the case of testicular transplants, the seminal tissues degenerating and the interstitial cells hypertrophying.

Knud Sand,[18] following the example of Steinach, was engaged from 1914 to 1917 in biological experiments on the sexual glands in mammals in the University of Copenhagen. In this work, Sand carried out experiments in:

Animal transplantations of testicles.

Autotransplantations.

Homotransplantations:

    (a) From male to male.

    (b) From male to female.

Simultaneous auto- and homotransplantations on the same animal.

Sand found that when the seminiferous tubuli atrophied, the Leydig cells augmented, thereby substantiating Steinach's findings. He considers this hypertrophy of the Leydig cells as dependent on atrophy of the tubuli.

Fifty-three experimental testicular transplantations were done.

In young castrated female rats, into which a testicle was transplanted, different degrees of hypertrophy of the clitoris were observed.

Similar results were obtained in homotransplantations of ovaries from females to males. Such males developed female characters and acted as females.

Experimental Hermaphrodism.—Steinach had expressed the opinion that prior castration was a condition *sine qua non* to obtain the results anticipated.

Sand made simultaneous transplantations of testicle and ovary in young castrated animals subperitoneally. The result was a pure somatic and psychic hermaphrodite. Thus by simultaneous transplantation of male and female glands, hermaphrodites can be experimentally produced. Sand also made intratesticular transplantation of ovarian tissue, the testicles being respected in their proper position, in rats. Artificial *ovariotesticles* were produced. Thus the two gonads increase in most intimate relationship without any prejudice, and both produce their special functional product.

Undoubted bisexual psychism was noticed in such animals.

Knud Sand deduces from his experimental work that the frequent almost absolute persistence of the Leydig cells in active transplants gives such reasonable proof that male sexual hormones are elaborated in them that he has reached an absolute certainty on the question, and that from the various researches and experimental findings the question may be considered as definitely settled. (Cf. Chapter on Hermaphrodism.)

Aside from Steinach's epoch-making investigations on laboratory animals the most important testicular transplantation researches in recent times are undoubtedly those of Voronoff.[19]

Voronoff carried out a number of experimental testicular grafts in animals in the Physiological Station of the College of France from 1917 to 1920.

Testicular grafts in young bucks two to three months old, in which their own testicles had been left, had a very marked influence on the development of the horns and hair. The accompanying illustrations are of bucks taken three years after the grafting. The horns are seen to be extremely well developed, attaining a length and thickness scarcely met with in normal male animals of this kind. These animals appear also to be more vigorous than normal animals of like age, and their beard is longer and more abundant. Such grafted animals reach their full growth earlier than normal animals.

Voronoff's animal testicular grafts were imbedded in the scrotum in their natural site. The histological examinations of the subsequently removed grafted testicles were made by Retterer.[20] In the grafts that survived, the nutrition was weakened, still they showed some tubes the epithelial cells of which evolved in such a way as to produce spermatozoa. The majority of the other seminiferous tubes survived also, but the evolutionary phenomena were checked in accord with the change in the epithelial cells. These latter were changed into a mass of proto-plasm containing numerous nuclei (syncytium) which filled the lumen of the tube. Besides, instead of producing spermatids and spermatozoa, the syncytium was transformed into a reticulated tissue. These testicular grafts in young animals previously castrated caused these animals to evolve normally as if they had not been castrated. Their horns continued to develop similar to those of non-castrated control animals. (Figs. 156 and 157.) The horns show extraordinary development. In general physical vigor these animals exceeded those animals of the same age and same

18

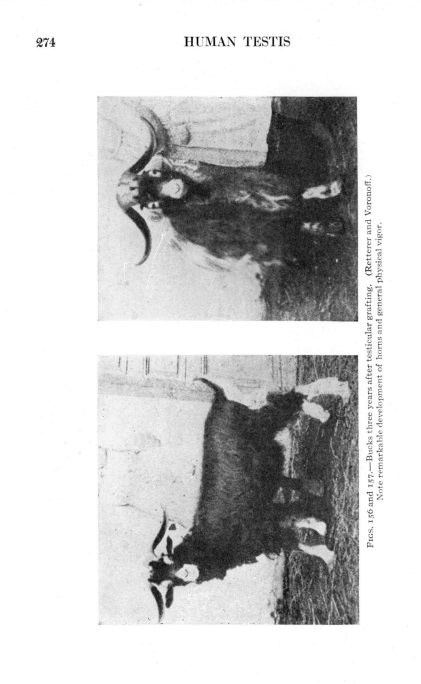

FIGS. 156 and 157.—Bucks three years after testicular grafting. (Retterer and Voronoff.) Note remarkable development of horns and general physical vigor.

specie. Their fleece is also longer and more abundant. Fig. 158 shows a small buck castrated at the age of two months, in which the horns had scarcely appeared. Fig. 159 shows the same animal at the age of six

FIG. 158.—Small buck castrated at age of two months. Here the horns have already made their appearance. (Retterer and Voronoff.)

FIG. 159.—Same animal at the age of six months after testicular grafting. Observe development of horns. (Retterer and Voronoff.)

months, and after the testicular grafts, with the horns normally developed. Fig. 160 shows a buck castrated at five months of age and photographed a year later (Fig. 161) with thick horns. The effect of the graft in these

FIG. 160.—Buck castrated at the age of five months. (Retterer and Voronoff.)

FIG. 161.—The same animal photographed a year later. Observe the remarkable development of the horns. (Retterer and Voronoff.)

castrated animals is not alone shown by the growth of the horns, but also by the general vigor, vivacity, combativity and general appearance showing lack of fatty invasion. A castrated animal subsequently transplanted, actually three years old, manifested, besides sexual desires, the same manifestations as if he had not undergone castration.

The effect of testicular grafting on old rams is not less striking. Figs. 162 and 163, known as ram No. 12, show the lamentable state of this old animal at the time of the graft and after transplantation. He was shaky in the limbs, and suffered from urinary incontinence owing to weakness of the vesical sphincter. He gave the impression of an animal exhausted by age and near the end of life. A graft was introduced in the right *tunica vaginalis* region above his own testicle. This graft consisted of four large fragments representing an entire testicle removed from a young ram. Some months later the animal was entirely transformed. There was no longer any shakiness, no incontinence, no dejected appearance. The general aspect was vivacious and aggressive with a remarkable appearance of youth and vigor. Soon after the grafting he was found

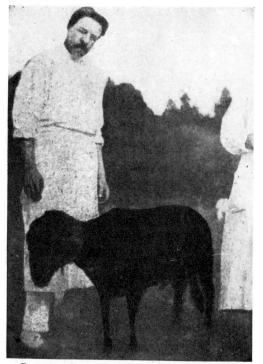

Fig. 162.—Aged ram before testicular transplantation. Note general attitude and depressed appearance of the animal. This ram is about 12 years old. (Retterer and Voronoff.)

Fig. 163.—Same animal a few months after testicular grafting. Note remarkable physical transformation. (Retterer and Voronoff.)

with a young sheep, which not alone showed a reawakening of sexual appetite and virility, which had been lost for some years, but also had a tangible result, as this sheep, isolated with this old ram for a month, bore a vigorous lamb in due course. The same result was obtained with ram No. 14, as old and miserable as the one just described. Figs. 164 and 165 show this animal before operation, and the effects of the grafting of a young testicle from an animal of the same species, a year after the operation.

FIG. 164.—Old ram before testicular grafting. (Retterer and Voronoff.)

In order to avoid any possibility of error, and to verify if the energy and sexual vigor displayed by these old animals was really due to the testicular graft, Voronoff removed the grafted gland from ram No. 12. Three months after removal, this formidable vigorous-looking animal aged with a disconcerting rapidity and again became docile and timorous. Six months later he was again a senile and melancholy-looking beast. A new testicular graft was then again made, and the effect was not long in becoming manifest. Once again he stood forth vigorously, with his head high. The sheep which had borne a lamb to this ram after his first grafting was

FIG. 165.—The same animal one year after transplantation of a testicle of a young animal of the same species. (Retterer and Voronoff.)

again isolated with him and bore a second lamb eight months after the second graft, which proved that the sheep had been mounted following the second graft.

These experiments were repeated on a number of other animals, either those castrated or afflicted with old age, and the results never failed when the grafting was done under good conditions, without resulting in suppuration or necrosis of the graft. In ram No. 15, a castrated and grafted animal, the same procedure of removal of the graft and re-grafting was done as in the case of No. 12, and the same effects were noted. All the grafts gave experimental confirmation of the stimulating effects of the testicular hormone and verified that the internal secretion of the testicle was the source of the energy and characters characteristic of virility.

In the grafts practiced by Voronoff he observed the viability of the cortical portions of the transplants, only the central portions were found to be necrotic. Microscopically the cycle of evolution in the transplant is different from that observed normally. A *syncytium* results which later becomes a *reticulum*. The cytoplasm becomes differentiated into (1): a fine reticulated tissue which shows an affinity for hematoxylin (*reticulum hematoxylinophile*); and, (2) a clear mass seen in the meshes of said network, the *hyaloplasma*. No mitoses were observed by these observers in the intertubular tissues. It is, therefore, they concluded, not the interstitial tissues that give rise to the apparent increase in volume of the interstitium.

These investigators furnish a number of illustrations showing the changes found by them in the transplants spoken of. A study of these, herewith produced, will aid in clearly understanding their interpretations. (Figs. 166–169.)

Steinach's transplantation experiments demonstrated that the internal secretion of the sex glands acts in a sex specific manner, *i.e.*, the male gonad furthers the development only of male sex characters and inhibits the development of female sex characters; whereas the female gonad furthers the development of female sex characters and inhibits development of male sex characters.

By the simultaneous transplantation of an ovary and a testis in castrated young male animals Steinach succeeded in producing a hermaphroditic condition. By transplanting ovarian tissue in castrated males and testes in females he succeeded in " feminizing" males and " masculinizing" females; that is to say, the animals, while showing the external sexual organs of males or females, developed the opposite secondary sexual characteristics and behaved in a manner corresponding to these character-

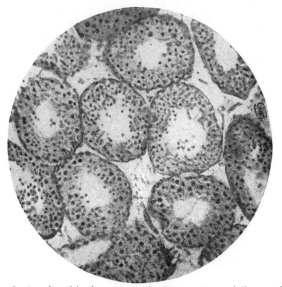

Fig. 166.—Section of testicle of a young buck. Between the seminiferous tubules that had not as yet developed spermatozoids the connective tissue is only slightly developed. (Retterer and Voronoff.)

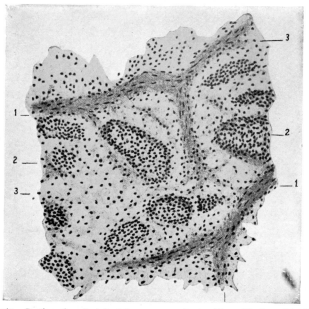

Fig. 167.—Portion of grafted testicle one year after grafting. (Ocul. 1; obj. 7.) Stiassnie. 1.1 fibrous strands; 2.2, remnants of seminiferous tubules; 3.3, reticulated tissue with wide meshes. (Retterer and Voronoff.)

istics. The experimental results were then observed for three years and
Steinach found that his " feminized " males had smaller and thinner bones
than their sisters; the " masculinized " females were longer and heavier

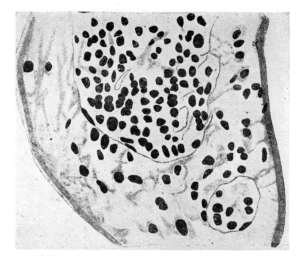

FIG. 168.—Two seminiferous tubules of the preceding preparation; showing the reticular tissue
between the tubules. Ocular 6; obj. Immersion 1/15th° Stiassnie. (Retterer and Voronoff.)

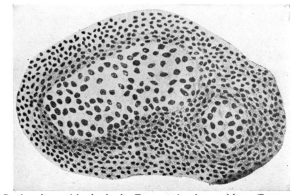

FIG. 169.—Portion of a testicle of a buck. Two months after grafting. (Retterer and Voronoff.)

than normal males. These results were denoted by Steinach as " hyper-
feminization " and " hyper-masculinization."

In the hermaphrodites the sex cycles alternated, the animals sometimes acting as males and sometimes as females. Steinach concluded that
the internal secretions of the gonads acted as a differentiating factor

sufficiently strong to cause deviation from the common path of somatic growth and to stimulate the development of sex characters.

Lipschütz has been able to verify Steinach's findings in animals in regard to the sex specific action of the internal secretion of the sexual glands. Examining the external urogenital organs of a female guinea pig operated on a few years before by testicular transplantation, which showed in weight, size and proportions of its body, and in its sexual behavior, all signs of a successful masculinization, Lipschütz observed the following changes: In the place of the small urethral tubercle, *i.e.*, the prominence at the uretheral opening in the female, there was a long fold of skin. It differed from a normal male preputium only by a slit in the under side. On drawing back this fold two red excrescences were seen, which, in their mutual position, in their color and in their dimensions were just like normal *corpora cavernosa* penis. The length of these excrescences was about 5 to 8 cms. No doubt through the action of the internal secretion of the implanted testis the *corpus cavernosum* of the clitoris had grown and changed into *corpora cavernosa* penis.

Near the increased *corpora cavernosa clitoridis* of the masculinized female there were also developed two horny spikes similar to those seen in the cavity of the intromittent sac of the *corpora cavernosa urethræ* of the normal male.

Thus it can be said that the implanted testis had evoked a transformation of the clitoris into a penis-like organ in the organism of a female. The findings suggest that the homology of two organs means the possibility of a mutual transformation, either by furtherance or inhibition.

The changes occurring in testicular tissue (especially in the Leydig interstitial cells), following testicular transplants in the peritoneal cavity of the same animals, the testes being removed from the normal situation in the scrotum, divided into small portions and scattered upon the peritoneum, have been investigated by Massaglia.[25] These experiments indicated that it was occasionally, but by no means always, possible to graft testicular substance upon the peritoneum in roosters. When a successful graft was made the tissue after some time underwent degenerative changes that involved all the elements of the testicular structure. With the progress of the degeneration changes the sexual instinct diminished. Since the degenerative changes involved all the testicular substance it was not possible for Massaglia to clearly distinguish which of the two, the Leydig cells or the epithelium of the seminiferous tubules, gave rise to the internal secretion.

In Bolognesi's [21] experimental testicular grafts in animals he endeavored to separate the seminal from the interstitial elements of the testicle. In previous experimental work Bolognesi, by an operation termed "total epididymo-deferentectomy," had demonstrated that sometimes it was possible to obtain complete transformations of the seminal epithelium with hyperplasia and hypertrophy of the interstitial cells such that the testicle was reduced to the condition of a small organ containing only interstitial tissue. This condition Bolognesi called an *interstitialoma,* a term which had previously been employed by Diamare.[22] The operation has for its basis the fact demonstrated by Alessandri,[23] that compression of the tunica vaginalis of the testicle and of the vasculo-nervous funicular supply causes seminal atrophy. By this operation Bolognesi considered that he obtained, without doubt, testicles reduced to interstitial tissue alone and fit for the investigation of the problem which he proposed to solve, *i.e.,* whether the sexual characters were referable to the seminal or to the interstitial portion of the gland. Barnabó [24] had, some years before, transplanted in castrated rabbits, testicles previously operated upon by resection of the vas deferens and which, consequently, contained an abundance of interstitial tissue. From his experiments Barnabó found hypophysary hypertrophy, due to the castration, persisted, although this is usually prevented by the transplantation of normal testicles. This result confirmed Barnabó's doubt that to the interstitial cells and to them alone belonged the elaboration of the internal testicular secretion.

Bolognesi's experiments consisted of two series. In the first, normal fragmental testicular transplants were made in guinea pigs, dogs and rabbits, the grafts being transplanted subcutaneously in the abdomen, in the testicular vaginal tunic, and the peritoneal serosa. In the second series the same kind of transplants were made, but instead of using normal testicular tissue Bolognesi used testicles reduced to interstitialomata.

From the first series of experiments Bolognesi found that when the graft "takes" it undergoes rapid transformation and resorption of all the seminiferous tissue with simultaneous hyperplasia and hypertrophy of the testiculo-interstitial tissue into large groups of giant-cells.

From his second series of experiments Bolognesi observed no modifications in the general condition of the grafted animal. Old animals unfit for reproduction remained so after the graft. There was no renewal of sexual instinct where such had been lost. Bolognesi also found that the interstitial tissue transplanted (*interstitialoma*) became rapidly reduced to a small nucleus of fibrous connective tissue traversed by areolar connective tissue and by ordinary glandular tissue; within a short space of time the interstitial cells themselves had, in fact, completely disappeared. The animals in which such grafts had been made did not show any modifications.

Bolognesi considered that seminal atrophy was accentuated by the interstitial transplant.

Bolognesi, therefore, from his experiments concluded that in order to obtain the beneficial results of testicular transplantation, grafting of the *entire gland* is necessary. He thinks further that the semen is not alone a product of external secretion, but that physiologically it can be absorbed by the lymphatics and contribute to sexual characters. He believes that in some of his experimental epididymo-deferentectomies, where the testicle became a closed gland, there was a freshing of sexual characters and desires. Bolognesi refuses to admit any value whatever of the interstitial testicular tissue in whatever regards the beneficial action of the testicular graft.

Bolognesi's experiments were repeated by the author with Bolognesi's technic, in which event the findings corresponded, but when the author's technic was used the results were entirely different. (Cf. Chapter on Technic.) The author believes that the site of implantation, the pressure to which the implant is subjected, and a number of other factors have a great deal to do with the results obtained. In other words, Bolognesi's grafts, undoubtedly, have been subjected to a great deal of pressure and he obtained therefore, in a measure, the results of Alessandri.

BIBLIOGRAPHY

[1] BERTHOLD: Transplantation d. Hoden. Arch. f. Anat. u. Physiol., 1849, p. 42.

[2] MANTEGAZZA: Della vitalité dei hemasperimi della rana e d. trapiantament dei testicolc da un animale all'attro., 1860.

[3] LODE: Wien. Klin. Wchnschr., 1895, viii, 345.

[4] GOEBELL: Centralbl. f. Allg. Pathol., 1898, ix, 737.

[5] RIBBERT: Arch. f. Entwickelungsmech., vi, H. I., 131.

[6] HERLITZKA: Arch. ital. di Biol. Turin., 1899, xxxii, 274.

[7] FOGES: Wien. Klin. Wchnschr., 1899, xii, 446.

[8] WAGNER: Pflügers Arch., lxv.

[9] SELLHEIM: Beitr. z. Geburts. u. Gynäk., 1918, H.2., 1.

[10] FOÁ: Arch. ital. di Biol. Turin., 1901, xxxv, 337.

[11] OBOLENSKY: Centralbl. f. med. Wissensch., 1867, p. 297.

[12] HARMS: Pflügers Arch., 1909, cxxviii; Exper. Untersuch. u. d. inn. Sec. d. Keimdrüsen. Fischer. Jena, 1914.

[13] BOUIN and ANCEL: Jour. de Physiol., 1904, vi, 1012.

[14] MEYNS: Arch. f. d. ges. Physiol., 1910, cxxxii, 433.

[15] GUTHRIE: Jour. Exper. Med., 1910, xii.

[16] CEVOLOTTO: Frank. Zeitschr. f. Chir., 1909, cxi, 331.

[17] STEINACH: Pflügers Arch., 1894, lvi; Pflügers Arch., 1912, cxliv, 71; Verjüngung durch experimentelle Neubelebung der alternden Pubertätsdrüse, 1920.

[18] KNUD SAND: Jour. de Physiol. gén., 1921, xix, 305; Acta. Chirurg, Scand., 1922, lv, 387.

[19] VORONOFF: Rev. de Chir., 1919, lvii, 697.

[20] VORONOFF and RETTERER: Jour. d'urol. med. et chir., 1922, xiv, 81.

[21] BOLOGNESI: Arch. ital. di chir., 1921; Jour. d'urol. med et chir., 1921.

[22] DIAMARE: Archiv. di ostet. e ginec., 1920.

[23] ALESSANDRI: Policlin., Rome, 1897, iv, C., 145.

[24] BARNABÓ: Policlin., Rome, 1908, xv, Sez. Chir., 134; Policlin., Rome, 1912, xix, Sez. Chir., 116.

[25] MASSAGLIA: Endocrinology, 1920, iv, 547.

CHAPTER VII

STEINACH'S VASOLIGATION EXPERIMENTS AND SO-CALLED REJUVENATION OPERATION

It has been the good fortune of the author to examine the results, both gross and microscopic, obtained by Professor Steinach in the latter's laboratories in Vienna, Austria. The invitation of Steinach to the author to witness the technic of vasoligation as practiced on the human by Steinach, was taken advantage of cheerfully. This will be referred to in the course of the following pages. It is needless to remind the reader that Steinach aside from being a pioneer in the study of sex-gland implantation has greatly enriched medical literature on sex-problems and allied subjects.

Vasoligature has been known as an experiment for more than a century. The first experiments date from 1785 (Brugnone [1]) and were continued later by a series of investigations (Cooper,[2] Brissaud,[3] Griffiths,[4] etc.), but it was not until the experimental work of Bouin and Ancel [5] in 1903 that the foundations were laid, not only for the question of the inner secretory functions of the tissue of the testicles, but for that which, properly speaking, forms the basis of the views which caused Steinach to use the operation in his experiments concerning " rejuvenation."

According to Bouin and Ancel, Griffiths, Wheelon, and others, ligation of the vas deferens results in cessation of spermatogenesis. Spermatocytes and spermatogonia degenerate, and after some months all spermatogenic elements disappear. At first there is apparently no change in the formation of the sustentacular (Sertoli) cells, but these, too, ultimately disappear. On the other hand, the interstitial cells retain their morphological and functional integrity; and, as long as these remain, alterations in the secondary sex characters do not occur. If they do disappear, the effects are the same as in castration.

The real purpose of vasoligature is that through it a *spermastasis* is created which, in a retrograde sense, causes a degeneration of the spermatic epithelium, *i.e.*, an atrophy of the whole spermatogenerative tissue, and subsequently a hypertrophy of the Leydig cells with a corresponding increase in hormonic production. Harms [6] has shown that it was possible

285

to almost entirely eliminate the spermatogenous tissue of the testis and at the same time (and probably on account of the hypertrophy of the Leydig cells) to retain and even intensify the sexual character (Cf. Chapter on Physiology and Function of Leydig Cells). Both in the ligature experimental work of Bouin and Ancel and the later work of Knud Sand [7] it was shown that the experimental animal became particularly virile with a most violent *libido sexualis,* a phenomenon which has lately been confirmed by Kuntz [8] (1921).

These facts form the basis of Steinach's [9] *theory of " rejuvenation."* From his investigations and observations, he drew the conclusion that the existence of the generative glands is the cause of the development and maintenance of the specifically masculine and feminine attributes of body and mind and of the secondary sex characters. He was further satisfied that the cause of sexual difference between the male and female lay in the interstitial cells, and that the internal secretion of these cells is responsible for sexual differentiation and for the phenomena of puberty. He termed the interstitial gland the *puberty gland.* By animal experiments, Steinach satisfied himself further that this internal secretion acted on the central nervous system through the circulation and gave rise to what he termed *erotization.*

In old rats, Steinach observed that after ligation of one or both *vasa deferentia* in the space between the testicle and the head of the epididymis, certain changes were noted in these animals within a few weeks. They lost their apathy, became lively, their fur grew dense and shiny, they looked like young males, and acted as such toward females. These old animals, who before ligation had lost the sexual and procreative power, were now, in case that only one vas had been ligated, able to procreate strong and healthy young. Life was, moreover, prolonged one-fourth of its usual span.

According to Steinach's researches, reactivation of the " puberty gland" leads to rejuvenation, procreative capacity and fruitfulness, both in males and females. This activation of the puberty gland is called by Steinach the *autoplastic treatment of old age.* If the rejuvenated " puberty gland " becomes exhausted, Steinach, by means of implantation of young testicles, succeeds again in increasing the energy of life, and this he calls the *homoplastic treatment of old age.* Improvement in the method by means of different combinations of the autoplastic and homoplastic procedures, with the object of postponing senility as long as possible, is the field in which further progress must be expected to take place with this procedure.

The immediate consequence of ligation of the vas deferens is a spermastasis, with absorption of the sperm contained within the testes as the result of the closure of the efferent ducts. A gradual atrophy of the spermatogenetic tissue follows. With the exception of the basal cells, all cells participate in this atrophic process; but, at the same time, a compensatory stimulation of the interstitial cells of Leydig is histologically evident. The histological picture is practically the same as that of a transplanted testicle with increase of the interstitial cells.

Wheelon [13] occluded, and *resected the right vas* in dogs, and examined the testis nine months later. On the operated side, the testicle showed that the seminiferous tubules, although the seat of some destructive processes, contained much spermatic tissue; sperm heads were readily identified, and in places spermatids were seen. The interstitial tissue in each gland seemed to be somewhat increased. The left gland appeared entirely normal. Wheelon's experiments do not, therefore, support the view that ligation destroys spermatogenesis in the testicle. Later Retterer and Voronoff arrived at the same conclusion.

Steinach described two types of intervention: (1) ligation of the vas deferens where it merges with the epididymis; and (2) ligature of the *ductuli efferentes* (*coni vasculosi*) between the head of the epididymis and the upper pole of the testis. This latter leaves the blood vessels supplying the testicle unimpaired. The important part of the technic consists in the exposure of the vas and its very careful dissection (with the ductus) from the fine arteries, veins and nerves connected with it and the testis. About 2 to 3 cms. of the ductus is resected.

Steinach's operation is only applied organotherapy, the patient being supplied with gonadal incretion prepared in his own testis and arousing a reaction of all other endocrines in the organism by the increased activity of the sexual hormone.

Steinach's operation might be regarded as indicated in patients the endocrinological examination of whom suggests *dysgonadism or hypogonadism*. The most suitable subjects are those with healthy organs who are growing prematurely old and who at the same time show loss of function by the impairment of secondary sexual characters.

Steinach formulated *contraindications* for the operation as follows:

(1) Well preserved power to produce spermatozoa.

(2) To be applied to excitable or nervously disturbed patients with great caution.

(3) Enlargement of the prostate.

(4) The existence of other organic causes for premature old age.

(5) Occlusion of vas deferens by previous disease.

(6) Deterioration of the secondary sex characters owing to a chronic disease of a different nature.

Lichtenstern,[14] with Steinach's coöperation, applied the method to man and reported improvements in five out of seven cases operated.

Kurt Mendel,[15] who carefully followed Steinach's method in a certain case, reported, however, that the result in this instance was disastrous. Mental disturbances followed the operation, as well as sexual aberrations. This patient had to be committed to an asylum for the insane.

Tiedje[16] also attacks the Steinach operation, and he thinks that the rejuvenation is only an effect of sexual superexcitation due to increase of albuminoids from the seminal cells.

Benjamin[17] and Wolbarst[18] have, however, both spoken highly of the results of the Steinach operation. Benjamin says that about 40 per cent. of cases of senility are positively regenerated objectively and subjectively. Wolbarst reported seven cases of actual senility operated on, with four patients showing a material benefit, continued from six to seven months, following operation. In five cases, also of premature senility, satisfactory results were obtained in three. Wolbarst considers that the operation has been distinctly advantageous to the patients who have been submitted to it, and there is reason to think that in the prematurely senile cases the sexual function has been materially stimulated.

Knud Sand has performed eighteen clinical vasoligatures in Copenhagen since 1920. The patients are divided by Sand into two classes:

(1) Senile patients, or those with a *senium precox*.

(2) Patients in whom some condition other than senility was the operative indication.

The technic employed by Sand was an *epididymectomy*. Right up at the caput several cms. of the epididymis were freed minutely but without injury to the fine vessels and nerves, all of which have importance in the nutrition of the testis. After the isolation a pair of Kocher crushing forceps is placed at each end, the interjacent space is resected, the ends strongly ligated and cauterized.

None of the patients have complained of any bad consequences from the operation. The time of observation has varied from about three to twenty-one months.

In considering the effects of vasoligature it is easy to understand that the organism of one patient, particularly his testicular tissue, is still comparatively healthy and able to regenerate, and that the organism of another may be in such a poor state that it is unfitted for any new process and the testicular tissue is unifluenced by a vasectomy.

Of thirteen patients in Group I, two gave negative results; one of these suffered from a condition of depression, perhaps melancholia, the other was a syphilitic. In two cases there was a temporary good result. The other nine cases gave favorable results to a greater or lesser degree; in some this result was astonishingly good.

In the five cases comprising Group II in which the operation was done for impotency, etc., there was one negative result. The other four cases gave a greater or lesser positive result.

Sand expresses his opinion of the value of the operation with reserve. He thinks that vasoligature (performed as an epididymectomy) is an operation free from danger and harmless, which, in cases of senility and impotency with depression, has sometimes given a negative result, but in others improvement, and in a number of cases astonishingly good results.

The visions raised in the popular press by the unfortunate denomination of " rejuvenation " must be dropped; and the work directed to more modest claims and ends which may be of value to the sick and suffering.

Steinach emphasizes the interdependence of the development of growth and the secondary sex characteristics as well as the psychic sex characteristics on the presence of the sex glands or on sex gland implantation. A great series of experiments brought out the fact that the sexual act is only possible after " erotization " of certain centres in the central nervous system, and that this erotization is the direct result of a chemical action

19

through the internal secretion of the testes, particularly of the interstitial elements of the male sex gland.   In collaboration with Holzknecht, Steinach was able to destroy the generative elements of the sexual gland through the action of the X-rays and in the same manner to increase the growth

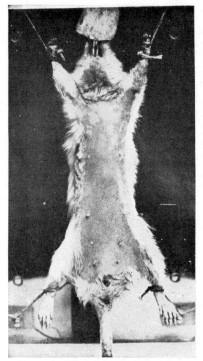 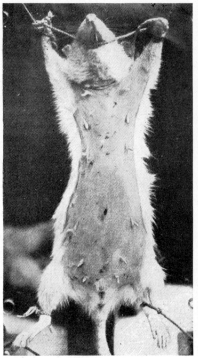

Fig. 170.—Before testicular implantation.   Fig. 171.—After testicular implantation.
(Senility.)   (Steinach.)   (Steinach.)

of the interstitial tissue.   This resulted in precocious puberty and hyper-feminization of the female animals.   In this manner these investigators think to have demonstrated the influence of the interstitial tissues on the somatic development of the experimental animals.   Steinach was able to transform female animals into males and *vice versa,* and he also succeeded in artificially producing hermaphroditism.   (Figs. 170–177.)

Peter Schmidt of Berlin, who has had quite a good deal of experience in following up Steinach's work, in a recent contribution expresses himself in part as follows: " The results of Steinach's investigations were too new

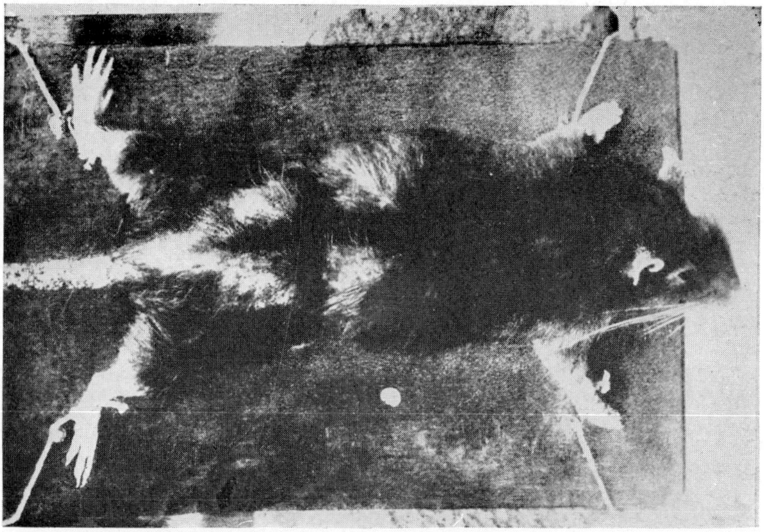

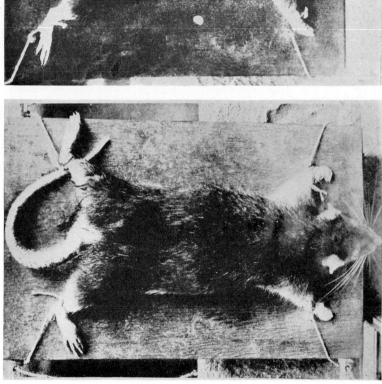

Fig. 172.—Senile appearance of rat before operation. (Steinach.)

Fig. 173.—Rejuvenated appearance of rat after operation. (Steinach.)

and too obvious to pass without creating comment. Like all new dis-
coveries, it had many champions and equally many adversaries. However,
the number of the former throughout the world is at present so large that
the voice of the latter pales into insignificance. Antagonism of that type
did not only exist in the lay world but also among the disciples of the
healing art who are bound to forget the proven biological studies and the

FIG. 174.—Senile rat before operation. (Steinach.)

FIG. 175.—Same rat after rejuvenation operation. (Steinach.)

tremendous labors of Steinach and his pupils. Very frequently the discussion of this theme has been made difficult or entirely void for many
who could not see anything else but a sexual question involved. Of
course, when Steinach wished to bring before us the rejuvenating effect of
his work on old rats it was necessary to objectively show the results of
increased sexual potency. While certain critics emphasize the impracticability of a comparison of the physiologic life of a rat with that of a man,
the only point of attack that remained to concentrate upon was the sexual
moment and to point out that the author would be unable to produce

evidence to show that the psychic life of the animal was in any way enchanced by his procedure."

He concludes by championing the feasibility of Steinach's work and the results obtained by others as well as himself from a therapeutic point of view, and propounds the following question: " Does the interstitial substance of the sex gland, be it through implantation of the sex gland of

FIG. 176.—Masculinization. (Steinach.)   Masculinated sister; castrated sister; normal sister; normal brother.

FIG. 177.—Feminization. (Steinach.) Castrated brother; normal virgin sister; feminated brother; normal brother.

the same species as practiced by Steinach and Harms, or through the ligation method as practiced by Steinach, produce any action on the development and perpetuation of the somatic and psychic sex characteristics?" This question he answers by giving a table and quoting the work of the results of Steinach, Sand, Lipschütz, Harms, Voronoff, Moore, Morgan and Boring, Massaglia, Goodale, Pézard, Athias, Heberlandt, and others, who were all able to answer the question in the affirmative through their experiments on animals. The same answer has been obtained by experiments on man by Lichtenstern, Mühsam, Lydston, Kreuter, Hocker, Faramiti, and others.

" Regeneration " by vasoligation, Schmidt says, has been obtained on animals by Steinach, Sand, Tiedje, Berblinger and Kuntz. On humans by Steinach, Lichtenstern, Levy-Lenz, Peter Schmidt, Loewy and Zondek, Finsterer, Rychlik, Chetwood, Kramer, and others. A splendid bibliography accompanies Peter Schmidt's brochure.

Summarizing the answers, it seems that in a great many instances transplantation is successful and according to the authors quoted vasoligation also gives positive results. The opponents of Steinach's theory and work emphasize *first:* that vasoligation causes spermastasis and increased spermatogenesis, and that the spermatogenetic tissue results in resorption of albuminous by-products. *Second:* that the interstitial tissue (the Leydig cells) is a purely trophic cell and that hormone production depends upon the germinative tissue and continues as long as spermatogenesis or resorption of the products above alluded to persist.

As stated at the beginning of this chapter, the author had the good fortune to visit Steinach in his laboratories and to watch the performance of his vasoligation operation, and also to study the specimens, both gross and microscopic, of his artificial sexualization or sex transformation, and also the results of his transplantations and vasoligation. Steinach emphasized to the author that while excellent results are obtained from vasoligation in selected cases, in some cases *transplantation is the method preferred,* all depending entirely upon the clinical manifestations in a given case and a thorough study of indications, clinical phases, etc., etc. In these views the author concurs most emphatically. The accompanying photographs of specimens examined by the author show the effects obtained by Steinach in rats after vasoligation as well as homo- and hetero-transplantation.

Very recently Macht and Teagarden,[22] of Johns Hopkins University, have performed the Steinach operation on six rats. All of these were senile and showed most of the manifestations of old age. Control animals were used to compare the results. Fourteen other animals were also operated on ostensibly to ascertain the results on these experimental animals and compare them with those obtained by Steinach and others. The greatest possible care was exercised in checking up the results from the rats operated on and from the control animals. After the operation a number of the rats showed distinct improvement in general appearance and

behavior. They were more active, and the observation made by Steinach
that the animals operated on by him developed new fur have been confirmed on some of the animals operated on by Macht and Teagarden.
However, the changes noted by these observers lasted only several weeks,
and the experimental animals regressed to their former senile state. Dis-

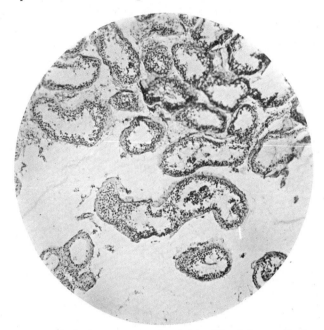

FIG. 178.—Testis of man 74 years. Scanty interstitium before vasoligation.
(Author's observation.)

tinct changes of improvement in muscular coördination and muscular
efficiency were also noted in the animals experimented upon, but this
also lasted a few weeks. The changes observed in these animals are
attributed by the experimenters to the operation that they have performed;
however, this statement they qualify by saying that more experiments are
necessary to enable them to positively assure them. The author experimented on the higher apes and operated on a number of humans, according
to Steinach's dicta, and he obtained, in some cases, good results; in others
again the results were disappointing. Figures 178 and 179, represent the
results in one of the author's cases on a human. In this instance prior to

vasoligation a great scantiness of the interstitial tissue was found, followed by an augmentation of growth four months after operation.

AUTHOR'S CONCLUSIONS

(1) I am opposed to the term " rejuvenation." It is misleading and

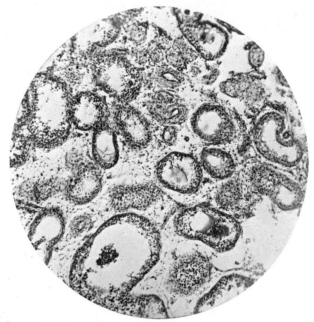

FIG. 179.—Same testis as in previous microphotograph after vasoligation. Note remarkable in-crease of interstitial elements, 7.5x16. Magnified 105 diameters. (Author's observation.)

may create a great deal of harm, particularly with the laity who are bound to exaggerate.

(2) More clinical data from unbiased sources are necessary to form definite opinions. Human data are the only reliable criteria, because what may hold true in the lower forms of mammalia may often be found reversed in the human.

(3) Clinical evidence supported by laboratory checking will in due time establish the merits or demerits of the Steinach procedure. Presently a mass of evidence is inclined to pessimism, although some good results are reported from some quarters.

BIBLIOGRAPHY

[1] BRUGNONE: Quoted by A. Bertrandi. Opera. Anat., Torino, 1786.

[2] COOPER: Observations on Structure and Diseases of Testicle, London, 1841.

[3] BRISSAUD: Arch. de physiol. normale, 1880, vii, 769.

[4] GRIFFITHS: Jour. Anat. and Physiol., 1895–6, xxx, 81.

[5] BOUIN and ANCEL: J. de Physiol., Par., 1904, vi, 1039.

[6] HARMS: Fortschr. d. Naturwiss., Forsch., 1922, xi.

[7] KNUD SAND: Acta. Chirug. Scand., 1922, lv, 387.

[8] KUNTZ: Endocrinology, 1921, v, No. 2.

[9] STEINACH: Verjüngung durch experimentelle Neubelebung der Alternden Pubertätsdrüse, Berlin, 1920.

[10] STEINACH: Geschlechtstrieb und Innersecretorische Function der Keimdrüsen. Zentralbl. f. Physiol., 1910, xxiv.

[11] STEINACH: Feminisirung von Männchen und Maskulirung von Weibchen. Zentralbl. f. Physiol., 1916, xlii.

[12] STEINACH: Pubertätsdrüsen und Zwitterbildung. Arch. f. Entwickel., Mech., 1916, xlii.

[13] WHEELON: Endocrinology, 1921, v, 307.

[14] LICHTENSTERN: Berl. Klin. Wchnschr., 1920, No. 42.

[15] MENDEL: Deut. Med. Wchnschr., 1921, xlvii, 986.

[16] TIEDJE: Deut. Med. Wchnschr., 1921, xlvii, 352.

[17] BENJAMIN: New York Med. Jour., 1922, cxvi, 203.

[18] WOLBARST: New York Med. Jour., 1922, cxv, 543.

[19] MASSAGLIA: Endocrinology, 1920, iv, 547.

[20] HARMS: Experimentelle Untersuchungen ueber die innere Sekretion der Keimdrüsen. Jena, Fischer, 1914.

[21] SCHMIDT: Theorie und Praxis der Steinachschen Operation. (Rikolo. Verlag. Wien.)

[22] MACHT, D. I., and TEAGARDEN, E. J., Jr.: Rejuvenation experiments with vasoligation in Rats, J. Urol., 10:407, November, 1923

CHAPTER VIII

THE SENILE TESTICLE

CURLING [1] appears to have been the first to give a definite description of the changes that occur in the testicle during, and as a consequence of, old age. Curling says: " As old age advances and the generative function ceases to be called into action the testicles undergo a diminution in size, their vessels grow less, and the seminiferous tubes become small, contracted and partly obliterated, their place being supplied by fatty matter."

In 1886 Arthaud published a thesis on the senile changes in the testicle. Arthaud devotes attention chiefly to the cystic formations that are found in many old persons in the globus major or head of the epididymis.

The next important contribution to the literature on the subject was that of Griffiths [2] in 1892. Griffiths observed that the bulk of the organ was not in most cases much altered, though in some it was so considerably. He saw one man ninety years old whose testicles were of normal size.

The testicles usually become softer and more flaccid and the tunics tend to become wrinkled. In the cases where the testicles were not much reduced in size, the internal structure was either soft and yellowish or granular and somewhat more firm than natural, the seminal tubules being less easily disentangled. In cases where the body of the testicle was much reduced in size there were large irregular-shaped fibrous patches scattered about, apparently containing no seminiferous tubules. The epididymis retained its normal size, but usually, in small, well-defined areas, its tubules (the *coni vasculosi*) were of a yellowish color like the seminal tubules, and occasionally in these altered patches and in other tubules of the head of the epididymis there were minute translucent cysts with clear fluid devoid of spermatozoa.

The yellowish color of the tubules of both testicle and epididymis is due to fatty degeneration of the epithelial contents of the tubules. Thus the chief and commonest change met with in the testicle of the aged, so far as can be determined by the naked eye, is fatty degeneration of the epithelial contents of the seminal tubules; but occasionally testicles are found that show transformation of their internal structure into patches of fibrous connective tissue.

298

Microscopical examination of the commonest type of testicles in the aged, and in which the organs are not much reduced in size, indicate two distinct stages in the retrogressive or involutive changes in this organ. (Fig. 180.)

In the earlier stage the changes in the tubules in both testicle and epididymis are but slight, except that fatty degeneration of the epithelial cells lining the seminal tubules is more or less pronounced. In Fig. 180, B., a transverse section of a seminal tubule is seen in which there is entire absence of the formation of spermatozoa in the cells and in the interior; and there is also a diminution of the number of the layers of cells lying within the contiguous peripheral one. The protoplasm of the cells is slightly granular, the granules being composed of fat. The degree of fatty degeneration is most pronounced in the cells lying just within the outer peripheral layer, in which latter degenerative changes are very slight.

In addition to this change, which is universal throughout the gland, there is another which accompanies it. This is the thickened and convoluted state of the *tunica propria*. In the normal testicle the *tunica propria* is a very thin membrane, whereas in the testicles of old men this membrane becomes several times thicker than it is originally and also becomes more fibrous in character. The convoluted disposition of this membrane corresponds with the diminution in the epithelial contents of the seminal tubules. There seems to be no increase in the intertubular connective tissue, but there is fatty degeneration of a few of the connective tissue cells and of those cells which may be regarded as the remains of the peculiar *interstitial* cells of this organ.

The second stage of degeneration is represented in Fig. 180, D. and E. The changes are mainly confined to the testicle. The seminal tubes are much reduced in size, the epithelium having in great part disappeared, the intratubular connective tissue is relatively increased and is loose in texture. Fig. 180, D., shows that there is only one layer of cells, which appear to be long columnar cells converging toward the centre of the tubule. These cells evidently represent the layer of cubical cells lying on the inner surface of the *tunica propria* of a normal tubule. The protoplasm is delicately fibrillated. The fibrillated protoplasm of the epithelial cells in the interior of the tubule often appears at first sight as if it were a continuation, or rather a prolongation, inward of the fibrillated matrix of the *tunica propria;*

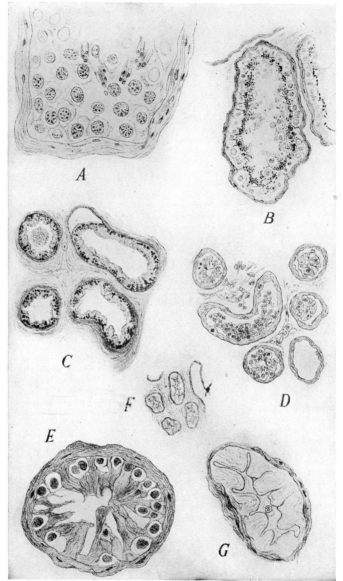

FIG. 180.—*a*, structural changes in testicle of aged persons. (After Joseph Griffith.) *b*, section of a seminal tubule from an aged man, showing disappearance of sperm producing cells and fatty degeneration. *c*, a section of testis showing the second stage in the changes that occur in old age. Seminal tubules reduced and epithelium only represented by a few cells; tunica much thickened. *d*, one of the foregoing tubules highly magnified. *e*, one of the tubules seen in foregoing figure, much magnified. *f*, section of fibrous patch in the testicle of an aged person. *g*, extreme magnification of foregoing figure.

but a careful examination will not fail to detect a sharply-defined line between the bases of the epithelial cells and the inner layer of that tissue.

Comment.—

The illustrations, while depicted with low magnification (Zeiss Komp. —Ok. 6. Apochrom. 8 mm.), have been subjected to higher magnification, Komp.—Ok. 18. The minute details, such as granulation of the protoplasm, distribution of chromatin, outline of cell bodies, etc., were controlled by careful drawings.

The changes that arise in the testicles of old men are, according to Griffiths, chiefly such as one would expect, confined to the epithelium of the seminal tubules. This diminishes in amount from fatty and other disintegrative degenerations of the cells which in great part disappear leaving only a single layer of columnar cells occupying the lumen.

More recent investigators have found that in the testicles of old men the interstitial cells are fewer and less voluminous than in the adult; Reinecke's crystalloids completely disappear and similarly for the other products of cellular activity. The senile interstitial gland shows progressive diminution, then abolition of the secretory activity and elaboration of abnormal (pigmentary) products.

Wheelon [3] thinks that in old men hypertrophy of the prostate is not normal, but that it may be the result of an overproduction of testicular hormone in combination with reduced external secretion.

Suppression of sexual activity in both men and women is frequently followed by the deposition of fat.

The final results of senescence as regards the testicle is more or less complete atrophy of both interstitial substance and seminiferous tubules as histologically exemplified in a case reported by Freiburg.[4]

In normal senescence, sexual power should be preserved till the seventieth or eightieth year, or even longer. After obliteration of the sper- matogenic cells the interstitial cells persist for a long time and hence *libido* outlasts generative power.

BIBLIOGRAPHY

[1] CURLING: Diseases of the Testes, 4th edit.
[2] GRIFFITHS: Jour. Anat. and Physiol., 1892, xxvii, 474.
[3] WHEELON: Endocrinology and Metabolism, 1922, ii, 480.
[4] FREIBURG: Lancet-Clinic, cxvl, p. 326.
[5] HALL: Senescence, 1922.

CHAPTER IX

THE MALE CLIMACTERIC

The word climacteric is derived from the Greek " Klimakter " meaning a step of a stair or ladder which was used to designate a dangerous period in life, and was originally equally applicable to either sex although it has been customary to apply it only in the case of the menopause in females.

It is an established anatomic fact that the early months of embryonic life show no sexual differentiation, and that the cellular elements that ultimately undergo variation and develop into the sexual apparatus of male and female are indifferently present in either sex, not only up to a certain period of intra-uterine life, but in a rudimentary form throughout the entire period of human existence.

Since it must be admitted that the sexes begin and end life in marked similarity, the period of differentiation commences at puberty, and this suggests that the second change, or the change that brings the sexes together again, occurs at about the same epoch after puberty in both sexes. At about the menopause age in woman, man also becomes unstable from a mental and nervous standpoint, and although he has no menstrual flux, as in the case of the female, he does show every other symptom, mental and physical, that characterizes the change in the female.

The man at this period has reached an age when functional vitality ceases to be sufficient to properly invigorate all his organism as in his younger days. He gives evidence of exhaustion in line with the physiological law that the last to develop is the first to show evidence of decadence. The man has reached his climacteric.

Sanctorius [1] seems to have been the first to mention the climacteric in connection with men in 1728. From the standpoint of body weight he found that in men there was a monthly increase of one or two pounds, followed by an increase in urinary output and accompanied by lassitude and a feeling of heaviness; this suggested a monthly cycle in the organism of men.

According to A. Church [2] the monthly increase of weight in men was confirmed by Belfield of Chicago who also observed a phosphaturia analogous to that experienced by women just before menstruation.

The accepted real climacteric period of menopause, which may be regarded as coinciding with life's full maturity, is a well recognized event in the life of women, but it is not so generally appreciated that men go through a similar readjustment of tissues, though after a less dramatic method and probably at a somewhat later age. The cessation of menstruation in women results from the functional death of the ovaries; it is usually accompanied by disturbance of the vasomotor and nervous systems as well as being a time of special liability to the development of disease or for the manifestations of disease previously more or less latent. In men, at a period of life from about seven to ten years later than the onset of the menopause in women, there is a similar liability to the awakening or arousing of latent diseases, and there seems to be at that period, just as is the case in women, an upset in tissue equilibrium conducive to the establishment of pathological conditions.

Halford [2] in 1831 noticed and described conditions in men which he termed climacteric diseases. Others asserted that there were rhythmic changes in the blood pressure in both sexes at definite periods. That some relation existed between certain critical ages in life and the activity of the sexual functions has long been maintained. In both male and female the fifteenth year corresponded approximately to puberty and in women the forty-second or forty-ninth year is not uncommonly the date of the menopause.

In man at the age of sixty-three—his *grand climacteric*—some assume that owing to the *cessation or marked diminution of the activity of the testicles* a profound change takes place in the body, and that this change corresponds closely to that supposedly dependent on the more sudden alteration in the function of the ovaries at the menopause in women.

An editorial in the *Journal of the American Medical Association,*[3] in discussing the male climacteric, remarks " that certain tolerably characteristic symptoms, not unlike those presented by women in the change of life, are undoubtedly manifest in many men about the age of sixty-three will be vouched for not only by physicians in general practice but also particularly by nerve specialists to whom these patients turn for relief. Attention has been focused on these symptoms by Mendel [4] when he speaks of the ' climacterium virile,' with lack of emotional control and a tendency to shed tears, combined with outspoken signs of depression, disinclina-

tion for exertion, lack of will power, and irritation; other symptoms sometimes prominent being dizziness, sense of pressure in head, hot flushes and
palpitation of the heart."

In connection with these observations the question at once arises
whether these symptoms are, in reality, due to a disturbance in the internal
secretion of the testicles, or whether they can be the result of the arteriosclerosis which develops almost with regularity at about this age; and if
there may not be a relation between testicular function and vascular
integrity in the male. Such questions are not easy to answer.

The defenders of the doctrine of the sexual origin of the male climacteric point to the nervous, emotional and vasomotor phenomena which
follow castration analogous to menopause symptoms which are brought
about artificially in women by bilateral oöphorectomy. The objection that
the natural male climacteric may depend upon arteriosclerosis rather than
upon retrogression of the activity of the sexual glands is met by the argument that the arteries are not always sclerosed when the climacteric symptoms are met in man; and that when they are, such sclerosis might be
considered as evidence of the importance of the internal secretion of the
testicles for the normal regulation of the circulatory apparatus and for the
welfare of the general metabolism.

Other opinions while regarding the symptom referred to as dependent
upon anomalies of internal secretion suggest that they owe their origin, not
to changes in the functions of the testicles alone, but in addition, to alteration in the activities of other related glands, notably the prostate. It seems
unquestionable that some functional connection exists between the prostate
and the testicles.

Studies by Paul [5] indicate that prostatic enlargement in advanced life
is a retrogressive process, comparable perhaps to the chronic atrophic or
inflammatory changes in the female breast at the menopause.

The large amount of investigations carried out within very recent years
showing the nature and functions of the internal secretion of the interstitial cells of the testicle renders it extremely probable that the climacteric changes in the organism of man are mainly dependent upon changes in
this secretion. The senile organism manifestations are generally accompanied by impotency even though sexual desire persists. The diminution of
vital capacity, with lessened activity of secretory and excretory vigor, is a

clinical manifestation that life has crossed its summit and that the bodily organism has entered upon the downward grade of its duration.

Acute illness in man or woman occurring within the limits of the climacteric is attended with more than the usual risks, the resisting powers of the organism being then apparently less competent to battle with infective or toxic invasion. But it is the chronic ailments existing at this period of life that demand the closest attention and interest. There are certain of them that, on account of their frequency, stand out conspicuously. Growths of all kinds, previously slow, at this time show great activity. Arteriosclerosis, interstitial nephritis, and diabetes form a group of diseases which with surprising frequency become manifest in men between the age of fifty-five and sixty-five. These conditions no doubt existed for a long time, but probably their development was checked by agencies charged with general defensory powers as well as with the maintenance of virility in the organism. The weakening of such defences at the period of the climacteric gives these chronic ailments referred to full opportunity to progress unchecked. The man may not feel ill but he is easily tired and quite unfit for the amount of exertion previously habitual to him. Although he eats and digests fairly, he fails to keep his nutrition to the correct mark, and he looks emaciated. He no longer has the same grip on things for which he was previously conspicuous.

In such men a process of sclerosis is probably being effected which reacts on the particular tissues determined by personal tendencies or inherited qualities. The common antecedent in all cases is strain, continued almost incessantly for fifty years. Domestic traits, financial worries, emotional storms, and mental anxieties, enter into the lives of those who are strenuous and ambitious to achieve worldly success. The stress and strain fall primarily upon the nervous centres, which become devitalized and unable to control organic functions.

None of the organs of nutrition and elimination are any longer equal to their task, a fact which is all the more important seeing that many such men have been habitually good eaters and that but few have taken exercise of any kind. The slowed nutrition, auto-intoxication, and the diminished vitality with neuropathic symptoms are the manifest symptoms of the failure of some governing power regulating the organic processes, and

20

which, as stated, are most probably, as far as our present knowledge goes, connected with the failure of internal secretions.

Neurologists are too prone to concentrate attention upon the psychical aspect of these cases, but what the patient needs is careful advice concerning the nature of the male climacteric and the changes that accompany it.

The good effects which in many cases have followed testicular transplantations in the senile, point to this method of therapy combined with proper treatment of existing pathologic states as that which offers the most hopeful relief in this field. (Cf. Chapter on Clinical Cases.)

Thewlis [6] refers to a typical case of the senile climacteric in a man of seventy-three years. In this case the principal change observed was in the mentality. Mental deterioration proceeded rapidly but irregularly, the usual mental attitude being agitated depression. This man also showed sexual recrudescence, the object of his sexual desires being a middle-aged married woman. Six months after the initial manifestations of the senile climacteric in this patient he is passing out of this period into the somatic state of senility and the mental state of senile dementia. His appearance bears out the statements of his friends that he aged ten years in six months. His bearing is less erect; he has lost weight; his face is wrinkled; his expression is apathetic; he is careless about his person, etc.; his walk is slower. The degenerative changes have been quite uniform.

During the climacteric this man showed maniacal outburst, periods of depression and amentia; there were delusions, hallucinations and phobias with lucid intervals. The mental aberrations gradually disappeared, leaving a weakened mind, the true dementia. The sexual recrudescence has entirely subsided.

Thewlis says that the senile climacteric, being one of the physiologic critical periods, cannot be prevented, nor need anything be done if the mental and physical deteriorations proceed uniformly and no active or distressing manifestations appear.

Therapy.—

In considering the therapy of individuals suffering from the effects of testicular retrogression and consequent clinical manifestations resulting in the symptom complex discussed in this chapter, two indications for treatment present themselves. In the first place, a thorough investigation of the physical status of the patient is essential. We must endeavor to eliminate the presence of organic disease of all sorts and rectify metabolic digressions which in themselves may give rise to symptoms analogous to those under consideration, in which case it would, of course, be wrong to advise or do anything other than eliminate or ameliorate the existing pathological process responsible for the patient's objective and subjective manifestations. Should there be no organic disease, nutritional disturbance or other factor responsible for the patient's condition, and if the diagnosis by a process of elimination directly points to endocrine disturbance, then the following avenues of relief are open to the medical man.

If the case be one where there is distinct gonadal pathology, often a homotransplant from a near relative of the patient or other human material, or perhaps a heterotransplant from the higher anthropoids, should be advised. (Cf. Chapter on Technic.) If in addition to gonadal dysfunction thyroid inefficiency is found (let it be said at this juncture that a metabolism test is always desirable in cases of this class and very often will throw light in an otherwise obscure field), then in conjunction with transplantation, thyroid therapy, either by transplantation or per os, is clearly indicated. In aberrations of other endocrines, clearly manifest in a given case by specific manifestations incriminating a given gland of internal secretion, the addition of therapeutic resource directed to that glandular dystrophy may be tried.

The following illustrative cases from a series observed by the author will perhaps aid in emphasizing these premises:

Male Climacteric; Psychic Depression; Asthenia; Transplantation; Improvement.—

Mr. F. X. V., aged sixty-two, American, a banker, four sons, three daughters.

Family History.—Negative. Has always been very active and in good health; no previous diseases. Moderate user of tobacco and alcohol. *Vita sexualis:* very active until four years ago. Then gradual decline with simultaneous development of general asthenia, impotency, psychic depression, great irritability of temper, at times, insomnia, irregular heart action, tachycardia alternating with bradycardia. Blood pressure, systolic 160, diastolic 90. Urinalysis and blood Wassermann reaction negative. The patient had submitted to various forms of cures, including a vasoligation done in New York City in February, 1920, without the slightest benefit.

He consulted the author in October, 1921. Transplantation was proposed, the patient acquiesced and homotransplantation according to the author's technic, was carried out.

The results were a gradual regression of the asthenia and psycho-depressive manifestations. The patient now has a brighter outlook on life; he has returned to work and his sexual power has gradually returned. At the present writing, eighteen months have elapsed since the transplantation and the patient's improvement continues.

A case very similar to the one just described has been transplanted by the author with practically negative results. In this instance ligation was done, supplemented by thyroid transplantation therapy, with most excellent results. Whether the good results obtained in this case are due to the vasoligation or thyroid-therapy is difficult to establish.

A series of cases carefully studied by the author leads him to the conclusion that every case must be judged upon its own merits and the indications present. A great deal of good may be accomplished in these cases, which is of real value, and the psychic element can be entirely eliminated in many instances. It must, of course, be kept in mind that the results are not uniformly good, and patients must be subjected to therapy of one type or another to meet the symptoms for which they apply for relief. The justification of the gynecologist and urologist for submitting their female patients for the relief of the untoward manifestations of the climacteric to various forms of therapy holds good in the male. Thus far this field has been sadly neglected, and offers much for the class of patients who travel from consultation chamber to consultation chamber, and finally fall into the hands of " quacks " or " faith healers " with ultimate and often untimely destruction, when in well-selected instances the physician can accomplish a great deal by the suggestions as to therapy given in this chapter.

BIBLIOGRAPHY

[1] SANCTORIUS: Ars de Statica Med. Lug. Bat., 1728.
[2] CHURCH, BELFIELD and HALFORD: Quoted by Turner, Texas State Journ. of Med., 1916, xii, 251.
[3] EDITORIAL: Jour. Amer. Assn., 1911, lvii, 1212.
[4] MENDEL: Die Wechseljahre des Mannes. Neurol. Centralbl., 1910, xxlx, 1124.
[5] PAUL: Lancet, Lond., 1910.
[6] THEWLIS: Geriatrics, St. Louis, 1919, p. 204.

CHAPTER X

THE MECHANISM OF THE ACTION OF THE INTERNAL SECRETION OF THE TESTIS ON THE CENTRAL NERVOUS SYSTEM

STEINACH has pointed out that in order to obtain a normal sexual reflex culminating in *libido* and performance of the normal sexual act certain influences are necessary to eroticize, or erotise the higher centres of the central nervous system, and such process of stimulation he designates by the name of *erotization*. Animal experiments as well as human investigations have afforded a mass of proof that such erotization of the central nervous system as to culminate in the psychosexual reflex can directly be traced to the testes.

To illustrate: The gonad elaborates through its internal secretions the chemical products, which are taken up by the circulation and carried to the central nervous system, and there erotization results. That these substances of internal secretion have a selective action seems probable, and that such chemical substances are stored in the central nervous structures seems, in view of recent experiments, quite certain. In this connection it is worth while to recite the experiments of Steinach who, in a certain group of castrates, injected a preparation made from the brain and spinal cord of a male animal in rut, and in a second series of animals he injected a preparation made from the brain and spinal cord of frogs that had been previously castrated. In the first series Steinach observed a typical sexual reflex, but in the second series the results were negative. He went a step further and injected the second series also with the same preparations that he used for the first series and the results were remarkably striking, for the frogs responded in the same manner as did the first series. He also called attention to the fact that frogs injected with brain and cord substance of sexually-active frogs gave the first manifestations of sex activity after ten hours, while in a series which he injected with testicular substances the manifestations appeared much sooner. Injection of preparations from organs of sexually-active frogs other than the cerebral spinal centres into castrates showed absolutely negative results. This, Steinach points out, proves conclusively that the substances elaborated by the testes have a selective action upon the central nervous system in which they are stored.

Nussbaum [1] has busied himself experimentally in an effort to ascertain what rôle, if any, the central nervous system plays as an intermediary between the sexual glands and the organs of propagation. During the summer months at the time when the secondary sex characters are most marked in frogs he conducted experiments by dividing the nerve of the forearm of the experimental animal on one side only. He observed that on the side where this operation was performed the characteristic sexual manifestations did not appear, and he therefore concluded that "inasmuch as the secretions of the testes entering into the general circulation of the body cannot reach the glands having to do with the sexual embrace in the divided nerve of the forearm such manifestations remain absent. This proves that the secretion of the testes taken up into the circulation acts as a specific poison on certain nervous centres and irritates certain groups of ganglia which can, through centrifugal peripheral nerve stimulation, accomplish metabolic changes in the organs supplied by such nerves."

Pflüger objected to this conclusion, stating that the division of centripetal nerves causes disturbance in the organs supplied by such nerves, and that such disturbance, being necessarily followed by atrophy of the muscles of the arm, causes the retrogression of the characteristic sex manifestations in that member.

BIBLIOGRAPHY

[1] Nussbaum: Cited after Pflüger on the question, Does the Development of the Secondary Sex Characteristics Depend upon the Nervous System? Pflüger's Archiv., B. 116—1907.

CHAPTER XI

THE INFLUENCE OF THE X-RAY ON THE TESTICLE

SINCE röntgenologists have made use of the X-ray in therapy, the fact has become established that workers in this field have frequently observed an increase of sterility in their own person. In other words, the *potentia cœundi* remains intact, while the *potentia generandi* becomes impaired. Outside of the inability to procreate, these individuals show no change whatsoever; their somatic and psychic characteristics do not suffer in the slightest degree. As early as 1903, Albers-Schönberg[1] called attention to this interesting set of clinical manifestations. This was followed by the work of Bergonié and Tribondeau[2] who have shown that röntgenization of the male sex gland was followed by complete degeneration of the spermatogenic structures, while the interstitial cells, as well as the cells of Sertoli, remained intact; also that it is not necessary to continually and repeatedly subject the testes to such action to produce such results. That one exposure, if it be of sufficient length and intensity, is sufficient to produce this destructive result upon the tubular components, has been amply demonstrated. The atrophy of the seminal tubules continues as the result of röntgen-ray exposure with the proliferation of the interstitial substances and increase in the number of Leydig cells. It has been observed that this increase in the Leydig cells is not a small or insignificant numerical augmentation, but that it is very considerable. The same holds true in some instances with reference to the Sertoli cells.

The results of Bergonié and Tribondeau have been substantiated by Villemin[3] and Tandler and Grosz.[4] The exposure to the röntgen-rays may be sufficient to permanently destroy the spermatogenic function and also to completely arrest the incretory function of the interstitial structure. However, if exposure to the X-ray has only been mild, regeneration of the tubular structures will follow. In other words, a restoration of the seminal epithelium to its previous state will ensue. Spermatogonia have been shown by Villemin to also resist the action of the ray.

We shall now discuss the author's experiments to ascertain the effects of X-ray on transplanted testicular tissues.

To ascertain the effects of the röntgen-ray upon transplanted male sex glands the following experiments were carried out. For sometime past the author thought that inasmuch as strong röntgenization of the sex glands will lead to their destruction, while mild dosage will increase their activity

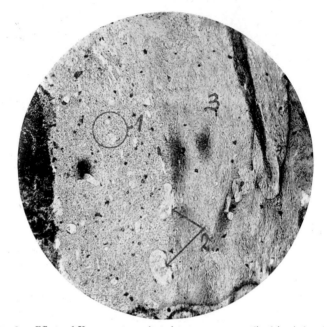

FIG. 181.—Effects of X-rays on transplanted testis. 1, area outlined in circle subjected to higher magnification (see following microphotograph). 2, new blood vessels and vascular sinuses. (Note tremendous increase of vascular spaces.) 3, muscles. Obj. 7.5; ocular 16. Leitz apochromatic. Magnified 105 times. (Author's observations.)

and stimulate their functions, particularly the interstitial elements, a series of experiments to throw more light on the subject would be of value. Space prevents entering into all phases of the experimental work done but the most important features will be recited.

Six rhesus monkeys were castrated on May 17, 1921. The testes were then interchanged between the castrates so that homotransplantations resulted. These animals were subjected to the following technic in

Röntgenization.—A filter of 5 mm. of aluminum was used, the distance being 18 inches for a period of (5 milliampere minutes) at a 5 inch spark gap.

Three of the animals were rayed according to this technic, the first application being made seven days after the transplantation and regularly repeated on each fourth day until a total of eight treatments had been given. The transplanted animals rayed and transplanted animals unrayed

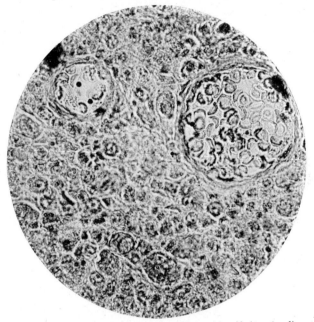

Fig. 182.—Area within circle "1" of foregoing figure.   Magnified to 1850 diameters.
(Author's observation.)

showed pictures distinctive of the effects of röntgenization, and I shall describe the findings in a typical case of each group.

The animals transplanted but not rayed showed the usual progressive retrograde changes observed in homotransplantations.

Microscopic section taken from an animal transplanted and subjected to the ray showed the following microscopic findings (Figs. 181 and 182):

The cells of the seminiferous tubules showed retrograde changes, the nuclei and cell walls were indistinguishable and the generative cells appeared as an undifferentiated mass. The stroma (connective tissue) is increased in quantity and many interstitial (Leydig) cells, occurring in groups throughout the stroma, are seen. Round cells and leukocytes are found disintegrated. The blood supply is very abundant, consisting of numerous newly-formed blood vessels; some of these might be classified as sinuses. Red blood corpuscles are seen in new formed vessels. Specimens were stained with Mallory stain and hematoxylin and eosin. Leydig cells in splendid state of preservation.

The microscopic findings of the control animal, not subjected to the X-ray, but transplanted in the same fashion at the same time, showed the following findings: No trace of a transplant could be found. The seminiferous tubules, stroma and blood vessels of the transplanted tissue have disappeared. The surrounding connective tissue is greatly hyperplastic, while round cells and leukocytes are very abundant both in the connective tissue and in place of interstitial cells. The blood supply of the transplanted area is very poor.

RESULTS OF THESE EXPERIMENTS:

The following significant facts were noted:

Rayed Animal.	Unrayed Animal.
Transplant thriving.	Transplant absorbed.
Dead leukocytes; little or no leukocytic infiltration.	Marked leukocytic infiltration.
Blood supply rich in blood vessels; blood sinuses traversed by blood.	Meager blood supply.
Tubular structures gone.	Tubular structures gone.
Leydig cells present in splendid state of preservation.	Leydig cells disappeared.

The following thought presents itself to the research worker in this field: Why does the implanted gland diminish so rapidly in size and and what causes its more or less gradual absorption? The diminution in size can be very readily explained if one will keep in mind the established fact that implanted testes will result in a disappearance of the tubular elements and a retention and proliferation of the interstitial tissue. Inasmuch as the tubular structures form, I should say, between 80 and 90 per cent. of the entire composition of the testicle and the interstitium the remainder, it will at once be seen that the disintegration and absorption of the tubular elements will of necessity cause the implant to become enormously reduced in size although the interstitial elements be proliferating. Be this as it may, however, from a study of the foregoing it will be noted that the author believes that the interstitial elements are the ones that give rise to sex characteristics and the qualities of hormone activity, so that the important part for the therapeutic effect is retained, although the transplanted gland in time assumes the proportions of a very minute nodule. *As long as that nodule, no matter how small in size it be, contains functionating Leydig cells, so long should there be a therapeutic effect and therapeutic value to the economy which it supplies.*

The second factor we have to cope with is the problem as to what is directly responsible for the regression in size of the implant. Is the necessarily marked leukocytic infiltration brought about by the introduction of the implant the cause? In a great measure this must be answered in the affirmative. This obtains, no matter what the type of the implantation be; the surrounding structures will at once react by the influx into the invaded territory of a tremendous number of lymphocytes and leukocytes of various types.

The problem then presenting itself assumes the following tone. The regression of the seminiferous tubules not being of consequence for our needs and purposes, how can we avoid leukocytic invasion, thereby retarding resorption of the implant for the longest possible time? The author believes that that question will eventually be solved and that a step in the right direction has been taken in instituting research as to the reaction of the leukocytes to the X-rays. If we refer to the table given above and closely scrutinize the findings in the rayed and unrayed transplants we will be impressed with the comparative absence of leukocytes in the rayed specimens and with the great abundance of them in the unrayed implantation. *The total disappearance of the implant in the unrayed specimen and its subsistence amidst a plentiful supply of blood in the rayed tissue seems rather significant.* We observe in the appended illustration an abundance of new formed blood vessels which are traversed by red blood corpuscles and between these cellular elements that have all the characteristics of living and functioning interstitial cells, particularly those of Leydig.

The conclusions drawn from these experiments may be summarized as follows:

1. A proper dose of X-ray will prevent excessive leukocytic invasion in the transplanted area.

2. The new formed blood vessels and blood sinuses, which are the result of the direct stimulation of the X-ray, carry sufficient pabulum to the Leydig cells to enable them to thrive and function.

3. The dosage of rays for the purpose of prevention of leukocytic invasion, enhancing vascularization and Leydig cell stimulation, should be of sufficient intensity to obtain these results *without carrying it far enough to produce the destructive effect.*

4. The proper doses to obtain these results in the author's hands were the following:

    300 to 400 milliampere seconds.

       1 milliampere.

       5 back up.

       5 minutes exposure.

       5 m.m. aluminum filter.

     18 distance from skin.

       4 day periods.

       8 exposures.

BIBLIOGRAPHY

[1] ALBERS-SCHÖNERG: Ueber eine bisher unbekante. Wirkung der Röntgenstrahlen auf den Organismus der Tiere. Münch. Mediz. Wochenschr., 1903, p. 1859.

[2] BERGONIÉ ET TRIBONDEAU: In C. R. Soc. Biol., 1904–1905.

[3] VILLEMIN: Rayons X et de activité génitale. C. R. Acad. Sc., T 142, 1906, p. 723.

[4] TANDLER and GROSZ: Die biolog. Grundlagen. usw. Vgl., S 97, u. ff.

CHAPTER XII

HOMO- AND HETERO-TESTICULAR TRANSPLANTS IN MAN

(A) Homotransplantations in Man.—

(a) *Autografts and Homografts.*—

THE results of transplantation of testicles, both homogeneous and heterogeneous, in animals, having fully demonstrated that such operations were often successful as regards the " taking " of the graft; and that, when successful, such grafts were followed by unquestionable evidence of the functioning of the transplanted tissue in the organism of the host, it was inevitable that the procedure should in time be applied to human subjects. Besides, for some time the surgical grafting of ovarian tissue having demonstrated that in women whose ovaries had been removed the effects of a premature menopause could at least, in a measure, be obviated, was an additional reason for carrying out a similar therapeutic procedure in man, and with equal hopes of success. The first attempt in the United States at transplantation of the testicle was carried out by Hammond and Sutton [1] in 1912.

Hammond and Sutton's case of transplantation was unique, as they attempted a direct anastomosis. In the case of a young man, aged nineteen, whose right testicle had been so considerably injured as to necessitate its removal for sarcoma, these authors transplanted the testicle of a man aged twenty-eight, who had died from hemorrhage following rupture of the liver. The injured gland was cut away from its connections and replaced by the transplanted organ which was anastomosed to the vessels of the cord from which the injured gland had just been removed. The tunica vaginalis was left in site. The artery was severed fairly close to the testicle well below the junction where the artery of the vas deferens joins the spermatic. The arterial ends in the patient and in the transplant were brought together and a tension suture brought the inner walls close together; this was followed by an overlapping suture around the circumference. The vein ends were similarly united and lastly the vas deferens joined. No attempts were made to unite nerve structures. The superimposed tissues were united and the wound closed. Before leaving the table, the arterial circulation had become reëstablished. The tunica vaginalis of the transplant soon began to slough and was gradually removed, but this did not seem in any way to affect the transplantation.

The patient left the hospital with apparently well-established union of the vessels and circulation through the testicle. Examined one month later, the transplanted testicle was, however, found much atrophied, but the cord anastomosis on palpation appeared in every way normal. Later on, the testicle was apparently increasing in size. No later particulars of this case have been published as far as known.

In 1913, Lespinasse,[2] in the case of a patient who had lost his testicles, cut some slices from the testicle of another man, 1 mm. thick, which were transplanted among the fibers of the abdominal rectus muscle and scrotum. Lespinasse says that the operation was successful, but gives no histological proof. (Cf. Chapter on Technic.) Lespinasse's single case of 1 mm. transplant cannot, in any case, be looked upon as offering any evidence whatsoever, either pro or con, in view of the inevitable absorption of such grafts. (Cf. Author's Experiments in Chapter on Quantity of Tissue Necessary for Transplantation.)

Undoubtedly, the first important work in the operative systematization of human testicular grafting is due to Lydston[3] who, in 1914, did a free autotransplantation on himself in order to better observe and study the effects of such transplantation.

Lydston says that whether or not there is eventual apparent disappearance of the gland tissue after a successful implantation, the method should be theoretically useful and its benefits permanent. This opinion is based on the view, first, because the interstitial gland tissue may remain and function, producing hormone; second, because the hormone may have done its work of regeneration. If the implanted testis should actually atrophy, it is still possible to have recourse to successive implantations of the same kind.

The results noted in his autotransplant case were: At the end of twenty-four hours, a marked exhilaration and buoyancy of spirits lasting for about twenty-four hours, which he thinks due to absorption of secretion from the gland. This was again temporarily renewed seven days later, probably beginning with the formation of vascular adhesions and functioning of the transplanted tissue. The well-being feeling and physical exhilaration returned again after some weeks and lasted for a considerable period, but were also greater than before implantation. Blood pressure conditions were much improved as long as the gland tissue apparently functioned. Eyesight improved, there was an improvement in the circulation of the skin, and increase in weight. Lydston had suffered from edema of the lower extremities for several years following a nephritis, and which was apparently improved. There was also an eczematous condition of the toes. This latter completely disappeared about four weeks after the implantation. Lydston used refrigerated material for transplantation. He exhibited several cases of transplantation in which the results were good, he says. He concluded from his experience that when the technic and material were right and the recipient properly selected, continuity of hormone production by the implanted gland for at least a long period is certain. Lydston implanted in the scrotum and believes the next best site to be the pelvic peritoneal space. His glands were obtained from recent cadavers or from living subjects, and placed in salt or physiological solution, then implanted within twenty-four hours after removal. He observed no case in which the implanted tissue, *when it took,* had completely disappeared within six to eighteen months following the transplantation. The good clinical results were in several cases observed for two years following operation. In 1921 Lydston reported what he calls two remarkable cases of testicular transplantation. The first was a case of hypopituitarism with infantile sexual organs and feminism. The scrotal implantation of one testicle in this case was followed by marked enlargement of the patient's penis and testes. He experienced erections and was able to perform coitus. In the second case, the testicles had been removed from a man aged thirty years, on account of tuberculosis. A double testicular transplantation four years later did not effect much improvement in the patient's sexual condition. This was followed two years later by a single implantation, which effected a pronounced physical and sexual improvement persisting for two and a half years.

Morris,[8] in 1914, did a homogeneous testicular graft in a man who had lost both his testicles by accident. A wedge of testicular tissue, cut from a hernia case, was sliced, and the slices transplanted in the scrotum, and beneath the abdominal recti muscles. This patient, according to Morris, experienced a renewal of muscular vigor and sexual power, both of which had previously been deficient.

A second similar case was reported in 1916. In this case, the scrotal graft was apparently absorbed, but at the same time the vestiges of the man's own testicle regenerated and began to grow; the vestiges of epididymis and cord also began to grow. A second graft was made to hasten matters and the patient was in a position to marry.

Stocker,[10] in 1916, in the case of a man of thirty years, bilaterally castrated for tuberculosis, resected a non-tuberculous part from one testicle, which was implanted in the scrotum. A year later the graft felt as large as when first inserted. The patient continued to have libido and erections.

Lichtenstern[11] in a traumatic injury case, sectioned a human testicle (removed from a man, aged forty years) in two parts. Each part was grafted by its sectioned face on one of the obliquus minor muscles. Erections were reproduced and the grafted patient was able to exercise coitus with ejaculation of prostatic fluid, results which were maintained for nine months.

In a later report, Lichtenstern[12] stated that an implanted testicle either sloughed or became absorbed in four other cases. These were cases in which the transplanted testicle was placed in the scrotum instead of a removed tuberculous testicle. In another traumatic case, Lichtenstern slit a testicle in two and implanted each half separately on scarified muscle tissue in the inguinal region. The results in this, and in twenty-one other cases done since 1915, confirm the therapeutic value of free testicle transplantation, and show that such technic offers favorable conditions for survival and continuous functioning of the transplanted testicle for years. Lichtenstern remarks that Lydston's high percentage of cases in which the transplanted testicle sloughed was due to his method of implantation in the scrotum (Cf. Chapter on Technic), the conditions there being far from favorable for vascularization as in a bed cut out for the graft in the fascia over the obliquus muscle in the inguinal region and slightly scarifying the muscle.

Lissmann,[13] in a case of bilateral orchidectomy for chronic tuberculous orchi-epididymitis, made a subaponeurotic homogeneous testicular graft.

There was a return of *potentia cœundi*, which, however, lasted only for a time, the graft apparently becoming absorbed.

Stanley and Kelker [14] did eleven human homogeneous testicular transplantations. In three cases the testicle denuded of parietal tunica vaginalis, following Lydston's technic, was placed in the scrotal tissues; in seven cases the testicles were grafted on the atrophied glands of the recipient, and in one case a double implantation was done, one testicle in the right scrotum and a denuded surface of the other testicle sutured on a similar section of the left gland. These transplantations, according to the authors, had a decidedly beneficial effect on the well-being of all the patients; they do not believe that the implant lives. The beneficial results probably last more than a year. One testicle removed eight and a half months after implantation showed that it was entirely necrotic.

Enderlen's [15] attempts of testicular grafting in four cases made him skeptical as to the value of the method in restoring sexual vigor.

In the first case, a eunuchoid of thirty-three years, half an ectopic testicle from a cryptorchid, aged twenty-two years, was implanted in the abdomen. The existence of spermatogenesis in this testicle was established. The objective and subjective phenomena were nil. After a vague hope of awakening virility at the end of six months the patient had become more frigid than before.

In the second case, an idiot of thirty-nine years had a goiter operation at the same time a man of fifty-four was operated for hydrocele. Two slices from the testicles of the latter were implanted in the pectoral muscles of the idiot. On the sixteenth day following the implantation one of the fragments was removed and examined and found almost completely necrosed.

In the third case a man of twenty-three years had been unilaterally castrated for tuberculosis of the epididymis. A further examination having shown that there was no tuberculosis present, a fragment of the removed testicle was grafted into the abdominal rectus muscle. Sixteen days later it was found that with the exception of a small peripheric zone, all the graft had degenerated.

In the fourth case a man of thirty-six years was bilaterally castrated for testicular tuberculosis. Three uninfected autografts were implanted in

21

the pectoral region. Fourteen days later one piece was removed and in its place an ectopic functioning testicle, removed from a man of thirty-nine years, was grafted. Four months later there was neither objective nor subjective symptoms, and on removal the graft was found almost entirely absorbed.

Foerster,[16] in a man of fifty-five years, a case of *dementia senilis,* transplanted the testicle from a healthy vigorous young man of twenty years. The testicle was halved and the pieces implanted in the fascia of the abdominal muscle bilaterally. There was no reaction observed. The grafted pieces were removed three months later and histologically examined; they were found almost completely necrotic.

Mariotti [17] reported a case in a young man of twenty-one years with thyreo-genital polyglandular dystrophia and persistent infantilism. In this case, Mariotti made a *subaponeurotic* graft of a testicle removed from a man operated for penile tumor. Fifteen days later, augmentation of the patient's infantile testicle was evident and its consistency was harder. The penis was also elongated about 2 cms. There was an increase of sexual desire and power of erection, but these disappeared later when the graft evidently became absorbed, about twenty months following operation.

In Kreuter's [18] case the right testicle was removed from a man aged thirty years for tuberculosis, later followed by removal also of the left testicle. An ectopic testicle from a youth of seventeen was split in two halves and the pieces implanted between the obliquus internus and fascia on each side of the abdomen. Erections were experienced after three weeks with physical betterment and capacity for coitus. Later there was regression.

Hammesfahr,[19] in a man of twenty-six years, with testicular atrophy following traumatism, and loss of sexual power, transplanted a piece of the testicle into the abdominal musculature. Sexual power was restored and has persisted for six months at time of report.

Muehsam,[20] in one case of bisexuality and two cases of homosexuality, reports that favorable results were obtained. The results were not observed immediately after the transplantation of testicles, but in the two cases of homosexuality it took six and four months before heterosexual signs were observed.

Both Lichtenstern and Pfeiffer [21] have reported good results from homogeneous testicular transplantation in cases of homosexuality.

The case reported by McKenna [23] concerned a man aged twenty-eight years, who had been bilaterally castrated for tuberculosis of the testicles. An undescended testicle, which had been removed during a hernia operation, was split in two; one half was implanted in each inguinal region and sutured to the cord. Slices from the grafts were placed also on the scarified tunica vaginalis. The patient's sexual desire had returned by the fourth day. The patient was discharged on the twelfth day. "His general condition was much improved; not only from a sex standpoint, but also from a mental standpoint, his condition was much brighter." Subsequent inquiries showed that these conditions persisted for seven or eight months up to the time of this report. He feels as strong sexually as he did between the ages of seventeen and twenty-one years.

(b) *Heterogeneous Testicular Transplantations in Man.*—

Perusal of medical literature shows but few attempts at practical transplantations of testicular tissue from animals to man, and in most of these cases the result was apparently a failure. The most probable cause was *the distance in the biological scale between the donor and recipient of the graft.*

In 1920 Falcone [24] reported four such cases, in all of which grafting of a sheep's testicle was done. In the first case, half a sheep's testicle was implanted subcutaneously in the abdomen of the patient, the sectioned face of the graft being applied next the aponeurosis. Seven days later there was a return of sexual desire and erections, and these persisted even after elimination of the graft about a month later. In Falcone's second and third cases the grafts were eliminated after forty and eighteen days respectively. Elimination of the graft in Falcone's first three cases did not give rise to any suppurative phenomena.

Stanley and Kelker reported that in five cases in the San Quentin Prison, California, they had transplanted testicles from young rams to human patients. One whole ram's testicle was embedded in the scrotum of each of two patients, but the grafts began to slough after seven and sixteen days respectively. *In the three other cases only half a ram's testicle was used, but in all sloughing began in about seven days after operation.*

The results of the ram testicular transplantations were not encouraging, although one man of sixty-five years seemed to have been benefited. Such grafts became absorbed.

Bolognesi [25] transplanted a dog's testicle in a man, having first reduced it to the form of what he calls an " interstitialoma," a condition in which all the seminiferous tissue had degenerated. The result was, however, a failure as regards function.

H. Lyons Hunt [26] recently reported three cases in which a testicle from a freshly-killed ram was transplanted abdominally in a man.

Case One.—A man aged sixty years, with loss of potency. Testicle implanted in abdominal wall *sloughed*.

Case Two.—A man aged sixty-five years. The same operation, *which also ended in sloughing of the graft*. The man had renewed erections and was able to perform coitus.

Voronoff's first *human testicular graft* was made June, 1920, in a man of forty-five, both of whose testicles had been removed on account of tuberculosis. The general aspect of the patient was that of a eunuch. A testicle from a cynocephalus ape was grafted, divided into four pieces. Two pieces were inserted on each side of the empty scrotum. Suppuration ensued on left side after six days. On the right was necrosis after three months and the graft was removed.

Similar results were noted in another tubercular case. In the first case, the man's beard reappeared during the retention of the graft.

A third ape graft was made November, 1920; a man of fifty-nine years, in whom there was almost complete loss of sexual power for eight years. The two testicles were removed from the ape; one divided into two and the other into four fragments. The two halves of the left Simian testicle were grafted on the scarified vaginal tunic of the left human testicle by catgut sutures. The albuginea was also scarified. The four fragments of the right monkey testicle were similarly grafted to the right human testicle.

Two of the four right fragments were spontaneously eliminated during the following month. The man has been followed up since then to the present time. His general state, both mental and physical, is much ameliorated, but his sexual frigidity remains.

The fourth ape graft was in a man of sixty-one years, with precocious senility, lack of mental vigor and impotency. Fragmental graft as before. Erections experienced twenty-three days later and have recurred very frequently. He has recuperated his virility and retained it perfectly for two years. Return of his mental and physical vigor of ten years before.

The fifth ape graft was performed in a man of thirty-three years, with sexual frigidity, asthenia, loss of mental vigor, etc. A cynocephalus testicle was divided into halves, and each grafted into the patient's testicles. Although his sexual frigidity was not much changed, his general virility has greatly improved.

The sixth graft: Man of sixty-six years; senility; physical and mental depression; much attenuated virility. Graft as in fifth case, erections experienced three weeks later, which became stronger and more frequent as time advanced. Twenty-two months later he reported that his genital power was maintained as well as his general vigor.

The seventh Simian graft was in a man of seventy-four years. Before the graft he had the aspect of a bent old man, dull-eyed, and walking with the aid of a cane. Completely impotent for twelve years. Fragmental graft as before.

The effect in eight months was that he apparently rejuvenated fifteen or twenty years. His physical and mental state, as well as his virility, all have changed, and his status has been altered from that of a senile old man into that of a vigorous man enjoying all his faculties. He has a juvenile aspect, his body is erect; he has an easy walk, all his physical and sexual functions have improved, and are maintained at the age of seventy-six years. This man was exhibited by Voronoff as a proof that in selected cases we may often successfully combat senility and physical and intellectual decay.

The eighth graft was in a man forty, impotent; graft as before. Erection experienced within one month, but the patient has been lost sight of since. Voronoff has not been able until quite recently to obtain the testicles of the higher anthropoid apes (chimpanzee) which he considers best suited for human grafts.

The Author has had considerable experimental and clinical experience in homo- and heterotransplantations of the testis. The results will be reported in this work under appropriate headings. (Cf. Chapters on Physiology; Functions of the Leydig Cells; Clinical Cases; Dementia Precox; The Male Climacteric; Interrelation of the Testes and Other Endocrines; Technic of Testicular Transplantation, etc.)

BIBLIOGRAPHY

[1] HAMMOND and SUTTON: Internat. Clinics, 1912, xxii, s. i.. 150.
[2] LESPINASSE: Jour. Amer. Med. Assn., 1913. lxi. 1869.
[3] LYDSTON: New York Medical Journal, 1914. c. 745.
[4] LYDSTON: Bulletin Chicago Medical Society, 1914, xiii, No. 24.
[5] LYDSTON: Jour. Amer. Med. Assn., 1916, xvi, 1540.
[6] LYDSTON: Jour. Amer. Med. Assn.. 1919, xxii, 1614.
[7] LYDSTON: Jour. Amer. Med. Assn., 1918, xx, 907.
[8] MORRIS: New York Medical Journal, 1914, c, 753.
[9] MORRIS: Jour. Amer. Med. Assn.. 1916, lxvii, 741.
[10] STOCKER: Corresp. Bl. f. Schw. Aerzte., 1916, xlvi, 193.
[11] LICHTENSTERN: Muench. med. Wchnschr., 1916, lxiii, 673.
[12] LICHTENSTERN: Mediz. Klinik. Berl., 1916. xii, 27.
[13] LISSMANN: Mediz. Klinik. Berl., 1919.
[14] STANLEY and KELKER: Jour. Amer. Med. Assn.. 1920, lxxiv, 1501.
[15] ENDERLEN: Mediz. Klinik. Berl., No. 48, 27, Nov., 1921. p. 1439.
[16] FOERSTER: Muench med. Wchnschr., 1921, xviii, 106.
[17] MARIOTTI: Riforma Med., Naples, 1919.
[18] KREUTER: Zentralb f. Chir., 1919, xlvi, 954.
[19] HAMMESFAHR: Zentralb f. Chir., 1921, xlviii, iiii.
[20] MUEHSAM: Deut. med. Wchnschr., 1921, xlvii, 354.
[21] PFEIFFER: Deut. med. Wchnschr., 1922, xlviii, 600.
[22] PFEIFFER: Deut. med. Wchnschr., 1922, xlviii, 660.
[23] McKENNA: Illinois Medical Journal, 1921, xl, 228.
[24] FALCONE: Riforma Med., Naples, 1920, xxxvi, 1177.
[25] BOLOGNESI: Jour. d'urol med. el dur., 1921, xii, 153.
[26] HUNT, H. LYONS: Endocrinology, 1922, vi, 652.
[27] VORONOFF: Greffes Testiculaires, Paris, 1923, Libraire Octave Doin.
[28] THOREK: Virginia Medical Monthly, Vol. 49, No. 6, p. 343, American Journal of Clinical Medicine, Vol. 29, No. 9, p. 662. The Medical Review of Reviews, vxxi, No. 1, Endocrinology, Vol. 6, No. 6, p. 773. The Urologic and Cutaneous Review, Vol. 26, No. 9, p. 542. Medical World, Vol. xv, p. 340. American Medicine, Vol. xxviii, p. 448. Northwest Medicine, Vol. xxi, p. 256.

CHAPTER XIII

BLOOD AFFINITY IN ANIMALS AND ITS IMPORTANCE IN TRANSPLANTATIONS

ONE of the most important conditions to be considered in connection with grafting of tissues is that there should be a close blood-relationship between the donor and the recipient of the graft. It has constantly been observed clinically and experimentally that the grafts of tissue which succeed best are autogenous grafts; homogeneous grafts come next, but heterogeneous grafts usually fail to become vascularized in the tissues of the body of the host. Such facts have too often been observed to consider that they are based otherwise than upon biological causes.

Whether a free testicular graft is adopted by its host and becomes vascularized and a functioning part of the organism, or the graft "takes" and is absorbed gradually and replaced by new tissue obtained and elaborated by the organism either from its own resources or from the elements of the grafts, in either case we have the object of the graft fulfilled; and we know that such fulfillment is more likely to follow when an autogenous or homogeneous graft is used than one which is heterogeneous to its host.

In testicular grafting, since the use of autogenous grafts or homogeneous grafts is frequently impracticable in the case of men, we are compelled to seek material from other members of the animal kingdom which are the most closely allied in blood relationship to man. In the natural zoological orders, Man belongs to the order of Primates, the other members of this order being the Simiidæ, Cercopithecidæ, Cebidæ, Hepalidæ, and Lemuridæ. The Primates are part of the general class of mammals, and all, except the Lemuridæ, are regarded as anthropoids, or man-like.

The question as to the degree of relationship between the anthropoids is one upon which there is some disagreement. Haeckel [3] contended that man was descended from Old World apes whose recent ancestors belonged to the tailless anthropoids and whose older ancestors belonged to the cynopithecidæ, a species of the Cercopithecidæ. Darwin supported this view. Comparatively recent investigations upon the eyes of mammals have shown a close relationship between the Old World apes and man in this respect, the *macula lutea* tending to disappear as we descend in the scale of New World monkeys, and being altogether absent in the Lemurs (semi-apes). This evidence has been directly corroborated by the blood findings demonstrated for anthropoids by Nuttall [1] which will presently be dealt with in more detail.

Nuttall's precipitin reactions with the bloods of Simiidæ gave results which closely resembled those obtained with human blood; the results with bloods of Cercopithecidæ came next in degree of similarity, and were followed by those of the bloods of the lower scale anthropoids, Cebidæ and Hepalidæ, which gave but slight reactions with antihuman serum, while the bloods obtained from Lemurs gave no indication of affinity of blood relationship with Man.

The reactions obtained by Nutall in these blood tests were in strict accordance with the relationship among anthropoids, hypothetically suggested by Dubois [2] in 1896, upon other grounds, and which may be seen in the following genealogical diagram. (Fig. 183.)

Comparative studies upon the constitution of the bloods of different animals by means of ordinary chemical methods have failed to demonstrate the delicate differences such as can be proved to exist by biological methods of investigation.

Nuttall used the biological methods, judging that the zoological relationship can best be demonstrated by noting the effects of powerful antisera upon blood dilutions from the animals. It is a remarkable fact that a common property has persisted in the bloods of certain groups of animals throughout the ages which have elapsed during their evolution from a common ancestor in spite of differences in foods and habits of life. The persistence of chemical and biological blood relationship between the various groups of animals allows us to bridge over spaces of geological time and will lead to very valuable results in the study of evolution.

Nuttall's object was to determine general broad facts of blood-relationship between animals, and for this he employed precipitating antisera.

Precipitins are substances (antibodies) formed in the blood serum of an animal as the result of repeated injections of some albuminous body; precipitins possess the property that when added to a solution of such albumen it causes its precipitation. The testing of animal bloods by

precipitating antisera will very clearly show that this method of investigation allows certain definite conclusions being drawn. Thus there are
reasons to show that precipitins are not formed in the serum of closely
related animals; no precipitin can be obtained for rabbit blood by treating

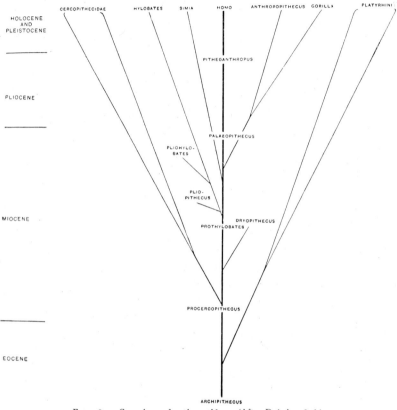

FIG. 183.—Genealogy of anthropoidea. (After Dubois, 1896.)

guinea pigs with rabbit serum, the serum from such guinea pigs only producing a very slight opalescence when added to rabbit blood dilutions, but
never precipitin. But when a powerful antiserum is added to a dilution
of its homologous blood, reaction is almost instantaneous; in other cases
the reaction takes place more slowly. Reaction takes place rapidly in
related bloods, but more slowly or not at all in distantly related
bloods. Generally precipitins appear in the blood serum of suitable animals

for a longer or shorter treatment by injections of non-homologous albuminous substances.

Nuttall tested nine hundred specimens of bloods in which he made, altogether, sixteen thousand precipitin tests. These tests were made by means of antisera for man, chimpanzee, ourangoutang, and cercopithecus, the effect of the newly-obtained antiserum upon blood solutions from different animals being observed. The antiserum injections were made intravenously in the marginal ear vein.

With antisera obtained from Primates, maximum reactions were obtained only with bloods from Primates. The degrees of reaction obtained indicate a close relationship between man and the Simiidæ, a more distant relationship with the Cercopithecidæ. The four antisera from Primates failed to produce reactions with the bloods of Lemurs from which it is concluded that Lemurs belong to an order separate from the Primates.

Examination of the very detailed tables presented by Nuttall for the nine hundred bloods tested, including those of all the usual mammals, birds, reptiles, amphibian, and fishes, and his results show, that generally the class antiserum gives a reaction for individual bloods of members of its own class, and that family antiserum gives marked reaction in the blood of members of the particular family. Thus, anti-human serum gives a very marked reaction in all human bloods, only a clouding which may be more or less marked in other members of the mammalian class, and no reaction in other classes. Pig antiserum produces a very marked reaction in the blood of pigs, with less reaction in other mammals, and none in other classes.

But bloods from the Simiidæ (ourang, chimpanzee, gorilla), and from the Cercopithecidæ (cynocephalus porcarius, macacus rhesus, etc.), generally gave reactions identical with those given by human bloods.

The antisera of the other mammalians, such as sheep, goats, dogs, etc., while giving strongly marked reactions for their own particular families, show no, or very slight, reaction for man or other primates, and only such as might be predicated for the general class of mammals. (Cf. Table.)

The results in general show the persistence of blood affinities in groups which have descended from a common stock; and vice versa where similarity is shown in the blood findings and affinities it argues for descent from a common ancestor.

The degree and rate of blood reactions to an antiserum appear to offer an index of the degree of the blood relationship; closely related bloods react more powerfully and more rapidly than do distantly related bloods, provided the latter react at all.

The table, which gives a few of the results obtained by Nuttall, only shows the general type of reaction in these cases; the degree of reaction for density of precipitation is not shown, but this in general follows the line of other reaction.

TABLE SHOWING REACTIONS OF ANTISERA WITH VARIOUS MAMMALIAN BLOOD SERA.*

$\oplus \oplus$ = strongly marked reaction; $\oplus$ = marked clouding.
$+$ = slight clouding; O = no reaction.

Class	Order or Sub-Order		Antiserum for								
			Man	Chimpanzee	Ourang	Monkey	Dog	Sheep	Ox	Horse	Pig
MAMMALIA	Primates Anthropoids	Man	$\oplus \oplus$	O	$+$	$+$	Occasional slight reaction.				
	Primates Anthropoids	Simiidæ	$\oplus \oplus$	$\oplus \oplus$	$\oplus$	$+$	Occasional slight reaction.				
	Primates Anthropoids	Cercopithecidæ	$\oplus \oplus$	$+$	$\oplus$	$\oplus$					
		(a) Cynocephalus porcarius	or $\oplus$				Occasional slight reaction.				
		(b) Macacus rhesus	$\oplus \oplus$	O	$+$	$\oplus$ or $+$					
		Lemuridæ	O	O	O	O	Occasional slight reaction.				
	Carnivora	Canis (Dog)	Occasional slight				$\oplus \oplus$	Occasional slight			
	Artiodactyla	Suidæ (Pig)	Occasional slight						$+$	$+$	$\oplus \oplus$
	Artiodactyla	Bovidæ: (a) Goat	Occasional slight					$\oplus \oplus$	$+$	O	$\oplus$
		(b) Sheep	Exceptional slight					$\oplus \oplus$	$+$	Occasional slight	
		(c) Ox, cow	Exceptional				Occasional slight	$\oplus \oplus$	O	$+$	

* Adapted from Tables given by Nuttal on p. 220 *et seq.*

In the American Hospital, Chicago, we have carried out a number of experimental investigations with anti-human rabbit serum on the blood of

Primates (cynocephalus (baboon) and macacus rhesus) in order to verify or contradict the results obtained by Nuttall.

The rabbit used for the production of the antiserum in the test described below weighed three pounds and eight ounces prior to the first injection of human serum. The injections were made intraperitoneally, and the animal weighed before each injection.

The following table will show amount of human serum inoculated, the interval of inoculation, and the weight of the rabbit before each inoculation.

*Date	Inoculation Weight		Amount human serum inoculated.
April 6, 1923	1st	3 lbs. 8 oz.	2½ cc.
April 8, 1923	2nd	3 lbs. 8 oz.	4 cc.
April 10, 1923	3rd	3 lbs. 7 oz.	5 cc.
April 13, 1923	4th	3 lbs. 6½ oz.	5 cc.
April 16, 1923	5th	3 lbs. 6 oz.	5 cc.
April 19, 1923	6th	3 lbs. 5 oz.	5 cc.

*Animal—rabbit; marking—shaved area on back; purpose—production of anti-serum——(human).

On April 22, 1923, the animal was bled from the ear and a preliminary test made for precipitins (test made against a 1:1000 dilution of human blood).

On April 28, 1923, the rabbit was prepared, the blood aspirated from the heart and collected in a flat bottle until the serum had separated off. The blood serum was then collected (aseptically), and placed in small test tubes, which were then sealed, and placed in the ice box for further use.

On May 20th, a preliminary test was made of the bloods of the cynocephalus (baboon), and the macacus rhesus (rhesus monkey) in dilutions of 1:1000. The tubes showed only a very slight reaction and the photographs failed to demonstrate same.

On May 27, 1923, a second test was made with better results. The dilutions in each case were 1:100. Below is a photograph of the tests, and following is the description of the findings (Fig. 184):

Tube One (Control).—Anti-human rabbit serum plus isotonic salt solution: No clouding at zone of contact.

Tube Two (Control).—Anti-human rabbit serum plus normal rabbit serum—1:100: No clouding at zone of contact.

Tube Three (Control).—Anti-human rabbit serum plus normal human serum—1:100: Marked clouding at zone of contact, slight precipitate.

Tube Four.—Anti-human rabbit serum plus serum of cynocephalus (baboon), 1:100: Moderate clouding at zone of contact.

Tube Five.—Anti-human rabbit serum plus serum of giant rhesus (rhesus monkey), 1:100: Faint clouding at zone of contact.

Tube Six.—Anti-human rabbit serum plus serum of macacus rhesus (rhesus monkey), 1:100: Almost imperceptible clouding at zone of contact.

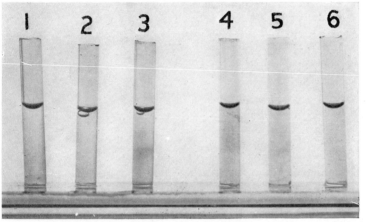

Fig. 184.—Precipitin reactions. Tube 1. (Control.) Anti-human rabbit serum plus isotonic salt solution: No clouding at zone of contact. Tube 2. (Control.) Anti-human rabbit serum plus normal rabbit serum—1:100: No clouding at zone of contact. Tube 3. (Control.) Anti-human rabbit serum plus normal human serum—1:100: Marked clouding at zone of contact, slight precipitate. Tube 4. Anti-human rabbit serum plus serum of cynocephalus—1:100: Moderate clouding at zone of contact. Tube 5. Anti-human rabbit serum plus serum of giant rhesus—1:100: Faint clouding at zone of contact. Tube 6. Anti-human rabbit serum plus serum of macacus rhesus—1:100: Almost imperceptible clouding at zone of contact.

The results show that while the anti-human serum gave marked clouding, with normal human serum similar, though slighter, reaction was obtained with the sera obtained from the cynocephalus and rhesus, thus verifying the findings of Nuttall that there was a biological similarity between the bloods of these animals and that of man.

These results furnish biological evidence in support of the fitness of grafts taken from the higher anthropoid apes, for use on the human patient, and give the reason why, a priori, such grafts might be expected to "take." The farther removed any animal is from man in the biological scale, the more dissimilar is its blood from human blood, and so much the slighter is any reaction of its blood serum to anti-human serum. There is, therefore, a strong biological reason why grafts from bovines, dogs, etc., are not successful when applied to man, and the same reason of blood similarity offers some assurance that in the transplantation of testicular tissue from higher apes to man, the graft, other things being equal, should have the next best chance of success to a transplantation of human testicular tissue.

BIBLIOGRAPHY

[1] NUTTALL: Blood Immunity and Blood Relationship, 1904.
[2] DUBOIS: Anatom. Anzeiger, 1896, xii, 1–22.
[3] HAECKEL: The Evolution of Man, New York, 1879.

CHAPTER XIV

DEMENTIA PRECOX AND THE GONADS

BEFORE it was evident that certain endocrine glands are in some way essential to the normal development and functional activity of the reproductive apparatus, it had been observed that frequently there were developmental defects of the reproductive apparatus and in the physical characteristics in sex in idiots, cretins, etc.

Gibbs [1] has recently made a study of sex development and behavior in 325 male patients and dementia precox. Forty-seven of these were under twenty-one years of age; the remaining 278 were over twenty-one. These were all unselected cases.

The testes of patients observed between the ages of sixteen and twenty compared favorably in gross size with those of patients between twenty-one and forty years of age. Small testes were no more frequent in patients admitted at an early age than in those admitted later in life. The majority of the patients examined had testicles which compared favorably in size with the normal, and in less than 5 per cent. of all patients both testes were small; typical infantilism was not noted. It was frequently observed that, especially in young patients, the testes felt unusually hard and rubbery. In many such, the epididymis and vas could be palpated only as a cord firmly adherent along the border of the testis so that it could not be separated out and palpated between the fingers. Many such testes were also misshapen. The findings suggested the possibility of a growth or overgrowth of tissue without proper differentiation or an excess of connective tissue.

That degenerative changes are to be found in the gonads in dementia precox is well known; the parenchymatous degeneration being accompanied by increased connective tissue, so that size and consistency cannot be taken as absolute criteria of degenerative changes. It might be expected that patients with a long duration of the psychosis would show smaller testes than recent admissions with short duration; and as a matter of fact, such was observed; but patients in whom degenerative changes would be most definite and rapid, usually do not live long enough, or an increase of

335

connective tissue might compensate for shrinkage of parenchymatous tissue.

A pure feminine type of distribution of pubic hair occurred in 13 per cent. of the younger cases of dementia precox, but in only 2.6 per cent. of those admitted after the age of twenty-one years. (Fig. 185.) A semi-feminine distribution was observed in 11 per cent. of the patients. (Fig. 186.)

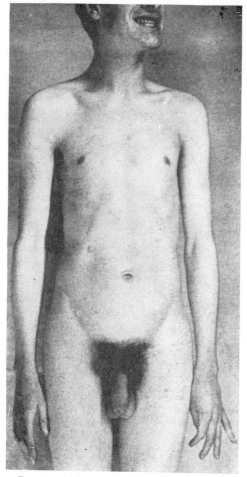

FIG. 185.—Patient with dementia precox. Age on admission, 18; present age, 23. Feminine pubic hair; deficient beard; no hair on the trunk; scrotal implant; testes average size; long thorax. (After Gibbs.)

Small testes were associated with the pure feminine type of pubic hair in only four of n i n e t e e n patients, and large testes occurred also in four. In only two patients were both testes small. In two patients one testis was undescended, and in one of these the other testis was unusually large. Likewise, in patients with definitely deficient p u b i c hair of the masculine type, there was no particular deficiency in the size of the testes.

Because of its persistence after puberty, the abundance of its growth, and the size of the testes, it would seem that the greater frequency of the feminine type of pubic hair in patients with early onset is something more than a retarded phase of normal sex development. It seems more definitely a perversion or unevenness of development.

Deficient beard was quite frequent in patients admitted at an early age, and gradually decreased in frequency in patients admitted at a later age. The hair was usually confined to the lip and chin as in females, with no hair on the jaw or neck. (Fig. 187.)

This deficiency persisted until after twenty-one in 34.6 per cent. of those first admitted between the ages of sixteen and twenty, and was

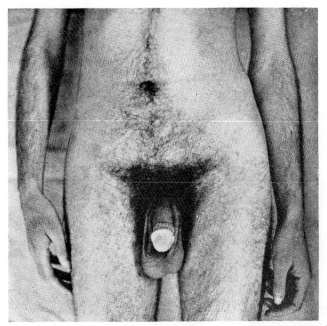

FIG. 186.—Patient with dementia precox. Age on admission, 19; present age, 30. Semifeminine pubic hair; scrotal implant; testes quite large; actively homosexual. (After Gibbs.)

still present in 21 per cent. of patients first admitted between the ages of twenty-one and twenty-five when those showing the deficiency had reached an average age of 25.8 years.

Deficient development of the secondary sexual hair did not depend on the size of the testicles, being associated with rather large testicles as frequently as with small ones.

The marriage rate of males developing dementia precox was definitely below that of males in the general population. Adult sexual relations with the opposite sex had never been accomplished in 64.1 per cent. of 120 dementia precox patients who answered the question in a satisfactory way.

22

Only 20.5 per cent. had reached an adult level of sex behavior and maintained it for even a short time, either married or single. The earlier the age on admission, the higher was the percentage of cases showing sexual inactivity.

By *scrotal implant* is meant having a fold of the scrotum on each side extended above and around the penis so that the penis seems to emerge

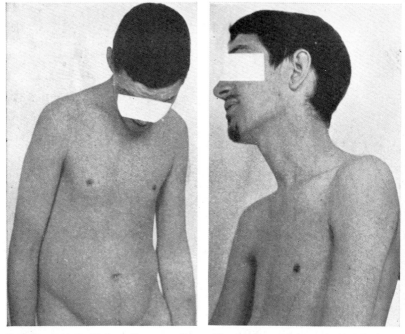

Fig. 187.—Patient with dementia precox. Same as Fig. 185. Two weeks' growth of beard; absence of hair of neck and sides of face. (After Gibbs.)

from the fold. (See preceding figures.) This occurred rather frequently, but was somewhat more frequent in those patients admitted at an early age than those admitted late.

Gibbs remarks that the findings cannot be easily interpreted in terms of internal secretions. Gonads, and especially interstitial cells, are essential to complete sex maturity, but they are not self-sustaining. Other internal secretions may stimulate or activate them. That the failure in sex growth and behavior is due to biologic inadequacy limited to the sex mechanism, probably should not be inferred. There is total functional deficiency in most of these patients. Adequate functional activity of the pituitary, thyroid and suprarenals seems to be necessary for sex growth and function.

From the necropsical investigation of a number of cases of dementia precox in both sexes, Obregia, Parhon, and Urechia [2] of Bucharest, have found some special conditions of the testicle in this condition. The seminiferous tubules are regularly attacked and absence of spermatogenesis is the rule, at least in cases of certain duration. Two of these patients who were married had no children.

These authors say that it is not impossible that the cells of the seminiferous tubules may have an internal secretion, and it may be asked if dementia precox might not be due to an alteration of this secretion. But it seems to the authors more probable that the functional spermatogenetic alteration was the effect of intoxication or some metabolic disturbance which produces the dementia precox itself.

The hypothesis of a perverted internal secretion of the cells of the seminiferous tubules is rendered untenable by the fact which Bleuler [3] raised against Bornstein's [4] hypothesis (exaggeration of puberty phenomena). This fact is that unilateral or bilateral castration does not exert any favorable action on the evolution of dementia precox. The foregoing arguments are equally applicable to the ovaries, which, in the cases observed by the authors, were very rarely normal. Bleuler had observed three cases of dementia precox in women in which the psychic disturbances ended after castration. But as normal ovaries may be observed in cases of dementia precox, and that this latter is not usual in castrated females, it may be concluded that operation in the cases quoted by Bleuler acted only as an accessory cause in the organism already predisposed by other causes.

The authors conclude from their investigations that disturbance of the internal secretion of the sex glands does not seem to be responsible for the appearance of dementia precox. But in the evolution of this condition we may find alterations of the genital glands, and that absence of spermatogenesis is the rule which, with other facts, such as alterations in the blood, shows that dementia precox, like general paralysis, is a systemic condition and not localized to the brain.

Todde [5] found that in mental disease generally, the testicles are smaller than in normal subjects, but that this diminution reaches its maximum in phrenasthenia; it is less marked in dementia precox. In these mental conditions also the function of the organ, especially the glandular secretion, is greatly altered. Such alterations usually are complete arrest of spermatogenesis involutive phenomena of the spermatogenetic and interstitial elements and complex alterations in the seminiferous canaliculi with increased intercanalicular tissue.

In dementia precox the functional disturbance and the structural alterations more especially involve the seminal gland. The alterations found at necropsy have no relation to age nor to the cause of death, but seem rather to be in direct accord with the gravity and duration of the mental disease.

In twenty-five cases of dementia investigated, Todde found diminution in the weight of the testicles in 88 per cent., diminished function in 44 per cent., and function abolished in 48 per cent.

Matsumoto [6] made a histological examination of numerous specimens of testes in twenty cases of dementia precox. These may be divided into three groups according to the time between onset of symptoms and death. The examination led to the general conclusion that the earlier the symptoms appeared, and the longer their duration before death, the more pronounced were the histological changes.

In the *first stage* of regressive atrophy only a few of the tubules show morbid changes, the most obvious being a diminution in size and fewer spermatogenic cells with fewer cells showing active nuclear mitosis, absence of spermatids and spermatozoa. The Sertoli cells are seen much more distinctly resting on the thickened basement membrane. The interstitial tissue in the region of the atrophied tubules, generally speaking, is correspondingly increased. The interstitial cells containing lipoid granules can be seen and numbers of lipoid granules are observed in the Sertoli cells.

In the *second stage,* many more tubules are similarly affected, but there may still be some tubules showing all stages of spermatogenesis. Examined with an oil-immersion lens, the heads of the newly-formed spermatozoa, both in the first and second stages, show appearances suggestive of degeneration. They are often of irregular shape and staining reaction; they present appearances like the degenerated forms described by

Mott as occurring in the fluid from the seminal vesicles in cases of dementia precox. Often they have an oxychromatin instead of a vasichromatin reaction with the hematoxylin and eosin dyes. In fact, there appears to be a general deficiency of the vasichromatin reaction of the nuclei of the spermatogonia and spermatocytes in all the tubules in the second stage.

In the *third stage,* which constituted the greater number of the twenty cases examined, there is almost complete or quite complete arrest of spermatogenesis. In the most advanced cases (and they are especially those which were admitted to the asylum in very early adolescence), the tubules show a very thickened basement membrane and no spermatogenic cells; a few Sertoli cells are seen within the tubule and an empty sustentacular network. Stained with scarlet red, numbers of large, coarse droplets of fatty matter of various sizes are seen in the spaces. The interstitial cells of Leydig can be seen in the first two stages containing fatty droplets, but they appear to be less numerous and less distinct in outline than those seen amidst the atrophied tubules in the testes of general paralytics. In the third stage, the cells of Leydig are still more difficult to find, and the interstitial lipoid is less observable. The interstitial connective tissue in some of these cases has undergone proliferation, and it is not uncommon to find, therefore, a fairly large testis in which there is a complete regressive atrophy of the spermatogenic cells. In other cases there is no interstitial connective tissue proliferation. In all the cases, however, there is thickening of the basement membrane; and, instead of one layer of flattened nucleated cells, there are several.

Quite recently, Sir F. W. Mott[7] has enriched the literature on dementia precox by some very interesting and striking studies. He reported his results in the proceedings of the Royal Society of Medicine. His first investigations along this line were published in the *British Medical Journal*[8] in a splendid contribution entitled, " The Investigation of the Testes in One Hundred Cases of Deaths in Hospitals and Asylums at all Ages from Birth to Eighty Years and Over." In collaboration with Prados Y. Such, after a thorough and painstaking study, these investigators formulated the following conclusions, which are given here from the proceedings of the Royal Society of Medicine.[9]

" 1. The interstitial cells prior to birth act as sexual determinants, and at birth form the greater part of the interstitial tissue which constitutes the major part of the testes. (Fig. 188.) They contain lipoid granules. Moreover, fine lipoid granules are seen between the embryonic epithelial cells of the tubules.

" 2. The interstitial cells after birth undergo a regressive atrophy and disappear. Inasmuch as the seminiferous tubules at four months are twice the size of those at birth and are approximated, it follows that the fine lipoid granules which are found between the epithelial cells have, in all probability, served as a pabulum for their formative activity. But, since there is still lipoid in the residual interstitial cells (Fig. 189), this correlation of function of the interstitial cells and the epithelial formative activity has not ceased, and it is reasonable to assume that

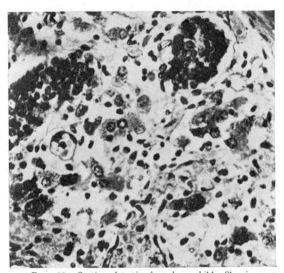

FIG. 188.—Section of testis of newborn child. Showing embryonic tubules and polygonal mature interstitial cells with round nuclei. Many small immature cells are present, but not so distinctly seen lying in loose areolar tissue. (Staining hematoxylin eosin. Magnification 410.) (Mott and Such.)

had the child been six months old at death, it would have ceased and no lipoid would have been found anywhere, and the following facts support this conclusion. At ten years the tubuli seminiferi are, for the most part, approximated and, as a rule, are only a little larger than those at four months; there is no lipoid in the interstitial tissue, or in the tubules. There are occasionally to be seen mitotic figures as if spermatocytes were commencing to be formed, but no Sertoli cells are observable. In the interstitial tissue are seen numbers of ovals, round and polymorphic nuclei, not nuclei of fibroblasts; and occasionally a definite small polygonal cell, eosin stained, can be seen, indicating that *pari passu* with the tubular epithelial formative activity there is a reappearance of the interstitial cells.

" 3. The appearance of these immature interstitial cells resemble, in many respects, the appearance presented by the interstitial cells in advanced cases of dementia precox.

" 4. At puberty and adolescence, the tubules have increased in size owing to active proliferation and spermatogenesis. Abundance of mature interstitial cells are present, which are undergoing active functional changes. They contain lipoid and lie upon a lymphatic space which s u r r o u n d s the tubule. Reasons are given why it may be assumed that this lipoid substance passes through the basement membrane to the Sertoli cells which contain fine lipoid granules, and serve as nurse cells to the spermatozoa.

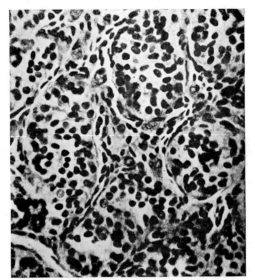

FIG. 189.—Section of testis of child, aged 4 months. The tubules are nearly double the size and approximated: here and there are small areas containing a few small faint pink polygonal cells, but for the most part the normal interstitial cells have disappeared. The portion of the section in the center containing the residue of the interstitial cells was found after search. (Staining hematoxylin eosin. Magnification 430.) (Mott and Such.)

" 5. M i c r o s c o p i c appearances indicate the continuous development of new interstitial cells which mature, actively function and decay. They are present in extreme old age, and sometimes when spermatogenesis has ceased.

" 6. The microscopic examination of the testes of twenty-seven cases of dementia precox, all commencing in prepubertal, pubertal or adolescent stages, are described, together with the age of admission and duration of asylum treatment, and the age at death, with cause of death and the principal mental diagnostic conditions, are given in Table I. (Mott and Such.)

" 7. It may be noted that a number of patients died of pulmonary tuberculosis, but a number died of acute disease, e.g., pneumonia and

TABLE I. (MOTT AND SUCH.)

Dementia Precox, Twenty-seven Cases.

Number of card and name	Age at death	Duration of time in asylum	Diagnosis	Cause of death	Weight of testis in grammes	Microscopic examination
(1) S. A. L.	25	6 months	Dementia precox; condition remained with slight change; symptoms of a stuporose, hebephrenic form of dementia precox; has hallucinations and delusions	Acute pulmonary tuberculosis	10–10	Second stage; no normal Leydig cells with low power; pale syncytium in which are numbers of pale chromatin; deficient nuclei of varied size and form; a few small cells with eosin staining; interstitial lipoid much diminished.
(2) W. R. M.	19	6 months	Adolescent insanity; made a violent attack upon his mother; irrational, deluded, sullen and depressed; masturbator	Wasting and exhaustion	8–8	Advanced third stage; no normal Leydig cells with low power; pale syncytium with pale chromatin; deficient nuclei of varied form and size; fibroblastic overgrowth; interstitial lipoid much diminished.
(3) A.	21	9 months	Dementia precox; threatened to kill his sister; suffered from insomnia, delusions; blind, the result of trying to gouge out his eyes; religious mania	Pulmonary tubercle, aortic hypoplasia	10–11	Advanced third stage; no normal Leydig cells with low power; pale syncytium with pale chromatin; deficient or diffuse purple nuclei; excess of fibroblasts; early history of symptoms; but inasmuch as the secondary sexual characters were well developed, it follows that Leydig cells have degenerated since puberty.
(4) M. G.	27	18 months (probably duration of symptoms much longer)	Dementia precox; history of manic-depressive insanity in father; hallucinations, delusions, katatonic; attempted suicide; admits excessive masturbation	Lobar pneumonia		Second stage; not much increase in interstitial tissue; groups of eosin-stained cells seen with low power, but fewer than normal.

	Age	Duration	Clinical	Cause of death		Gonad
(5) H. W.	21	18 months (for 3 years previously history in Army of delinquencies)	Recent melancholia; had hallucinations; morose and confused; refuses to speak, with bursts of aggressiveness	Lobar pneumonia	13.8–15.8	Second state; no Leydig cells seen with low power; isolated small eosin-stained cells; pale vacuolated syncytium with oval, irregular pale nuclei; deficient in chromatin (*vide* Fig. 191, Plate C).
(6) F. A. E.	28	18 months	Primary dementia; fixed, stupid expression; never speaks unless addressed and then makes silly replies	Dysentery	19–19	Early first stage of regressive spermatogenic atrophy; active spermatogenesis in many tubules, but degeneration of many of the spermatozoa (*vide* photomicrographs 1 and 2); diminution of Leydig cells as compared with normal; fewer mature cells (*vide* Fig. 191, Plate B).
(7) L. Wm.	26	20 months	Dementia precox; dull and apathetic with occasional outbursts of excitement; masturbation	Dysentery and commencing pneumonia (died after a few days illness)	11–10	Second stage; no normal Leydig cells seen with low power; irregular and oval pale nuclei in vacuolated syncytium pale pink or pigmented; excess of fibroblasts.
(8) T.	27	22 months	Dementia precox; "makes grimaces and laughs without cause...; wanders about gesticulating and doing strange things;" has delusions; dull, stupid, no initiative; no note of masturbation	Broncho-pneumonia	19–16	First stage; no normal Leydig cells seen with low power; number of oval, pale, rounded or irregular nuclei in a pale unstained syncytium.
(9) C. U.	24	2 years (about 2 yrs. duration of definite symptoms)	Dementia precox; auditory hallucinations; violent at times, otherwise stuporose; no mention of masturbation	Broncho-pneumonia	15–16	Third stage; no Leydig cells low power; pale or pigmented syncytium with oval, round imperfectly stained nuclei; fibroblastic overgrowth.

TABLE I. (MOTT AND SUCH.)—Continued.
Dementia Precox, Twenty-Seven Cases.

Number of card and name	Age at death	Duration of time in asylum	Diagnosis	Cause of death	Weight of testis in grammes	Microscopic examination
(10) H. P.	20	2 years (6 months before admission character changed)	Dementia precox; duration one year, "attributes present state to a row he had with his brother;" was suspicious	Pulmonary tuberculosis	9–9	Third stage; no Leydig cells, high power; occasionally a pinkish vacuolated syncytium of cells with pale oval and irregular-shaped nuclei; fibrous tissue overgrowth.
(11) S. E.	25	2 years	Dementia precox; "confused, restless, reacts slowly to questions, deluded, dull, apathetic"	Acute lobar (death after a few days illness) pneumonia	21.2–16.1	Early second stage; only a few small imperfectly stained groups of Leydig cells, seen deficiently stained with eosin; there are numbers of oval, round and irregular-shaped pale nuclei; many fibroblasts; fair amount of interstitial lipoid.
(12) A. M.	25	2 years	Dementia precox; dull and confused; indifferent to self and surroundings	Pulmonary tuberculosis	10–10	Advanced second state; generally diminished interstitial lipoid; dense interstitial tissue fibroblast overgrowth; ill defined pale syncytium with pale nuclei oval or varies in shape and size; deficient chromatin or diffuse pale purple.
(13) G. R. D.	22	2½ years	Dementia precox; dull, stupid, very rarely speaks to anyone; untidy, habits faulty	Acute pulmonary tuberculosis	15–16	Third stage; greatly diminished interstitial lipoid; no normal Leydig cells; vacuolated eosin-stained cells with pale nuclei or vacuolated unstained syncytium with pale, oval, irregular nuclei; deficient in chromatin.

(14) S. T.	27	3 years	Dementia precox; sullen and very taciturn, laughs silly manner, no cause; very impulsive and at times very violent and destructive	Dysentery	12.5–16	Second stage; atrophy of Leydig cells; many cells pigmented.
(15) C.	29	3 years	Dementia precox; "he takes no notice of his surroundings;" mannerisms, mutism and periods of impulsive excitement at one time associated with cataleptoid state or katatonia; family history *nil*	Phthisis	10–10	Third stage; no normal Leydig cells; occasional small isolated cells seen with low power, otherwise vacuolated syncytium with pale oval and irregular nuclei; pigment in vacuolated cells.
(16) M. J.	29	5 years (commenced before 25 for certain; how long before this not known)	Primary dementia of adolescence; hallucinations, delusions, attitudinising; grimacing and other signs noted	Acute pulmonary tuberculosis	8.5–9	Third stage; no normal Leydig cells; numerous pigmented cells; pale syncytium with numerous pale nuclei of irregular shape.
(17) C. F. G.	30	5 years	Paranoidal form of dementia precox with masturbation, mannerisms, stereotypism; periods of katatonia and excitement	Exhaustion (blue hands and feet at death)	13.5–12	Third stage of regressive atrophy of tubules; no fibroblastic overgrowth; no normal Leydig cells; here and there an islet of Leydig cells seen with oil immersion; cytoplasm pale pink or pigmented; nuclei deficient chromatin, oval or irregular in size and shape.
(18) B.	26	5 years	Primary dementia of adolescence; no history of masturbation in the notes	Tuberculosis, broncho-pneumonia, ulcerationofintestines	13.5–11.5	Second stage; very little interstitial tissue and lipoid; no normal Leydig cells; pale syncytium with nuclei of varied size and deficient chromatin, a few isolated Leydig cells.

TABLE I. (MOTT AND SUCH.)—*Continued.*
Dementia Precox, Twenty-Seven Cases.

Number of card and name	Age at death	Duration of time in asylum	Diagnosis	Cause of death	Weight of testis in grammes	Microscopic examination
(19) S. H.	28	7 years (11 months prior to admission gradually became dull, apathetic and anergic)	Dementia precox; did not brighten up at all; sat or stood for hours in one position; movements grotesque, showed some stereotypy; much addicted to masturbation before and after admission	Pulmonary tuberculosis		Third stage; interstitial tissue increased; islands and islets of Leydig cells containing lipoid; Sertoli cells contain abundance of lipoid; no normal Leydig cells but vacuolated syncytium containing nuclei of varied form and size; deficient in chromatin; excess of fibroblasts.
(20) U. T.	33	7 years	Dementia precox; dull, listless, only speaks in whispers; occasionally faulty in habits; some katatonia; sits in one place gazing as long as allowed; no masturbation during residence	Chronic dysentery, bronchopneumonia	8.5–6.5	Third stage; interstitial tissue increased; no normal Leydig cells; vacuolated pale syncytium with here and there groups of pigmented cells; nuclei deficient in chromatin; variable in size and shape; excess of fibroblasts.
(21) C. W. J.	35	8 years (about 8 years duration, commenced at 27)	Dementia precox; history of hallucinations, delusions; masturbation and terminal dementia	Broncho-pneumonia, pulmonary tuberculosis (probably 3 months' duration)	16–15	Early third stage; abundance of interstitial lipoid, and in Sertoli cells minute lipoid granules can be seen passing through basement membrane; lipoid granules visible in Leydig cells accounting for vacuolation in hematoxylin eosin preparation; no normal clumps of cells; with oil immersion pale vacuolated syncytium with pale nuclei of varied form and size; here and there pigmentation.

(22) M. Wm.	35	10 years	Dementia precox; two years after admission notes state that he is suffering with secondary dementia; stands in various attitudes in corners of grounds and wards with bowed head; cannot converse rationally; poor idea of time and place	Dysentery	17.5-14.5	Third stage; all the tubules are deficient in epithelial cells, many are only lined by Sertoli cells; a striking feature is the unequal nuclear staining of the remaining cells in the tubules; the interstitial tissue consists of an overgrowth of fibroblasts and a number of pale nuclei of varied size and shape, around which in places are little collections of pigment indicative of degenerated Leydig cells; no normal cells were observed.
(23) M. A. G.	27	10 years	At age of 17 certified as mania; year before as suffering with delusions of persecution, possessed by devil, hopelessly lost; attempted to commit suicide; progress of case shows typical dementia precox	Broncho-pneumonia	20.5-17	Advanced second stage; the most obvious change is an increase of interstitial tissue, excess of fibroblasts; no normal Leydig cells; with oil immersion isolated pale syncytium cells with nuclei deficient in chromatin of varied size and shape; no pigmentation observed.
(24) G. A.	36	11 years	Typical dementia precox of ten years' duration, commenced at 26	Apical tubercle and cholelithiasis	12-0 Left testis absent; left suprarenal 6.5 grm., right 12 grm.	Third stage; increase of interstitial tissue, a few scattered islets of Leydig cells and vacuolated syncytium with pale nuclei of varied form and size; excess of fibroblasts; the spermatogenic cells more profoundly affected than the interstitial cells.

TABLE I. (Mott and Such.)—Continued.
Dementia Precox, Twenty-Seven Cases.

Number of card and name	Age at death	Duration of time in asylum	Diagnosis	Cause of death	Weight of testis in grammes	Microscopic examination
(25) W. H.	35	14 years	Dementia precox; "earned his own living until six years ago," four times sentenced to prison; masturbator; had delusions, hallucinations; was irrational, exalted, incoherent, and had innumerable mannerisms; verbigerations; no signs of congenital syphilis	Exhaustion	5–5	Third stage; capsule of testes greatly thickened; seminiferous tubes, extreme regressive atrophy; no lipoid in Sertoli cells; nodules of Leydig cells, many containing lipoid granules; these nodules stained with hematoxylin eosin show a vacuolated syncytium of cells with abundant nuclei of varied form and size containing a fair amount of chromatin, but there is no eosin staining of cytoplasm; the specimen is not unlike that of a cryptorchid (*vide* photomicrograph, Fig. 5).
(26) D. F. Wm.	33	15 years	Dementia precox; dull, morose and taciturn; tried to cut his throat; sometimes violent and excited; confirmed masturbator	Adherent lungs, probably tubercular	7.5–9	Early third stage; very little interstitial or intertubular lipoid; no normal Leydig cells seen.
(27) B. F.	35	15 years (15 years' duration at least)	Katatonic dementia precox; masturbation and adolescence are given as causes; he suffered with emotional indifference, mutism, katatonia and acrocyanosis; did not obey calls of nature, and required constant supervision; destructive tendencies.	Acute bronchopneumonia	10–10	Advanced second stage of spermatogenic atrophy; no normal Leydig cells seen; syncytium with *very* marked pigmentation everywhere; nuclei varied in size and shape with deficient chromatin excess of fibroblasts; suprarenals very small, deficiency of medullary substance.

dysentery, and after a few days or a week or two of illness. The micro-scopic conditions did not differ essentially from those dying of pulmonary tuberculosis. In some there was no history of masturbation, whereas in others there was definite information, but the microscopic examination did not reveal any difference.

" 8. The regressive atrophy found microscopically corresponded, gen-erally speaking, but not always, with the loss of weight of the testes and the naked eye appearances. As a rule, the longer the duration of the mental symptoms, the more pro-nounced was the atrophy, but duration of asylum treatment does not strictly connote the length of duration of symptoms.

" 9. T h e regressive atrophy, as determined by microscopic examination, has led me (F. W. M.) to divide the c a s e s into three groups. The first stage in which the changes i n d i c a t e the forma-tion of normal and degen-

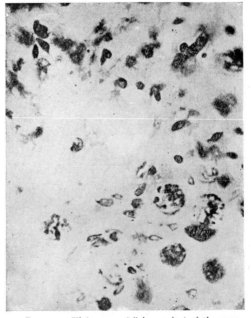

FIG. 190.—High power (oil immersion) of the same section, showing a group of these degenerated spermato-zoa. Observe the heads of the spermatozoa are of unequal size and shape, and do not take the nuclear stain, although the chromatin in the adjacent cells is well stained. Mag-nification 1,200. (After Mott.)

erate spermatozoa (Fig. 190), and commencing failure in the formation of normal interstitial cells and by special staining an increase of inter-stitial fibroblasts. In the second stage, there is, in addition, an obvious shrinkage of many of the tubules, increase of fibroblasts, thickening of basement membrane and failure of spermatogenesis. The mature intersti-tial cells are fewer in number and there are numbers of immature cells with pale nuclei deficient in chromatin. In the third stage, the tubules either show no spermatogenesis, or only a few tubules relatively show

TABLE II. (MOTT AND SUCH.)

Summary of Results Obtained in Nine Cases of Psychoses other than Dementia Precox Occurring in Post Adolescence.

Number of card and name	Age at death	Duration of time in asylum	Diagnosis and symptoms	Cause of death	Weight of testes in grammes	Microscopic examination
(1) G. J. A.	50	3 years	Subacute melancholia, epilepsy	Broncho-pneumonia; gangrene of lung; epilepsy	9–9	Advanced second stage of regressive atrophy of tubules and Leydig's cells; pigmentation.
(2) B. G.	..	18 months	Persecutory insanity	Edema of glottis; fatty heart	9–7	Second stage of regressive atrophy of tubes; islets and islands of Leydig cells seen with low power; eosin stained, some pigmented.
(3) D. E.	48	20 months	Confusional insanity, serous meningitis; operation for tumor	Lobar pneumonia		First stage advanced of regressive atrophy; atrophous pigmentary degeneration of Leydig's cells.
(4) M. T. G.	58	4 months	Melancholia, hypochondriasis	Exhaustion; bronchitis; emphysema	18–13	Tubules active, spermatogenesis in most of the tubules; nothing abnormal except diminution in numbers of Leydig cells.
(5) A. T.	65	22 years	Korsakoff psychosis	Cirrhosis of liver; carcinomatous; ascites paracentesis	12–12	Complete arrest of spermatogenesis; thickened basement membrane; Leydig cells considering age fairly normal in numbers and staining reaction; not pigmented.
(6) N. P.	53	9 years	Recurrent manic-depressive insanity, dementia	Pulmonary tubercle	14–14	Third stage of regressive atrophy of tubules and Leydig cells; pigment granules in syncytium.
(7) H.	36	First attack at puberty; four times in Claybury; subsequently 40 days the last time, then died	Recurrent manic-depressive insanity	Acute broncho-pneumonia	9–11	Many normal tubules showing active normal spermatogenesis and spermatozoa; Leydig cells for the most part pale syncytium with faint eosin staining; some normal groups of eosin-stained polygonal cells seen; some pigmentation; no overgrowth of fibroblasts.

(8) H. T. L.	41	22 years	History points to alternate periods of depression and excitement. Clinical notes: melancholia, restless, miserable and depressed, a furtive expression; answers questions readily, but becomes incoherent; has hallucinations of sight and hearing; memory fair for remote events, poor for recent events; poor health and condition	Pulmonary tubercle	15–20	Spermatozoa from vesicular alive eight hours after death; many tubules show all stages of spermatogenesis; normal staining and shape of spermatozoa; no failure of nuclear staining; Leydig cells in small clumps seen with low power; oil immersion examination: no pigmentary degeneration; no excess of fibroblasts; occasional groups of normal nucleated polygonal cells, well stained; majority vacuolated syncytium with fairly normal nuclei; fair amount of interstitial lipoid and in Sertoli cells.
(9) B. C.	50	History of attack 4 yrs. previously present attack 40 days	Manic-depressive insanity	Pulmonary tubercle	10.2–12.2	Vesicula seminalis abundant spermatozoa; spermatic tubules fairly normal for the age; quite one-half show all stages of spermatogenesis; basement membrane not thickened; interstitial tissue much diminished; no excess of fibroblasts; low power; only slight evidence of interstitial cells; with oil immersion; a vacuolated faintly pink-stained syncytium; nuclei pale, irregular, small crenated as if they had undergone atrophy or were immature; pigmentation of the cytoplasm. Conclusion: interstitial cells affected out of proportion to the spermatogenic.

23

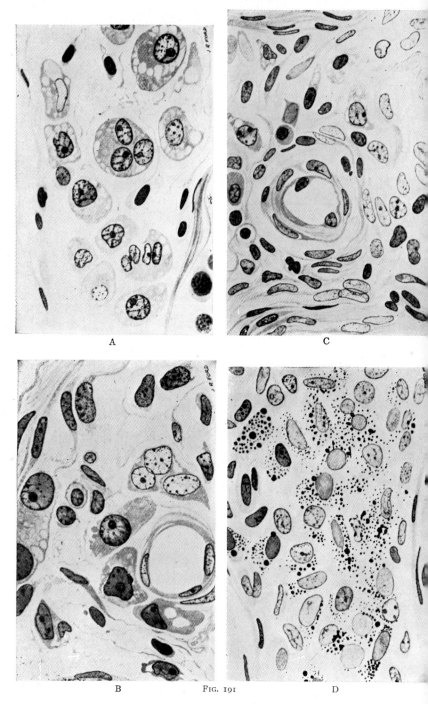

A

C

B   Fig. 191   D

FIG. 192.—Interstitial cells. Examination of hematoxylin eosin preparations.

A. Section of testes of man, aged 81, suffering with senile dementia. On the left a portion of tubule is shown exhibiting spermatogenesis with normal stained heads of spermatozoa the basement membrane of this tubule and the adjacent one, which shows normal staining spermatogonia and spermatocytes, is thickened by an increase of fibroblasts. Above is an isolated small interstitial cell and above this a group forming a syncytium by vacuolation; the nuclei of normal shape and staining; one cell contains pigment granules.

B. Section of testis of normal case dying of shock showing abundance of normal interstitial cells lying between the tubules. They are most of them mature and contain a good amount of eosin staining substance, although the vacuolation would show that for the most part they contain lipoid. There are three young cells together showing no vacuolation.

C. Section of testis of a case of juvenile tabo-paralysis. Spermatozoa were found in the vesiculæ living eight hours after death. Most of the tubules showed normal active spermatogenesis. There was some thickening of basement membrane of tubules; this is seen in the tubule on the right by the increase of fibroblast nuclei. There are abundant normal interstitial cells which are visible as eosin-stained clumps with a low power. The nuclei are well stained and there are no fibroblast nuclei intervening. This should be compared with D.

D. Section of testis from Case 19, Table I. Observe the great fibroblast nuclear proliferation of the basement membrane, upon which lies only a syncytium of Sertoli cells. The interstitial tissue consists of a very vacuolated syncytium of cells with pale nuclei of irregular form and size. The elongated more deeply stained nuclei are the nuclei of intervening fibroblasts. (After Mott and Such.)

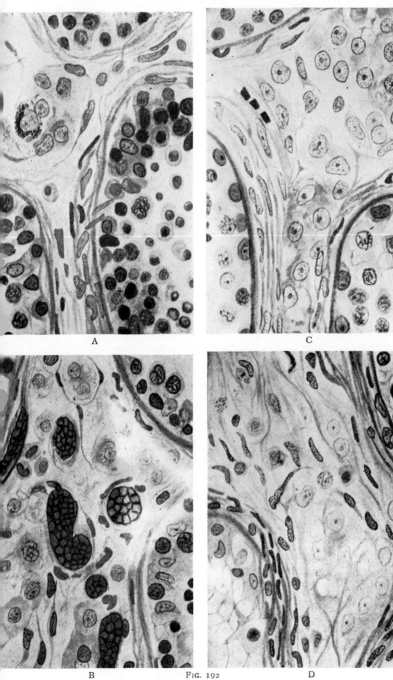

A   C

B   FIG. 192   D

some spermatozoa, some being degenerate; there is a failure of formative nuclear activity and many, or, in advanced cases, all the tubules consist only of a very thickened basement membrane lined by Sertoli cells. These cells usually contain lipoid granules in the syncytium, and when this occurs there is lipoid in the interstitial tissue and cells. This indicates that the essential feature of the atrophy is a primary germinal defect.

" 10. In seven of the cases of dementia precox, a pigmentary deposit was found in the interstitial cells which is not seen in normal conditions except in old age, and therefore may be regarded as evidence of presenile change."

In the preceding table, the authors give a summary of the results obtained in nine cases of psychoses other than dementia precox.

" 12. There are four cases in Table IV in which symptoms of dementia precox came on in postadolescence, and all of these showed marked regressive atrophic changes of the tubules and the interstitial cells similar to those observed in cases commencing in early life.

" A recurrent manic depressive insanity may terminate in dementia, and then regressive atrophic changes are found exactly similar to those met with in dementia precox. Otherwise, manic depressive insanity does not show these regressive atrophic changes in the testes. It will be interesting to see whether there are changes in the brain corresponding to those I have described in dementia precox in these cases.

" 13. As a contrast to these regressive atrophic changes occurring in the biogenetic psychoses are the changes in the testes of cases of general paralysis, an acquired disease. Whereas, in the former the atrophy is primary and affects more or less the whole organ, in the latter it is secondary to inflammatory changes in the epididymis, either gonorrheal or syphilitic, and causing a complete disappearance of the epithelium of the tubules by obstruction of the *vasa efferentia*. The result is local patches of dense fibrous tissue affecting especially one testis, sometimes both. In the immediate neighborhood are tubules showing normal active spermatogenesis and Leydig's cells. Not infrequently, amidst the atrophied tubules consisting only of thickened basement membrane interstitial cells are present.

" In spite of this secondary atrophy which affects the testes of so many paralytics, the average weight of the pair, after removal of the tunica vaginalis and epididymis, is eight gm. heavier than the testes of cases of dementia precox. Whereas, in the great majority of cases of dementia precox an emulsion of the testes showed no spermatozoa, the converse was found in general paralysis."

The accompanying photographs illustrate the work of these authors and emphasize the important points in the conclusions cited. (Figs. 191 and 192.)

Cases of Dementia Precox and Homotransplantations.—

A case reported in the *New York Medical Journal* of April, 1911, by the late G. Frank Lydston may be of interest in this connection: " Young man aged twenty-two years, no occupation, heredity bad, paternal grandfather and one paternal aunt committed suicide. Another paternal aunt had seven children, five of whom developed dementia between the ages of sixteen and twenty years. This aunt was insane for twenty years after the birth of her last child and died insane. Patient was very bright at school. He suffered with a head injury of some kind four years ago, which his parents are inclined to believe had something to do with his condition, as their attention was first attracted to his mental state not long afterward. For some time he complained of headache. This injury, in our opinion, bore only a coincidental relation to the mental state that subsequently developed. Taking into consideration the family history and the typic nature of the case and the absence of history of really severe trauma and of present evidences of previous trauma, my position regarding the possible etiologic relation of the head injury to the mental state would seem to be justified. About three years before I saw the case, a Neisserian infection was contracted. Recovery apparently was satisfactory. The contraction of this infection, according to his mother, ' preyed upon his mind a good deal and may have had something to do with his mental condition.'

" Something over three years before the author first saw the patient mental symptoms began to be noticeable. Dr. Archibald Church was consulted, September 13, 1914. His report in brief was as follows:

' The case impresses me as being the initial phase of a dementia pre-cox. I anticipate that he will develop a phase of activity, perhaps with a good deal of excitement and boisterous conduct, or he may become more and more stupid and catatonic. At any rate, it will be some time before he is better and his ultimate prospects are extremely bad.'

" Soon after the case was brought to our attention we referred it to Dr. Bayard Holmes for an Abderhalden test. His report was as follows:

' The hemoglobin was 80 per cent., the whites 12,400, the reds 4,800,000, the polymorphonuclear neutrophiles 57 per cent., small lymphocytes 30 per cent., large lymphocytes 8 per cent., transitionals 1 per cent., and eosinophiles 4 per cent. The form and character of the red corpuscles were normal and no parasites were to be observed.

' The serum of this blood was centrifugated for two and a half hours, and 1.5 cc. of the serum was placed in each of six dialyzers, in which was also placed one gram of the following: Human organ albumins prepared according to the method of Abderhalden and each tested free from ninhy-drin reducing elements before being used, namely against cerebral cortex, pancreas, thyroid, ovary, testicle and one control. They were incubated in Erlenmeyer flasks, each containing 20 cc. of sterile water for a period of sixteen hours at a temperature of 90 to 100° F. At the end of that time they were each tested against the ninhydrin solution and boiled for one minute. Every tube proved negative, being perfectly clear at the end of a half hour.

' The blood serum in this case does not give any of the reactions of dementia precox. Neither does the blood picture of the microscopical examination correspond with the blood picture in cases of dementia precox. Although I made no considerable examination, the ocular reflexes and the mental picture did not suggest to me even the possibility of an embry-onic case of that disease. I do not hesitate to state that this is not a case of dementia precox.' "

Commenting on this case, Doctor Lydston had the following to say: " That the subject was insane is beyond the possibility of doubt. With due deference to Doctor Holmes' opinion, that the case must be classed as dementia precox is obvious. The prevailing nomenclature of psy-choses is faulty, it is true, and, in the case of dementia precox, absurd, in a way, the term having only a symptomatic-chronologic basis, with no definite pathological foundation, but at present, it is the best nomenclature available. It is possible that the Abderhalden test and hemologic observations eventually may enable us to resolve dementia precox into several distinct pathologic types, one of which responds positively to the Abderhalden test, while the others do not. This would facilitate a more scientific nomenclature and classification. It, of course, is possible that our conclusion regarding the head injury in the case is incorrect; if so, this naturally might explain the negative Abderhalden. Even granting, however, that the head injury was an exciting etiologic factor, the same nomenclature would confront us.

" The evidence of mental deterioration in the case in point is distinct, and of a character which leads me to classify the psychosis as hebephrenia of the paranoid type. Hallucinations have been a dominant feature. Voices whispering, adverse comments, and insults were daily complained of. Lack of energy, and the complaint that he was too weak to work, were salient points. The most prominent feature of the case was the patient's notion that he was a great architect and builder. His particular obsession was that he was in the employ of the City of Chicago, his special business being the remodelling of every large building within the loop. He spent many hours each day in writing ' specifications ' for such remodelling. The following are samples of his lucubrations:

' 1. The Mallers Building was built as large in city as neither Building contribute to Herbert at all. Fine stones on Mallers Building has stones representing the ends of earth. One on each side of the door has two poles or ends of earth. Have building largest in world and fine stones as Equator higher up as students dont know. Have lights showing these stones.

' 2. The Hub store built before Marshall Field & Company Building. Both sell men's suits. Buildings has no opposition on Account of neither seeing each other. Mostly for two hotels or Theatres. Blackstone and LaSalle Hotel, leaving both tops off both hotels and they will be eighteen or Blackstone Theatre and Majestic Theatre, Blackstone takes off one of Majestic leaving Eighteen. 4 Buildings and 4 stories make same as largest Printer Building. Both see Monadnock Bldg.

' 3. The LaSalle Hotel built after McCormick Bldg only a Hotel. Built same distance from railroad and McCormick Bldg. and not hurting I. C. R. R. Have large smoke stack running up side of Hotel for no interruption of I. C. smoke stacks. Built also on account of Taft. Same height as McCormick. Top of Seats are higher in LaSalle Hotel on account of foreign countries and Washington and also Quaker City Church. People must not think they are Queen and King seats here on that account. Little like Blackstone on Top of Build, only larger and different altogether.

' 4. The Franklin Bldg. is the building supposed to be finest printers building in city to honor *Benjamin Franklin* the same man discovered telephony. Same can be used as business building as close to Heisen Bldg, as Heisen Bldg. built for high telegraphy today, bringing telephony and telegraph together on account of printing paper being very precious, and two fastest ways of protecting same. Offices to be used as same making Franklin Bldg. *Finest* in city.'

" October 3, 1914, by request of the patient's mother and with complete understanding on her part of the experimental nature of the procedure, the author implanted two testes upon the patient, one in the suprapubic region and the other in the left side of the scrotum. The result of the suprapubic implantation already has been related. In passing, it may be stated that faulty technic probably was responsible for the loss of this testicle. The gland was very large and firm, and the implantation bed was hardly ample enough, the resulting pressure being disastrous. Even as matters were, a considerable portion of the gland was living, adherent, and, had it not been removed, possibly would have survived for some months.

" The scrotal implantation was perfectly successful. December 16, 1914, there had been no diminution in the size of the implantation mass that could not be explained by resolution of the defensive exudate surrounding it.

" Beginning about one week after the implanation, considerable improvement in the patient's mental condition was noticeable. His ' architectural ' writing became a little more coherent, and he would not write unless urged to do so. He was encouraged to correspond with his friends.

Comparison of a letter written by him soon after the implantation with another written later, showed a marked improvement. The latter missive is herewith submitted:

' Miss. . . . .

  G. . . . . Bldg.

Dear Miss . . . .

  I received your flowers and was glad to know some kind friend remembered me. The flowers were beautiful and my mother was down to see you as she said. Now you know I am here. Will want to see you next time I get a chance myself.

  Your friend,

  . . . . '

  " Obviously, the improvement may have been of no special significance, although it was sufficient to arouse great enthusiasm on the part of his relatives and friends.

  " The improvement continued for several weeks, during which time the patient did not do any writing. He began reading assiduously, expressed a desire to ' go to work,' and showed interest in many matters to which he hitherto was indifferent. This state of affairs lasted for several weeks, during which time his response to various tests showed a marked change for the better. The aspect of the case now again changed, and the mental condition was as bad as ever. He now showed some irascibility and resumed his writing. Several weeks later he again improved, and after a few weeks was distinctly better. He had ceased writing, seldom heard voices, and was working in a drug store for a portion of the day. On question he admitted the ' foolishness ' of his literary effusions and hallucinations, but if these matters were discussed at length, his expressions still were unsound, although not so markedly as formerly. There was a change in the aspect of the case in that there was now a tendency to melancholy, and, as a special source of worry, an imaginary defect of eyesight, which had been carefully tested and pronounced normal by Dr. Harry Gradle. There also was a new delusion. He attributed the ' lump ' in his scrotum to a large marble which he had swallowed when a boy.

" November 3, 1914, Dr. Ralph Webster reported a blood examination as follows:

'Red cells .... 5,050,000 per c.mm.
White cells .... 16,400 per c.mm.
    Polymorphonuclear neutrophiles .... 85 per cent.
    Polymorphonuclear eosinophiles .... 2 per cent.
    Polymorphonuclear basophiles .... 1 per cent.
    Large mononuclears .... 1 per cent.
    Small mononuclears .... 11 per cent.
    Myocytes .... 0 per cent.
    Transitional .... 0 per cent.
Hemoglobin .... 88 per cent.
Color index 8
Coagulation time—
Nucleated red cells .... Negative.
Polychromatophilia .... Negative.
Degenerations .... Negative.
Blood pressure (systolic) .... 120 mm.'

" Comparison of Doctor Webster's reports with that of Doctor Holmes is suggestive, although by no means conclusive. The improvement in hemoglobin and the number of reds is, however, consistent with what we have observed in previous implantation experiments.

" February 8, 1915, the patient was surprisingly improved both as to mentality and general condition. The ' melancholy ' had disappeared and his mother reported that he was quite industrious and ambitious.

" About December 15, 1916, the patient reported and was found to be still improved mentally. His general health, however, seemed to be failing, without any especial reason therefor. Quite recently the author was informed that the patient had developed tuberculosis. There has been no opportunity of verifying this.

" It will be evident from the foregoing account of this case that the author by no means is claiming indisputable therapeutic results from the implantation. There, nevertheless, is abundant encouragement for further experimental work in dementia precox. The case may still further improve, and in any event, it may later be shown that there is a form of dementia precox which, if taken early, is susceptible of improvement, or possibly even cure, by implantation. If there is such a form, it probably will be found to be that which shows a positive Abderhalden reaction."

Author's Experiences.—

F. R. R., aged twenty-two years, a designer by occupation.

Family History.—Mother highly nervous; suffered a number of " break-downs " for which she had to be taken to a sanitarium. Father in robust health. Two brothers; no sisters. Younger brother homosexual tendencies; older brother normal. No history of syphilis in the family.

Personal History.—The patient was examined by a prominent neurologist, and diagnosis of a dementia precox was made. The usual forms of treatment were of no avail; in fact, the patient showed tendencies to become worse instead of better. The neurologist who referred the patient to the author became very much impressed with the work of Sir Mott of England, who has proven a deficiency and morbidity of the Leydig cells in dementia precox, and in view of the fact that everything possible had been tried to ameliorate the patient's condition, without success, he, after consultation with the author, proposed an experimental implantation. Consent was obtained from the immediate members of the family to perform this operation for they were much concerned about the patient. The older brother offered a portion of his testis for implantation.

Operation.—On May 4, 1922, the operation was performed by the author's technique. The patient left the hospital four weeks after operation, the wound having healed *per primam*.

Postoperative Course.—The patient's mental condition four months after the operation, September 5, 1922, showed some improvement. On November 11, 1922, the neurologist reported further progress. At present, ten months after the operation, the condition is about the same. Last report, November 28, 1923. " Patient is mentally much better than before operation," writes a near relative.

Comment.—Recovery cannot be spoken of in this case, for certain manifestations on the part of the patient are still present and do not permit of definitely labeling the case as one of recovery. However, he undoubtedly is improved, and, what is more important, the gradual mental retrogression that was evident before the transplantation may, perhaps, in the opinion of the author, have been arrested because of the implantation, and a degree of improvement reached which may be assumed not to have been possible of accomplishment without this form of therapy.

A similar case, transplanted by the author in July, 1921, was followed by no improvement whatever. In view of Mott's researches, more clinical evidence is necessary to establish definite indications for implantation of the type of implant best suited to these cases, though the rationale of the procedure is self evident. Another case, of dementia precox, with heterotransplant. Harold H. K., was referred to the author by Doctor Pfister of Chicago. He was twenty-two years of age (Hospital No. 13,667); family history negative; no insanity, epilepsy or other discoverable familial taints.

Habits.—He never slept well at night; his appetite was good; he occasionally was constipated.

Previous History.—He has never been seriously ill; always has been melancholy and " by himself;" otherwise mentally normal. He graduated from the public school when he was fourteen years old and was then admitted to high school. When he was fifteen he left high school and began to work for an electrical company. A year later he was readmitted to high school.

Clinical History.—His present condition began four years ago when, during an altercation with a street car conductor, he was struck over the head with an iron control bar. There was no discoverable injury to the head. Two weeks later his mental condition began to change. He developed ideas of persecution and said that the boys in school were accusing him of having killed one of his friends. (Inquiry disclosed that one of his friends had been killed by an automobile.) He claimed that there was a dictagraph in the wall which always talked (aural hallucinations). His conduct became intolerable and his parents sent him to a sanitarium, where his condition was said to have shown some improvement. After his return home he became apathetic, sitting at home and showing no interest in his surroundings. He still had delusions and hallucinations of various sorts, so that he stopped his ears with wax to avoid hearing the noises.

The patient was admitted to the hospital June 19, 1922, at which time he was examined by our neurologist, Dr. Sigmund Krumholz, of Northwestern University, and a diagnosis of dementia precox was returned with the clinical records.

The noteworthy findings of the physical examination at the hospital were as follows: The general appearance was that of typical dementia precox. His temperature was normal, pulse eighty and of good quality. The thyroid was markedly enlarged. Systolic blood pressure was 120, diastolic 65.

He was kept under observation at the hospital for some time and on August 1, 1922, a testis of a giant macacus rhesus was transplanted, according to the author's technic, into the right side of the abdomen. On the day following the operation the temperature rose to 102°, and the following day to 103° F., but gradually subsided by lysis. During the height of the temperature the mental faculties of the patient became almost normal, a fact observed by his attendants.

On November 20, 1922, it was reported that the patient's mental condition had retrogressed to the former state and appeared hopeless.

On April 1, 1923, nine months after the operation, to the great surprise of the author, the patient presented himself to extend his Easter greetings. He has gained considerably in weight, his general appearance was brighter, and his gait much more steady. He could never remember the author's name on former occasions. At this time I said to him, "Harold, do you know my name? " and without hesitation he answered, " Yes." I then asked, " What is it? " and he immediately answered " Thorek."

There is a marked retrogression at present of the thyroid enlargement, his neck being normal. Prior to the transplantation the patient had a great desire and tendency to destroy things, particularly by burning. He always built fires in the yard, using as fuel satchels, books and anything he could lay his hands on. This tendency to destruction has now entirely disappeared. His great tendency to be disobedient prior to the operation, has given place to calm and obediency. His mother says, " I have not the trouble with him I had before."

He is very much improved, but he still has periods of depression, during which he becomes melancholy and introspective. The aural hallucinations have all disappeared. Another transplantation has been suggested the results of which will be reported later.

A year after the primary operation the patient was readmitted to the hospital. At this time the thyroid of a cynocephalus was transplanted into his own thyroid, and a testicle of the same cynocephalus implanted at the site of the previous testicular implantation. The first testicle implanted was found very much shrunken in size, but thoroughly vascularized and apparently in full functional activity.

A small section was removed for the purpose of microscopic study, hardened in formol, and after imbedding in paraffin, sections stained with hematoxylin and eosin, the findings were shown in (Figs. 193 to 196). In this section of small magnification, one observes tissue of the syncytial type first described by Ribbert and later by Retterer and Voronoff. The cellular elements are composed of large protoplasm cells surrounded by areolar-shaped syncytium. The vacuolization is very marked. There are many leucocytes and an abundance of Leydig cells, the nuclei of which are colored intensely dark. In some places the nuclear stain of the Leydig cells is not so intense, but appears lighter.

The patient left the hospital a few days after the operation and the further progress of the case will be noted later. The author was fortunate to get a verbal report from the father of the boy, while reading the proofs of this work, twenty months since the patient came under our observation.

The father reports that all destructive tendencies have disappeared, hallucinations have vanished, and a marked improvement has been noted.

The author believes that the improvement is remarkable here and that the case should be further observed for future developments.

The author has at the present writing a number of cases of dementia præcox under observation, in which human testicles have been implanted. I believe Sir Mott has pointed to an important phase in the possibilities in the treatment of dementia præcox and that further researches and studies are urgently needed in this direction.

BIBLIOGRAPHY

[1] GIBBS : Arch. Neurol. and Psychiat., 1923, ix, 73.
[2] OBREGIA, PARHON and URECHIA : L'Encéphale, 1913, viii (i), 109.
[3] BLEULER : Cited by Obgregia from Aschaffenburg's, Hand b. d. Psychiatrie, 1911,
[4] BORNSTEIN : Cited by Obregia from Aschaffenburg's, Hand b. d. Psychiatrie, 1911,
[5] TODDE : Rivist. Sper. di freniat., 1914, xl, 233.
[6] MATSUMOTO : Jour. Ment. Sc., 1920, lxvi, 414.
[7] MOTT, F. W.: Proc. Royal Society of Medicine, xiii, No. 8, 1920, pp. 25–63.
[8] MOTT, F. W.: British Medical Journal, ii, 1919.
[9] MOTT, F. W., SUCH, PRADOS Y.: Proc. Royal Society of Med., xv. Psychiatry.

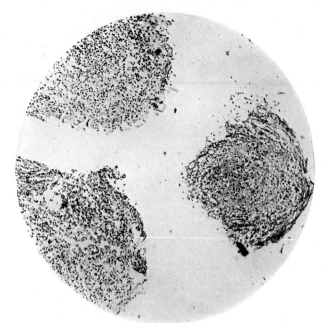

Fig. 193.—Dementia precox. Microphotograph of transplanted testis one year after implantation. Ocular 4x; objective 16; magnification 64 diam. Leitz apochromatic micros.

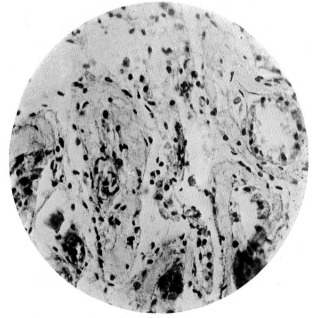

Fig. 194.—Dementia precox. Same section magnified 268 diam. Ocular 4x; objective 4.

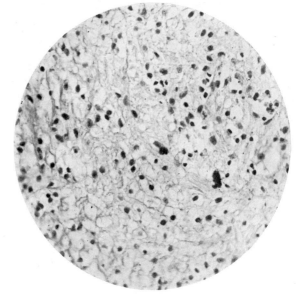

FIG. 195.—Same as preceding. Magnified 470 diam.; ocular 4x; objective 2.

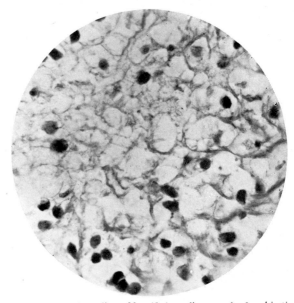

FIG. 196.—Same as preceding. Magnified 710 diam.; ocular 8x; objective 2.

CHAPTER XV

AUTHOR'S EXPERIMENTS WITH HETEROTRANSPLANTS FROM ANTHROPOIDS TO MAN AND VICE VERSA

THE difficulty often encountered in obtaining material for implantation from proper human sources and the possibility of success from hetero-transplantation from the higher apes, as advocated by Serge Voronoff, who was clinically able to produce remarkable results from such implantations, prompted the author, some years ago, to enter into the study of this phase of research. Up to the present time there is nowhere to be found in the literature histological proof that gonads from apes transplanted into the human will thrive. Such proofs were first histologically offered by the author in 1922.

The experiments on the human to be described presently were carried out with the full understanding of the recipient that the tissues from anthropoids were to be implanted for experimental purposes solely and that after the lapse of a certain time they would be removed for scientific study. Experiments carried on in this fashion bearing on this question had been entirely lacking up to the time of the author's reports above referred to. Proper consent having been obtained and the patients placed under obser-vation, the materials used for implantation were taken from sexually mature, normal macaci or cynocephali. After much experimentation the proper site for implantation was first ascertained by means of autotrans-fers and homotransplants in lower animals and the site selected as described by the author in another chapter (Cf. Chapter on Site of Implantation) in this book.

Fig. 197 depicts a homotransplant. A study of the photograph will enable the student to observe the relationship of the implanted testis to the surrounding structures, very clearly. The implant in this case was removed after a period of three months and shows that the transplanted testis is alive and has formed intimate relationships with the contiguous tissues. Inasmuch as homo-transplantations from ape to ape were suc-cessful without much, if any, reaction and without suppuration in a rather considerable series of cases, by employing the technic worked out by the

24   369

author, a typical example of which is depicted in the photograph referred
to, it occurred to him that a step further might be taken without risk to
the patient by implanting tissues from the very same type of animals into
the human.   This, however, had been done successfully previously by

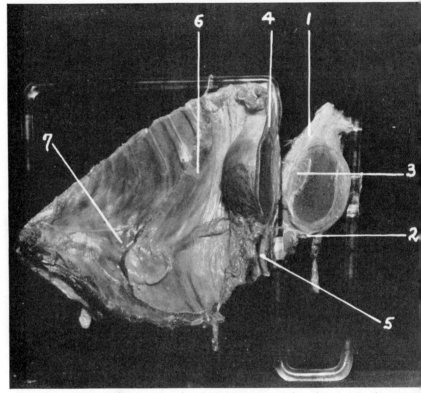

Fig. 197.—Homotransplantation of testis of macacus nemestrinus three months after transplantation.   1, musculus rectus abdominis; 2, peritoneum parietal; 3, epididymis; 4, portion of
muscle and tunica vasculosa; 5, same, lower pole of implant; 6, internal surface of peritoneum
parietal.

Serge Voronoff.   A great many of these experiments were made, however,
before risking heterotransplantation as outlined.

The first heterotransplantation from ape to man was made by the
author in 1920, following Voronoff's technic, with the following results:

1. Clinically no untoward manifestations were observed as far as the
recipient was concerned.

2. Outside of a rise of temperature during the first twenty-four hours,
and in some cases for forty-eight hours, with a feeling of exhilaration on

the part of the patient perhaps due to the introducion into the system of a rather large, suddenly set free, dose of testicular hormone, the post-operative course was normal and without any unpleasant manifestations.

3. After a period of seven months the implant was removed from the recipient with his consent and the transplanted testicle found to be vascu-

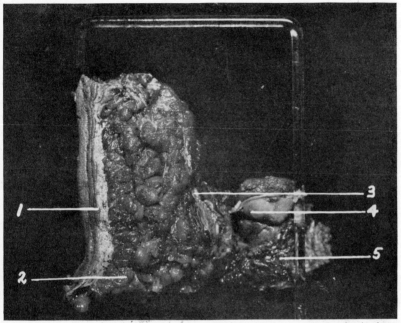

Fig. 198.—Heterotransplantation from cynocephalus to man, seven months after implantation. 1, cutis and scar of original incision; 2, panniculus adiposus; 3, musculus rectus abdominis; 4, implanted testicle of cynocephalus; 5, parietal peritoneum showing vascularization of implant.

larized and alive. The only macroscopic change was a diminution in its size, which, of course, is to be expected for the reasons given in a different chapter of this book. (Fig. 198.)

4. Sections taken from the implant in this case offer the following microscopic proofs: (Fig. 199.)

    (a) The seminiferous tubules were regressing.

    (b) The interstitial elements were proliferating.

    (c) An adequate vascular supply had been established to keep the graft alive.

    (d) The Leydig cells were of normal structure and functionating. (Fig. 200.)

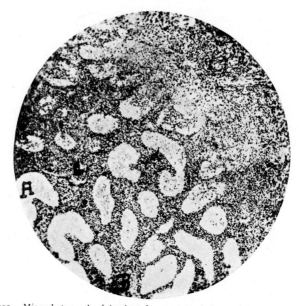

Fig. 199.—Microphotograph of implant from cynocephalus to human seven months after implantation showing: *a*, regression of seminiferous tubules; *b*, proliferation of interstitial elements; *c*, adequate vascularization of implant from contiguous structures; *d*, Leydig cells normal in structure and apparently functionating.

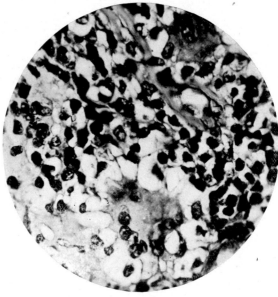

Fig. 200.—Same as preceding. Magnification 560 diameters. Observe Leydig cells, giant cells and abundance of cell life in well nourished area

Figs. 201 and 202 show an implant removed eight months and fifteen days after transplantation, the gross and microscopic findings being practically the same as in the description of the case given above. A rather large number of other such experiments were made with the same results. In these instances of successful heterotransplantation of testicular tissue from ape to man it has definitely been proven, clinically as well as histologically, that for therapeutic purposes if human material is not obtainable heterotransplants of the proper type may in indicated cases be an entirely feasible procedure.

That transplantation from the human to the anthropoid is possible, has for the first time been proven by the author in the experiment in which a transplanted cryptorchid testis from a human into an ape was able to produce in this impotent castrate the same results (erections, copulation and increased physical vigor) as were shown to result in transplanting the testes from apes into the human. (Cf. Chapter on Function of the Leydig Cells.) These experiments, to the mind of the author, are of great importance for two reasons: *First*, these experimental studies may, perhaps, add their quota of enlightenment to Darwin's concepts of evolution. *Second, the practicability of therapeutic transplantation from the higher apes to man is proven beyond any doubt, if one is to rely upon clinical manifestations and histological examinations as criteria for unbiased deductions.*

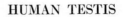

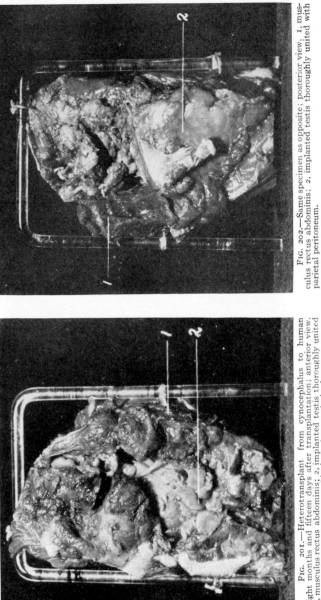

FIG. 202.—Same specimen as opposite; posterior view. I, musculus rectus abdominis; 2, implanted testis thoroughly united with parietal peritoneum.

FIG. 201.—Heterotransplant from cynocephalus to human eight months and fifteen days after transplantation; anterior view. I, musculus rectus abdominis; 2, implanted testis thoroughly united with contiguous structure and intimately vascularized.

CHAPTER XVI

THE MATERIALS USED FOR SEX GLAND IMPLANTATION: A DISCUSSION OF THEIR VALUE

I. Human Transplants.—

WHEN the question of sex gland implantation has been decided upon the next phase to consider is what is the best material to use for a given case and which transplant, or implant, will yield the very best results. All observers and workers in this field unanimously agree, of course, that *the best material for implantation is human glandular tissue.* However, to obtain the proper human material a number of obstacles often present themselves. In the first place the following important factors must be kept constantly in mind:

First, the age of the donor.

Second, the absence of pathological conditions within his body (syphilis, tuberculosis, malignancy, etc.).

Third, under what circumstances has the implant been obtained, and how was it treated immediately before implantation.

As to the age of the donor, it is, of course, best to obtain testicular tissue from an individual who is neither too young nor too old. I would say that the ages between nineteen and thirty-five would be a fair average. It must be kept in mind that sexual maturity is arrived at in some individuals earlier than in others, and again, sexual virility is extinguished in some persons at an earlier age and retained for a longer period in other individuals. The best rule to adopt in this connection is to select a donor who is known to be at a period of sexual maturity and activity in a normal and active manner. A thorough examination of the donor as to the presence or absence of syphilitic taint, the presence or absence of tuberculosis and the presence or absence of other communicable diseases or systemic aberrations, are criteria which are to be very earnestly considered. The general physical condition outside of the *vita sexualis* are also of paramount importance. It would be malpractice of the grossest kind to implant into a normal individual the testis of a tubercular individual, the testis of a syphilitic or the testis of an otherwise diseased person.

The third problem presenting itself is: Has the donor (if living), earnestly consented to part with a portion of his sex gland to help someone in physical need for such aid; or is he simply parting with it for monetary consideration? The latter practice offers, in the opinion of the author, serious objections. The reason for this is that under stress of poverty young individuals may part with one, or part, of their sex glands and later regret their action and, perhaps, become remorseful or introspective. Although the fact has been thoroughly established that an individual can continue throughout life with one testicle just as well as with two, yet these facts are known principally to physicians, and the uninitiated may attribute every ailment that may befall him later in life as being the direct result of the loss of a testis from which he has parted for pecuniary reasons.

On the other hand, inasmuch as close blood relationship, say between father and son, is the best tissue for implantation purposes, the question naturally presents itself, cannot the son who owes his very existence to his father part with a portion of one of his testes, should the father need it for his well-being and usefulness? The donor may in turn expect the same therapeutic help from his own son. The same rule may apply to near relatives. If such arrangement can be effected the full understanding of the question at issue must be impressed upon the donor, emphasizing that only a portion of one testis will be required and that the amount of testicular tissue remaining will be sufficient to carry on the functions of internal secretion and propagation in a normal manner and without in the least jeopardizing his somatic and sexual functions.

Some observers have made use of testicles of young individuals who have died by accidental means. *If disease in these individuals can be absolutely eliminated, and, above all, if the implantation can be done a reasonable time after the death of the donor, such method may be resorted to.* L. L. Stanley, who has used refrigerated material, in a personal communication to the author writes as follows: " I always prefer the fresh gland to any that are preserved. However, the preserved seem to be as efficient as the fresh. Sometimes it is difficult for us to secure the fresh just when we want them and we have to ' take the current when it serves.' As a result we have removed the testis from the tunica vaginalis and immersed it in vaseline which was still in a liquid state, being slightly heated, and then placed on a cake of ice in our ice manufacturing plant. In this way the material is frozen solid and then when removed cuts something like ice cream bricks. By this process the air is kept away from the material and the freezing prevents any decomposition. When thawed out it is as sweet as when put in. I have preserved these glands for months by merely keeping them immersed in vaseline at room temperature. We have made a number of microscopical slides of the material, both of the fresh and the preserved, and I have been unable to find any marked change in structure.

" The longest period in which we have used preserved glands has been one month."

Carrel has shown that tissues may be kept refrigerated for some time and that such tissues may retain their vitality. However, how much damage accrues to the delicate structure of the Leydig cell from such refrigeration has not definitely been ascertained, but it stands to reason that the injury to the cell protoplasm must be considerable if one keeps in mind the delicacy of the composition of these cells, their high specialization and their complicated function.

Carl Michel believes that gland tissue kept at 37° C. for about twelve hours loses its functional activity, which he terms " functional autolysis."

The author desiring to ascertain just how long tissues of the glandular type may be kept alive and available for transplantation, has instituted a series of experiments, as follows: A testis was removed and submitted to examination, to Dr. Charles E. M. Fischer of Chicago. Another portion of the same testis was placed in the hands of Dr. R. B. H. Gradwohl of St. Louis, and a third portion was submitted for study at the American Hospital Laboratories, Chicago, Ill. The reason of this distribution was the desire to arrive at conclusions at different sources and compare results, the question being a vital one from the standpoint of implantation, the greatest care had, of course, to be exercised to arrive at definite conclusions. The report of Doctor Fischer, dated December 14, 1920, was as follows:

" Reporting on the examination of testicular tissue to determine its viability when preserved by refrigeration as demonstrated by microscopical appearance of the interstitial cells, beg to advise:

" The testicle which was received from you November 1, 1920 was washed with ice-cold Ringer's solution having the following formula:

NaCl	....	0.9	per cent.
KCL	....	0.042	per cent
CaCl₂	....	0.024	per cent.
HaHCO₃	....	0.02	per cent.
Dextrose	....	0.1	per cent.

" A portion thereof was cut off and fixed in 5 per cent. formalin solution, and the rest being put into about six ounces of Ringer's solution and placed on ice.

" Portions similar to the first were cut off at twenty-four hour intervals for five more days and preserved with formalin as above, the remainder being placed in fresh, ice-cold Ringer's solution and put back on ice.

" In addition to being placed in fresh Ringer's solution at the time the daily specimen was taken, the remainder was also washed with some of the solution and placed in a fresh quantity thereof, at two other periods each day.

" The testicle was thus divided into seven portions, each being out of the body twenty-four hours longer than the preceding one, before preservation.

" The testicle was first placed in Ringer's solution about 6 P.M., four hours after it was removed from the body. From the time it was first washed with Ringer's solution until the last portion was preserved, the tissue was kept continuously at ice temperature.

" After fixation, the portions of the testicle were imbedded in paraffin, and sections cut therefrom. The sections were stained with hematoxylin and eosin. Microscopical examination showed the cells in the first portion to be normal. The cells in the second portion showed signs of degeneration, the cytoplasm being granular and taking the stain to a lesser degree than the first.

" This degeneration continued progressively each day until, at the end, the cells showed more or less definite masses with much degenerated nuclei."

The report from Doctor Gradwohl, dated December 23, 1920, was as follows:

" We beg to report as follows on sections of testicle which you transmitted to us on November 11th, Laboratory number 29433. We understood that this testicle came to us in sterile physiological salt solution. As per your directions we kept this organ in this fluid during the entire period of observation, keeping it constantly in our refrigerator at an average temperature of 3° C. On the first day upon which we received it we made a section of same, returning it to the saline fluid at once, and on each succeeding day we did the same, until eighteen sections on eighteen successive days had been made. We ceased sectioning on the eighteenth day for the reason that we had used up the entire organ. We wish to call your attention to the fact that when we made cuts from the organ, we did so with the strictest asepsis, picking it up with sterile forceps and incising it with sterile scissors.

" The sections were stained with hematoxylin and eosin, after freezing.

" Microscopically we noted on the first day very distinctly the classical markings of testicular tissue; namely, the lining cells of spermatogonia; the adjacent layer of intermediate cells or spermatocytes and finally the third layer of spermatozoids which are simply ill-defined granular masses of protoplasm. Beneath this were seen very clear and well-stained the supporting cells of Sertoli, which were elongated and columnar. The sections on the first day showed perfect staining characteristics and very clean cut nuclei. Beginning changes were noted on the third day and very distinct changes on the fourth day and all succeeding days until the last or eighteenth day of observation; to wit: the cells showed poorer staining characteristics, the granular cells seemed shrunken, the protoplasm becoming hazy and indistinct. In other words, as early as the third day in salt solution, cellular disintegration seemed to be taking place. This process became more and more pronounced the longer the organ was kept in saline solution. The deep purple color of the hematoxylin nuclear stain became a peculiar brown. The nuclei finally became indistinct and there remained merely a shadowy appearance of the protoplasmic structure. We have preserved these slides, serially numbered, for your observation and further study."

The accompanying two microphotographs on the work done by Gradwohl (Figs. 202a and 203), show on the first day the normal structure

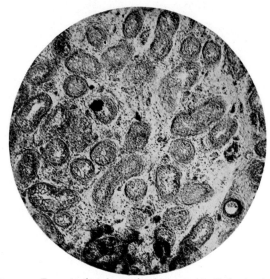

FIG. 202a.—Frozen testis 24 hours, showing normal testicular structure.

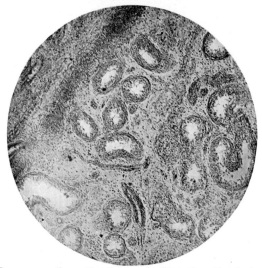

FIG. 203.—Same as preceding on the third day of refrigeration. Note beginning changes.

of the testicle; on the third day there is a beginning paling of the nuclei
with disintegration of the tubules and on the fourth day still further
advanced disintegration until finally complete dissolution takes place. The

protoplasm gradually became cloudy until the cellular structure degenerated into a homogeneous mass, failing to stain. The following are the results of our studies in our laboratories.

AUTHOR'S EXPERIMENT NO. 1

On the 23rd of February, 1921, at three o'clock in the afternoon, a testicle of a normal dog was removed. A portion of this testis was fixed in formol, and another portion in Müller's solution. After hardening, imbedding in paraffin and staining in hematoxylin and eosin, the picture presented the normal appearance of the testicle revealing all stages of spermatogenesis. The bulk of the testicle was placed in Ringer's solution, packed in ice and deposited in the ice box of our refrigeration plant. Small pieces of this specimen were then removed at the hours indicated below, imbedded in paraffin, sectioned and stained with hematoxylin-eosin.

Date	Hour	Time refrigerated	Microscope shows
Feb. 23, 1921	4 P.M.	1. Hour	All component parts of testicle normal.
Feb. 23, 1921	10 P.M.	7 Hours	Normal appearance.
Feb. 24, 1921	7 A.M.	16 Hours	Normal appearance.
Feb. 24, 1921	11 A.M.	20 Hours	Seminal cells do not stain as well.
Feb. 24, 1921	7 P.M.	28 Hours	Leydig cells normal, some changes of dissolution in sperm cells.
Feb. 25, 1921	7 A.M.	40 Hours	Sperm cells regressing.
Feb. 25, 1921	4 P.M.	49 Hours	Same condition.
Feb. 26, 1921	7 A.M.	64 Hours	Tubular content partly destroyed, in other places spermatogenic elements still visible.
Feb. 26, 1921	7 P.M.	76 Hours	Same condition.

EXPERIMENT NO. 2

This was done on guinea pigs and on human testes, with practically the same results as in previous experiment.

CONCLUSIONS

It will be readily seen from the results above cited that the conclusion is justified that the ideal manner to proceed in implantation is to have, if the donor be alive, the operation performed on the donor and recipient at the same time; both being simultaneously prepared for the operation and the implantation properly performed. (Cf. Chapter on Technique.)

It needs no emphasis that biochemic changes will commence in the transplant as soon as the surgeon's scalpel divides the testes or the portion of the testes from its normal surroundings, from its normal vascular supply and from its usual neurohematogenic environment. Highly specialized tissue, such as seminal tubules, interstitial cells and other component parts of the delicate gland structure are very susceptible to thermic, mechanical and chemical influences. This is a well known fact. It is, therefore, of the utmost importance to bring the transplant as quickly as possible into an environment and into as nearly normal a bed of surroundings as it reposed in prior to its ablation. The natural conclusion, therefore, follows that *immediate transference, wherever possible, according to the technical steps given in the chapter on technique, should be made. If such immediate transference be not feasible or practicable the tissue should be subjected to refrigeration for as short a time as possible, certainly not longer than forty-eight hours.*

II. Implants from Animals other than Apes.—

An attempt has been made in certain quarters to transplant testes from rams, goats, and animals of similar specie into the human economy. Reports from serious investigators in this field have shown absolute failures in the vast majority of cases. *Experimental investigations conducted by the author on this question have resulted in all instances where these animals were used for transplantation, in absolute failure; to-wit, necrosis of the implant; aseptic or septic suppuration with final extrusion of the transplanted testis.* This is not at all surprising, for if we consult the results of the studies in blood relationship between the human and the lower forms of animals a wide divergence and an insurmountable biologic gap is at once encountered. (Cf. Chapter on Blood Relationships between Apes and Humans.) Furthermore, a histologic comparison between the blood elements of these animals and humans will at once display the greatest variation and disproportion. In other words, the implantation of sex glands from these lower animals into the human body is a physical, physiological and biologic impossibility, and in view of my own researches and those of other investigators it is a fallacious undertaking and should *never* be attempted, for biochemically and structurally the hiatus thus far remains unconquerable. Microscopic studies invariably emphasized these conclusions in showing that there was no tendency of regeneration and an influx of cellular elements is at once set at work to extrude the invading foreign body—for the implant is a foreign body in the strictest sense of the term and is, therefore, dealt with by the body juices as such from the moment of implantation to its final extrusion.

To recapitulate: *For transplants to be successful they must come from a member of the human family or its nearest biologic relations—the higher apes (anthropoidea), of which we shall speak directly.*

III. Transplants from Higher Apes.—

The most logical animals to serve the purpose for implantation, next to the *homo sapiens,* as donors, are the groups belonging to the anthropoidea. Of these the chimpanzee and the ourangoutang are most desirable. To Serge Voronoff of Paris, France, belongs the credit, unreservedly, of having pointed out to the scientific world that in the absence of, or in the case of, impracticability of human specimen for implantation, we may resort with success to the animals under discussion in this chapter, *i.e.,* the higher apes. Experimental studies and the comparison of the embryology, dentition, analogy of the skeleton and visceral relationship, as well as the histology of the internal organs, have caused him to conclude that the possibilities of implantation from higher apes to humans may be successfully accomplished. This has been proven by Voronoff and others, from a number of transplants so done, to be a fact. In comparative studies between anthropoid apes and humans, Voronoff is upheld by Gruenebaum, Uhlenhut, Bruch, and others. Clinical manifestations verify the feasibility of such implants in cases subjected to this treatment. In following up Voronoff's work the author was able to prove by implanting a number of testes from this class of apes into humans that the implants do live for a certain period and clinically often give results akin to those obtained from homo-transplantation. (Cf. Chapter on Clinical Cases.)

The difficulty of obtaining these animals at the present time is due to conditions created by the World War and is a rather difficult task. Occasionally one can obtain a specimen or two, however. In procuring a proper animal the very same rules as to the investigation of its health must apply as though the donor were a human being. A thorough examination of the lungs is indispensable. The proper age of the donor must be ascertained. *The prepuberal period bars the animal as a donor. The period of sexual maturity is the desirable one.* As soon as the beginning signs of senescence in the animal are observed it is to be discarded as a donor for implantation.

The author has made use of some of the animals above referred to and in their absence, through difficulties of procuring same he made use of the class of apes known as *Cyrcopitheci* and *Cynocephali.* This class is very closely related to the above mentioned group and are classified by Hartman as " Anthropoideæ." The blood relationship in these apes is very close and histologically the same as in the higher anthropoids and humans. The lower forms, such as the small rhesus, lemurs, ringtails, etc., are entirely to be discarded for implantation purpose. (The giant rhesus may form an exception.) Their blood agglutination tests are too distant, their life cycle and *vita sexualis* too remote to give the desired results to be of proper therapeutic value in this work. (Cf. Chapter on Blood Relationship between Humans and Apes.) It is a wise plan to select the proper animal and keep it for observation for about a week. From experience, the author has learned that immature animals were sold by unscrupulous dealers which were discovered to be in the prepuberal or senescent stage, and therefore, unfitted for the purposes for which they were desired. All facts pertaining to the general condition of health of the donor must be taken into consideration, must be carefully weighed, and every angle thoroughly considered for a proper selection of the material to be used. One should always remember that: *for implantation, human material offers the best prospects for therapeutic results.*

CHAPTER XVII

INDICATIONS AND CONTRAINDICATIONS FOR SEX GLAND TRANSPLANTATIONS IN THE MALE

A. Indications.—

1. Loss of the testicles through trauma or pathology resulting from such conditions as tuberculosis, neoplasmata, suppurations, etc. This class of cases represents a distinct and clear-cut set of indications where the greatest possible good may be done by sex gland implantation.

2. Individuals who suffer mentally and physically through the manifestations of the " male climacteric." (Cf. Chapter on this condition.)

3. Cases of premature senility, pure and simple, depending upon endocrine dysfunction where sex gland implantation, perhaps combined with other implantations (thyroid, etc.), and supplemented, if need be, by other forms of therapy as indicated in a given instance, is frequently followed by surprisingly good results.

4. In sexual neurasthenia where hormone dysfunction results by reason of the neurasthenia primarily or as a secondary accompaniment in correlated conditions.

5. Based on recent studies, particularly of Mott and others, showing a dysfunction with gross alterations of the Leydig cells in cases of dementia precox, and in view of some good results obtained by Lydston and the author as cited elsewhere in this volume in this class of cases, implantations seem to be indicated.

6. The same holds also true in the various psychoses of puberty resting on an endocrine basis. (Combined with other methods of treatment.)

7. In Fröhlich's disease beneficial results have been observed by some from sex gland implantation coupled with hypophysis therapy.

8. In certain cases of impotency, particularly those not dependent upon organic or constitutional diseases (such as tabes, gout, diabetes, etc.), or other forms of organic disease of the central nervous system; implantation offers a field of fruitful therapy in properly selected cases.

9. In carefully selected cases of eunuchoidism and infantilism benefit may be obtained from testicular implants and in certain forms of homo-

sexuality, particularly when taken early before somatic and psychic ingraining of homosexual tendencies has taken place.

10. In well selected cases of hermaphrodism where the coöperation of the patient is assured and clear indications for implantation exist, the existence of the individual may be rendered more comfortable with less humiliation and ultimate tolerable happiness.

11. Under-development of the genitalia in young individuals.

12. In certain forms of sterility, it may be tried. (?)

13. In chronic nutritional diseases implantation may be successfully combined with other methods of therapy.

14. In sexual asthenia, resulting from excesses, dissipation, etc.

15. In all cases of testicular dystrophy and malfunction from any cause.

16. In cases where testicular function has been seriously interfered with through the action of X-rays (X-ray operators: therapeutic applications). The author observed four such cases.

B. Contraindications.—

1. The implantation of testicular substance is absolutely contraindicated, where the physician cannot find a distinct indication for such procedure. To implant gonadal tissue on general principles without having made a thorough diagnosis and established a definite reason for the procedure, is unjustified as well as unscientific. Charlatans, of course, will advise implantation of gonadal tissue for almost anything, but those will gradually be eliminated by educating the lay public concerning the truths in this field of therapy and by emphasizing the real possibilities and benefits of gonadal therapy in properly selected cases and its absolute contraindication in others.

2. In patients suffering from acute conditions of any sort, transplantation should never be done. If one keeps in mind that following transplantation there often is a period of reaction with a rise of temperature which a normal individual throws off without any untoward manifestations it will be seen that a person affected with a febrile condition may fare badly in the added systemic effort necessarily following the procedure of implantation and its post-operative manifestations, brief though they may be.

CHAPTER XVIII

TECHNIQUE

THE RELATION OF THE QUANTITY OF INTERSTITIAL SUBSTANCE TO THE INTENSITY OF ITS INCRETORY ACTION

LACASSAGNE [1] has shown that there is an accentuation of the sexual activity in individuals who have an increase of the interstitial elements of their testes. Such increase has been observed in cryptorchids, as well as after transplantations, after ligations, and as a result of röntgenization.

These findings of Lacassagne have been verified by the studies of Steinach,[3] as well as those of Sand. On the other hand, Alfred Kohn [2] denies such effects, pointing out that the relation of virility to the activity of the interstitial substances, as stated by the above authors, do not behave as stated by these observers. Alexander Lipschütz,[4] arguing the question, points out that during the metabolic processes in the organism only such proportions of a given substance are utilized by the body as are necessary for the function or functions in a given instance, and that a superproduction of such products are either oxidized or eliminated, as is the case with the albumins and salts of which only a limited quantity can be stored and the rest must be eliminated. In other words, these incretory products, like the various aminoacids or the various ions having specific biochemical functions, are not necessarily exercising such biochemic functions, by an overproduction in the organism and the organic functions depending upon their production; nor do they cause disturbances in metabolism, provided certain limits are not exceeded. Such increased supply results only in greater demands upon the digestive, resorbatory, circulatory, and excretory organs, and in the course of these events a marked increase in oxidation ensues. Lipschütz compares these bodies to the introduction of other toxic products into the system, such as morphin for instance, in which case gradual administration in minute doses will permit the organism to accommodate itself to the drug so that after a time enormous doses are not followed by toxic manifestations. Of course a suddenly increased supply of the testicular hormone may so stimulate the organism as to increase sexual functions greatly, as exemplified in animals during the rutting period.

From experimental work on lower animals and humans, it has been established (Lacassagne, Steinach, Lipschütz, Voronoff, Sand, Thorek, and others), that if there is an increase in functionating interstitial elements

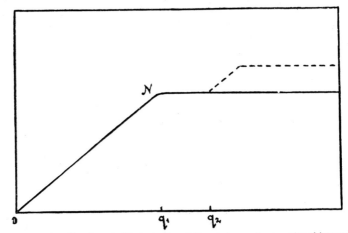

Fig. 204.—Graphic scheme to illustrate the relations between the quantity of internal secretion of the male sex gland and the intensity of the manifestations of internal secretion. (After Alexander Lipschütz.) Abscissa=quantity of internal secretion of the sex gland. Ordinate=the internal secretory action as represented by the development of somatic sex characters. q. 1=quantity of internal secretion through which the normal development of secondary sex characteristics (N) develop. q. 2=quantity of internal secretion normally reaching the circulation.

that simultaneously with such increase there is increased psychosexual and somatosexual capacity.

There is a certain group of observers who point out a certain parallelism between the quantity of the testicular substance and corresponding intensity of incretory function. Steinach insists that it is not as much the quantity of the testicular tissue as the amount of interstitial elements that plays the important rôle in the development of secondary sex characters.

Lipschütz [4] affirms that such interdependence holds true only to a certain point, after which the intensity of the action of the internal secretion is mitigated or nullified. He expresses his views graphically by the above schematic representation of existing conditions. (Cf. diagram.) (Fig. 204.) Of course, Lipschütz pleads for more proof to verify his hypothetical suggestions exemplified in his graphic illustration. The author is inclined to agree with Lipschütz that the autonomic regulations of body functions on a physiologic basis will consume only that quantity of internal secretion necessary for their immediate needs, storing a great deal in the central nervous system, and that a great surplus will be eliminated from the body through the usual emunctories.

A study of the diagram in Fig. 204 shows that the proportionate incretory function of the action of the quantity of the internal secretion of the sex organ is seen in the space between o and q. 1. If the quantity of internal secretion should rise above q. 2, temporarily, the result will not be permanently increased incretory function (prolonged line). A transient rise above q. 2 leads to a transitorily increased action such as is observed during the rutting period (dotted line).

BIBLIOGRAPHY

[1] LACASSAGNE: L'Etude histologique et physiologique des effets products sur l'ovaire par les rayons X. Thése med. de Lyon, 1913, Vgl., p. 213.

[2] KOHN, ALFRED: Morphologische Grundlagen dor Organotherapie. Abschnitt über die Generationsorgane. In Jauregg und Bayer, Lehrbuch der Organotherapie. Leipzig, 1914, Vgl., S. 80.

[3] STEINACH: Geschlechtstrieb und echt sekundare Geschlechtmale usw. Zentralblatt f. Psysiologie, B. 24, 1910.

[4] LIPSCHÜTZ: Die Pubertätsdrüse, Bern, 1919.

B. Site of Implantation.—

The site of implantation plays a rather conspicuous rôle in transplanting sex glands for therapeutic purposes. If we analyze the sites of implantation resorted to by various authors, two prominent features impress themselves upon the careful observer. First, that a great number of implants have either suppurated or were extruded. Second, that there is too rapid regression in the size of the implanted testis.

Lydston did an extravaginal implantation. In other words, in experimenting upon himself and advising implants upon others, he placed the testis in a pocket situated between the skin and the parietal layer of the tunica vaginalis of the testis. In his reported cases, numerous suppurations were noted and the testicle implanted into himself has also been lost to a very great extent through necrosis and suppuration.

Voronoff implants the testis with the cut surface of the implant against the tunica albuginea. This author also has observed, in some cases, suppuration and extrusion of the implant. Dartigues,[1] however, has recently modified Voronoff's technique, by placing the cut surfaces of the grafts

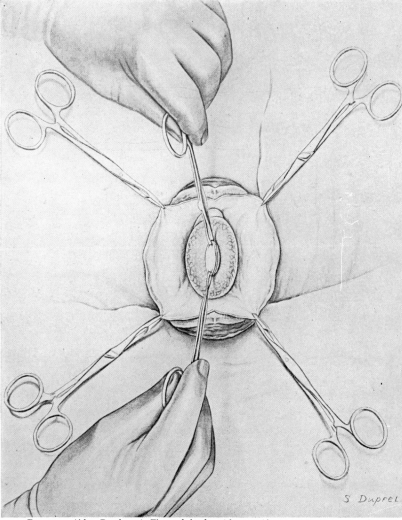

FIG. 205.—(After Dartigues.) The graft is of oval form and is attached to the tunica albuginea with delicate catgut in such a manner that the parenchymatous pulp of the graft faces the external surface of the parietal layer of the tunica vaginalis testis.

against the external surface of the parietal layer of the tunica vaginalis (Fig. 205).

The same fate befell (suppuration: extrusion) some transplants of Lichtenstern, who grafted testes with sectioned face on one of the obliquus minor muscles of the abdomen.   In a later report, Lichtenstern stated that in four other cases in which he placed the testicle in the scrotum, they either sloughed or became absorbed.   In still further experiments, Lichtenstern placed the testicle to be implanted on the scarified muscular tissue of the inguinal region.   The conclusion that Lichtenstern reaches is: " Lydston's high percentage of cases in which the transplanted testicle sloughed was due to his method of implantation into the scrotum, the conditions there being far from favorable for vascularization as in a bed cut out for the graft in the fascia over the oblique muscle in the inguinal region, slightly scarifying the muscle."

Lissman did a subaponeurotic testicular graft, but this graft absorbed more rapidly than Lissman expected.

Stanley and Kelker, used in three cases, Lydston's technic, and in seven cases the implantations were grafted on the testes of the recipient.

Enderlen uses as the site for implantation the rectus abdominalis muscles.   Foerster used the fascia of the abdominal muscle.   Mariotti placed the graft subaponeurotically.   Kreuter implanted one-half of the testicle between the obliquus abdominis internus and the fascia.   Hammesfahr implanted into the abdominal musculature.   Other observers have placed the testes underneath the pectoralis major.   McKenna implanted into the inguinal region and sutured the implant to the spermatic cord.

While, undoubtedly, a great many cases operated upon by the authors above mentioned have healed *per primam intentionem,* yet the fact remains that a large number of the grafts suppurated and sloughed according to the statements of the various observers.   The author is inclined to believe that the site of implantation had a great deal to do with the suppuration in these cases.   Keeping in mind the extreme delicacy of texture of the sex gland and its vulnerability to pressure, to which it is not subjected in its normal habitat, the thought projected itself upon the author that a space where the implant may be placed without subjecting the delicate structure to compression might, perhaps, prevent suppuration and pressure necrosis.   A glance at the following photographs (Figs. 206, 206a and 207) will illustrate the point in view.

Two testes were transplanted into the same individual for experimental purposes. One was placed entirely in accord with Lichtenstern's method

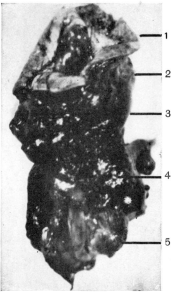

and the other according to the method evolved by the author (Cf. below). The operation was performed on the same individual at the same time, the glands weighing the same amount. After a given time both implants were removed and it was found that the gland transplanted by the Lichtenstern method had remarkably decreased in size, whereas the one implanted by the author's method was only slightly reduced in size. Pressure was responsible for the decrease in size in the specimen subjected to the Lichtenstern technic, and the happy result in the other instance was due to placing the implant in an area calculated to be free from pressure. Microscopic examination of the Lichtenstern transplant showed all testicular elements to have vanished save small islets of interstitial

FIG. 206.—A. G. (Case No. 11551.) Successful transplant of testis of macacus nemestrinus into human. Author's method. 1, skin; 2, subcutaneous tissue and fat; 3, musculus rectus abdominis; 4, living transplant testis; 5, peritoneum.

cells (Figs. 208 and 209), while in the other specimen, the usual manifestations observed in a transplanted testicle, such as seminal cell regression and interstitial cell proliferation, were to be seen in full activity. (Figs. 210–212.)

The author's experiences in operating by the Lichtenstern and other technics were discouraging; most of the implants being either too rapidly absorbed if healing *per primam* was the case, or suppuration ensuing, as was the case in the autotransplantation practiced by Lydston upon himself and others. This clearly illustrates the necessity of implantation in localities free from pressure.

FIG. 206a.—A. G. (Case No. 11551.) Unsuccessful transplant of testis of macacus nemestrinus into human. Lichtenstern's method. Transplanted same day as transplant by author's method.

After a great deal of experimentation the *site found by the author to be ideal for implantation is the supraperitoneal space with its mobile and free areolar tissue forming the base upon which the implant rests, it (the implant) being gently secured in its position by slight pressure exerted*

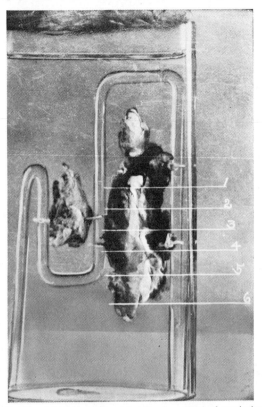

FIG. 207.—Results of Lichtenstern's and author's method of testicular transplantation. Right: Four months after transplantation of testis of nemestrinus into human. 1, skin and subcutis; 2, skin, subcutis and muscle; 3, muscle and transplanted testis; 4, same; 5 and 6, transplant and peritoneum. Left: Transplant according to Lichtenstern's method; same size; same patient; same date. Note comparative results.

from above by the rectus abdominalis muscle. The " give " of the loose peritoneum prevents any pressure upon the implant by reason of the contraction of the abdominal muscles or from other extrinsic causes.

As will be seen, with the other methods, pressure is not eliminated, and in scrotal implantation there is the added discomfort due to the mobility of the scrotum to contend with, which subjects the implants to more or

FIG. 208.—Gross specimen, Case No. 11551. (Slide No. 103.) Magnification 75 diameters.
About four months after transplantation of testis of macacus nemestrinus by Lichtenstern's technic.
1, rapid replacement of tubuli seminiferi by connective tissue; 2, limited areas of interstitial islands.

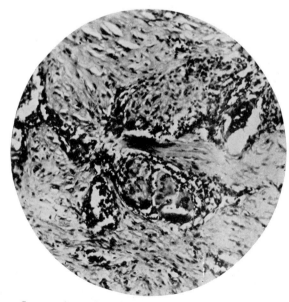

FIG. 209.—Gross specimen, Case No. 11551. (Slide 103.) Magnification 160 diameters.
About four months after transplantation of testis of macacus nemestrinus. Lichtenstern's method.
Note rapid replacement of tubuli by connective tissue and displacement of islands of interstitium.

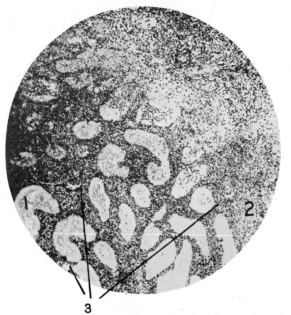

FIG. 210.—Results with author's method of transplantation. Gross specimen, Case No. 11551. (Slide No. 101.)   Magnification 60 diameters.   About four months after transplantation of testicle of macacus nemestrinus.   1, tubuli seminiferi in process of resolution; 2, interstitium in process of hyperplasia; 3, new blood vessels.

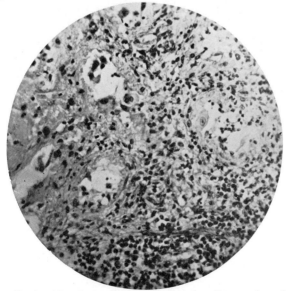

FIG. 211.—Results with author's method of transplantation. Gross specimen, Case No. 11551. (Slide No. 102.) Magnification 225 diameters. About four months after transplantation of testicle of macacus nemestrinus. Author's method, showing giant cells, macrophages, Leydig cells, metamorphosed interstitium.

less trauma from extrinsic sources. In implanting supraperitoneally, as practiced by the author, freedom from pressure is at once obtained, and, aside from the occasional oozing of some serosanguineous fluid, there should at no time be suppuration if the technic has been aseptic and thorough.

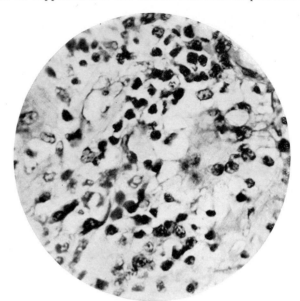

Fig. 212.—Results of author's method of transplantation. Same section as preceding. Magnified 560 diameters.

In a series of a considerable number of cases at the hands of the author, this statement has been amply verified.

Another important factor as to site is the vascularity of the surrounding tissues. The tunica vaginalis, as is well known, has a rather meager blood supply. The vascularity of the tunica albuginea if not denuded so as to expose the tunica vasculosa is also poor in blood supply. The site, therefore, that the author selected is better adapted to receive the implant, for the peritoneum is very vascular and rich in blood and lymph spaces in the vicinity of the deep epigastric vessels, and these supply a pabulum which is most ideal for blood and lymph circulation about the transplant.

While in this situation the implant fared best, the thought that the superimposed muscular contractions might influence, to a certain extent the transplanted testes, and the necessity of making an incision in the anterior abdominal parieties, a series of investigations have been carried on with the following results.

It was thought by the author that the retrorenal space between Gerota's capsule and the endo-abdominal fascia might still further improve the

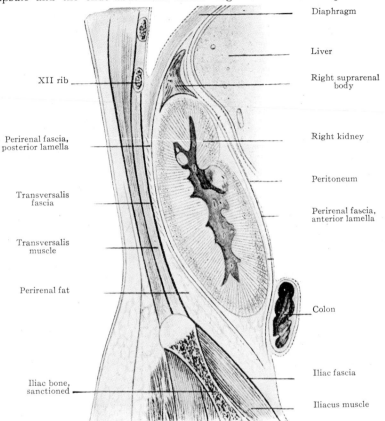

Diaphragm

Liver

XII rib

Right suprarenal body

Perirenal fascia, posterior lamella

Right kidney

Transversalis fascia

Peritoneum

Perirenal fascia, anterior lamella

Transversalis muscle

Perirenal fat

Colon

Iliac fascia

Iliac bone, sanctioned

Iliacus muscle

FIG. 213.—Schematic longitudinal section, showing relations of supporting tissue to right kidney. (After Gerota.)

technic, and after much experimentation such was found to be the case. A technic was then further evolved which we shall designate technic No. 2, describing the foregoing procedure as No. 1.

Figs. 213 and 214 depict the retrorenal space very accurately.

BIBLIOGRAPHY

[1] DARTIGUES: Greffes Testiculaires du Singe a l'homme, Paris, 1923.

C. Quantity of Gland Necessary for Implantation.—

Some observers have used the entire testicle and its epididymis; others have " halved " it; still others have used only the body of the testis and discarded the epididymis. Voronoff splits the entire testis into four or more

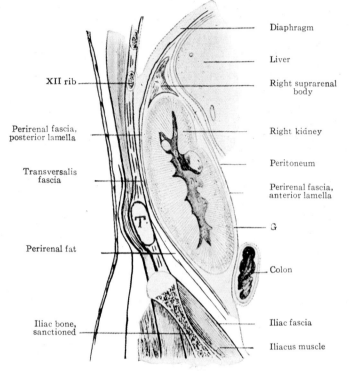

XII rib

Perirenal fascia, posterior lamella

Transversalis fascia

Perirenal fat

Iliac bone, sanctioned

Diaphragm

Liver

Right suprarenal body

Right kidney

Peritoneum

Perirenal fascia, anterior lamella

G

Colon

Iliac fascia

Iliacus muscle

FIG. 214.—Schematic longitudinal section, showing position of transplant to surrounding structures.
t, transplant; *g*, Gerota's capsule.

segments and implants all of them. (Fig. 215.) Occasinally he modifies his technique by merely splitting the testis into two segments and implanting one or both halves as need be. Still another group of operators use variable sections ranging from 1 mm. to larger portions of tissue. There are, of course, occasional extremes met with as to the quantity of tissue used for implants. In 1913, Lespinasse transplanted a man for the relief of impotence by means of " slices " of testicular tissue 1 mm. in thickness. This was a homotransplant and transferred from the donor to the scrotum and rectus muscle of the recipient who had lost both of his testicles, one through a hernia operation, and the other through accident. These delicate bits of testicular tissue were placed in a bed between the fibres of the rectus abdominis muscle which was prepared by plunging an artery forceps between the fibres of the muscle and opening it. On the fourth day after this procedure, the patient told Lespinasse that he had strong erections,

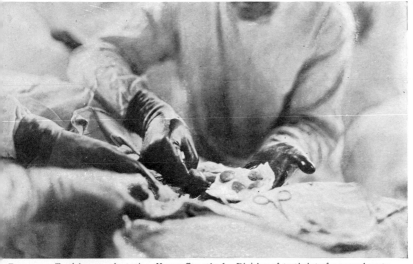

FIG. 215.—Testicle transplantation, Voronoff method. Division of testis into four equal parts, epididymis removed.

accompanied by marked sexual desire. " He insisted upon leaving the hospital to satisfy this desire," says Lespinasse. He also adds that the desire and power of erection have continued for two years, and that at the time the case was reported it had been two years and six months since the operation.

Author's Experiments.—

The possibility of grafting in the fashion of Lespinasse stimulated the author to undertake some experimental studies to ascertain the fate of such grafts. These experiments were carried out as follows: On August 25, 1921, homotransplantation was practiced on a group of six apes (macacus rhesus). While it was difficult to cut slices 1 mm. thick, we were able to get some thicker slices and deposited them between the rectus abdominis muscle fibres as suggested by Lespinasse. The first examination of the implant was made two weeks after the implantation and the others were studied three, four, five, and six weeks after grafting respectively. *Microscopic examination revealed that at the end of two weeks the implants were well on their way to absorption, and that at the end of the twenty-fourth day not a vestige of the implant could be found, while in others, the implant or suggestions of one, could be found as late as the fourth week, and none thereafter.*

The conclusions arrived at from these experiments justify the establishment of the fact that hormone production in animals transplanted by the Lespinasse technic can only continue as long as the Leydig cells persist, which in our experimental animals was not longer than *two to four weeks.* The author repeated these experiments on two men with practically identical results. It is difficult for the author to reconcile the good result reported by Lespinasse in his particular case in view of the microscopic findings in the author's series of experiments.

The rule adopted by the author in transplantation is: 1. *If the donor is a young man in good health closely related to the recipient, and who of his own free will, and with a full understanding of the conditions, is willing to part with a portion of his testicle, approximately one-half of the testicle is excised, reconstructed and implanted into the recipient with a reconstruction of the remaining one-half of the testis of the donor.* (Cf technic below.)

2. *If the testis is taken from a dead person or from the higher apes, the entire testicle should be used for transplantation according to the technic which will be described below.*

GENERAL TECHNIC

A. Anesthesia.—

Those who are engaged in the transplantation of endocrines from the higher apes to humans for experimental or therapeutic purposes will frequently meet with numerous obstacles with which the author had to cope, and which he was able to surmount by meticulous attention to the general rules of asepsis, coupled with painstaking regard for every detail. In the first place, the transportation of animals from their cages to the anesthetizing room presented some difficulty. A special anesthesia chamber was therefore constructed which eliminates a great many drawbacks with which the operator so often is confronted. The author's anesthesia chamber is so constructed that it can be attached to the door of the cage. (Fig. 216.) The arrow points to a sliding door which, when the chamber is attached to the cage door, is lifted up and the animal permitted to enter. As soon as this is accom-

plished the sliding door is permitted to drop, and from that moment on the animal is under absolute control, and the anesthesia can proceed without any further trouble. There is an observation window in the anesthesia chamber, (1) which permits the anesthetist to observe the actions and the general condition of the animal at all times; (2) indicates the aperture in the anesthesia chamber through which the anesthetic (usually ether) is permitted to enter; (3) is a screened window

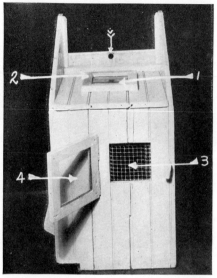

FIG. 216.—Author's special anesthesia chamber.

which permits the ingress of air. As soon as the anesthesia is commenced a glass door (4) is closed tight to intensify the effects of the ether. This can be opened at the pleasure of the anesthetist to permit the entrance of air *ad libitum*.

Fig. 217 depicts to better advantage the aperture through which the anesthetic is introduced. This can be accomplished either by plugging the aperture with absorbent cotton and permitting the anesthetic to drop from its container on this plug, or a funnel may be introduced into it which is lined with an absorbent cotton floor.

Fig. 218 illustrates the upright position of the anesthetizing chamber during the administration of the anesthetic. A to and fro motion of the chamber will indicate to the anesthetist whether the animal is completely under the influence of the anesthetic or not.

26

As previously stated, the author prefers ether for general anesthetic purposes, as his experiences with cholorform have not been as satisfactory as with this agent. Some authors (Voronoff, Dartigues, Moutard) commence the anesthesia with ethyl chloride.

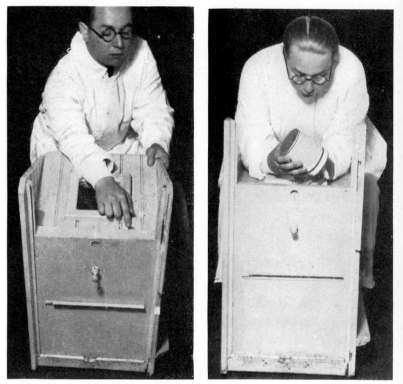

FIG. 217.—Aperture in anesthetizing chamber.   FIG. 218.—Position of anesthetizing chamber during anesthesia.

B. Preparation of Donor and Recipient.—

The recipient shall be prepared surgically, the site of implantation selected (Cf. Chapter on Site of Implantation), and rendered as aseptic as possible. The anesthetic used for the recipient is scopolamin-morphin supplemented by gas, oxygen or ether; or any one may use, if he so desires, local anethesia throughout the entire procedure. If the material to be implanted is a refrigerated specimen, the implant is kept in the container until the time it is to be transplanted. The setting up of the operating

ɔom, with the relative positions of the donor and recipient, is depicted in
ig. 219. Of course, two anesthetists are necessary, one for the donor
nd one for the recipient. The donor, if human, is prepared at the same
me as the recipient; if an animal, it is shaved and rendered surgically
septic after complete anesthesia has been induced. It is then draped and
rought into the operating room for ablation of the testes, and the recipient,

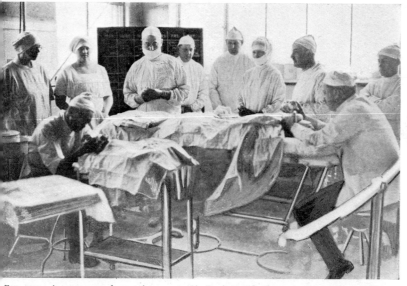

FIG. 219.—Arrangement of operating room. (Author's technic of sex gland transplantation.)

ter complete relaxation has set in following anesthesia, has the area pre-
ared for the reception of the implant. If the author's technic is decided
ɔon and the space between the peritoneum and rectus abdominis muscle
 selected as the site for the implant (Technique No. I) in the region of
ιe deep epigastric vessels, this area is exposed, by dissection, through a
attle-Kammerer incision, keeping in mind that *hemostasis is of the
'most importance.* The space is prepared as shown in Fig. 220. Next
ιck the bed so prepared with a dry gauze tampon, and proceed to ablate
ιe testis that is to be implanted as shown in the accompanying illustration
'ig. 221).

Immediately upon removal of the testis, strip it from its tunica vagin-
is testis, leaving the epididymis intact, and snip out small pieces of tunica

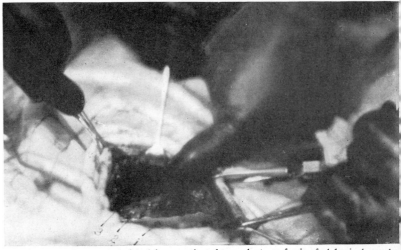

FIG. 220.—Preparation of bed for reception of transplant. 1, fascia of abdominal muscles 2, rectus abdominis muscle; 3, bed between supraperitoneal structures and muscle. (Author' technic of sex gland transplantation, No. 1.)

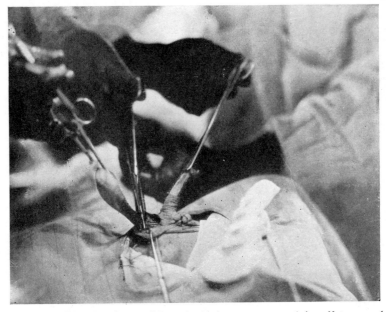

FIG. 221.—Dissection of parts of donor, in this instance a cynocephalus. Note removal o testis in its unopened tunica vaginalis and high amputation of funiculus spermaticus. (Author technic of sex gland transplantation No. 1.)

buginea with a sharp scissors curved on the flat, as shown in Fig. 222.
he author calls this step " lanternizing " for the reason that small fenestra
e created as a result of snipping away portions of the tunica albuginea.

FIG. 222.—Proper position of instruments and gland to obtain "lantern" denudation effect.
(Author's technic of sex gland transplantation.)

he ablation of the tunica albuginea, as described, results in the protru-
on of the testicular substance, as shown in Fig. 223.

In the earlier operations performed by the author, he removed larger
rips of the tunica albuginea than he does at present. It was found that
·moval of the large strips permits too much eventration of the testicular
·bstance, as shown in the figure, and contributes to too rapid absorption.
 one desires to resort to the " lanternizing " method, only small sections
· the albuginea should be removed. The author recently has abandoned
·is method, however, and now prefers to expose the tunica vasculosa which
 to come in contact with the peritoneum by employing the elec-

tric thermo cautery (Figs. 224 and 225). During this procedure
great care is necessary not to permit the penetration of the heated cauter
point to too great a depth. It must be remembered that the object i
destruction of small areas of tunica albuginea and exposure of the tunic
vasculosa sufficiently to cause union of the vascular and lymph element
between it and the contiguous similar anatomic structures whose func

FIG. 223.—"Lantern" denudation completed. (Author's technic of sex gland transplantation.)

tion it will be to nourish and keep the implant alive. The accompanyin
illustrations (Figs. 226 and 227) show to what depth the tunica albugine
should be penetrated.

After preparing the implant by lanternization or cauterization, it
deposited in the bed previously prepared for its reception in the deptl
of the abdominal wall (Fig. 228).

The important point to be kept in mind at this stage of the operatic
is to have the operative field dry and free from blood. The rectus abdomin
is now permitted to resume its normal anatomic relation, its fascia
closed with interrupted catgut sutures and the skin united with silkwor
gut, dermal sutures, or skin clips, as the operator may select. A coat
iodin is applied to the wound (Fig. 229), which is then covered with
gauze pad and the patient is returned to bed.

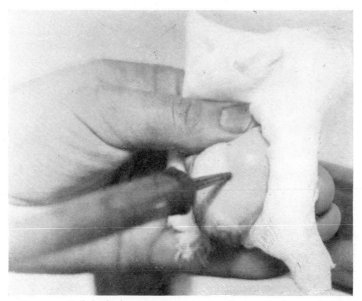

FIG. 224.—Technic of using electro-thermo-cautery to expose tunica vasculosa. (Author's Technic No. 1.)

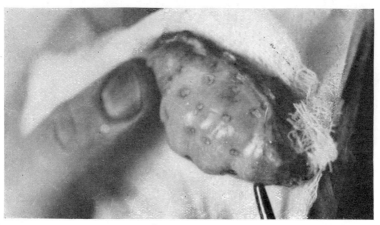

FIG. 225.—Same as preceding (close-up).

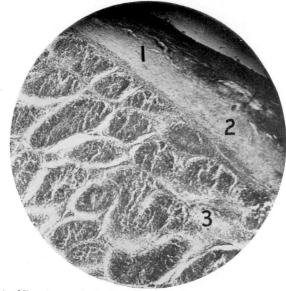

FIG. 226.—Microphotograph, showing degree of destruction of tunica albuginea with electro-thermo-cautery in exposing tunica vasculosa (proper method). 1, normal tunica albuginea; 2, effects of heat on albuginea; 3, slight thermal effects on tubuli seminiferi. (Author's Technic No. 1.)

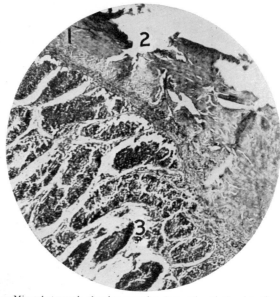

FIG. 227.—Microphotograph, showing excessive destruction of albuginea (improper method). 1, border of normal tunica albuginea; 2, excessive destruction (thermal) of albuginea; 3, excessive destruction of contiguous tubular structures.

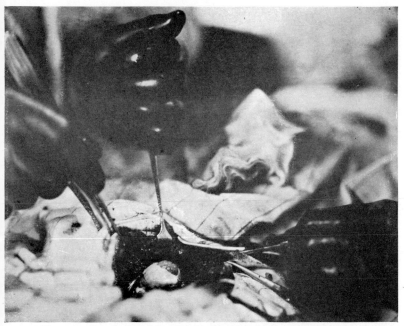

FIG. 228.—Introduction of denuded transplant into bed previously prepared.
(Author's Technic No. 1.)

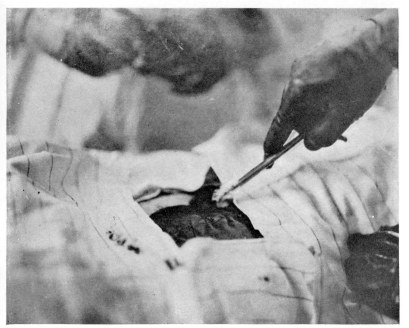

FIG. 229.—Final aseptization of the skin with tr. of iodin; dressings. (Author's Technic No. 1.)

AUTHOR'S TECHNIQUE NO. 2.

To still further improve the technic by placing the implant in the most favorable position for function, the author experimentally discovered that the retrorenal space between Gerota's capsule and the endo-abdominal fascia offered such opportunities. The accompanying illustrations (Figs. 230–233) nicely depict this space, as well as the results obtained by the author in his experimental transplantations on animals which led to the evolution of Technique No. 2 now used. A study of these illustrations (taken from higher apes) offers conclusive proof of the vascularization of the transplant through the lumbar vessels.

In using this technic (author's Technique No. 2) the patient is placed in the position usually employed for kidney exposure (Fig. 234). An incision about two inches long, or longer if the patient is obese, is made (Fig. 235), and muscular and fascial planes are separated by blunt dissection, either with the finger or a blunt instrument (Fig. 236), and the retrorenal space is then exposed, bringing into view Gerota's capsule and the perirenal fat cushion (Fig. 237).

The testicle to be implanted is then treated as described in my Technique No. 1 (Fig. 238), and is then deposited loosely *without any sutures whatever* in the retrorenal space, (Fig. 239). Figure 240 shows the testis resting freely in this space, entirely unsubjected to pressure. Two or three catgut sutures (Fig. 241) unite the superimposed muscles and fascia and the skin is closed with dermal sutures, linen, silkworm gut or clips, according to the fancy of the operator.

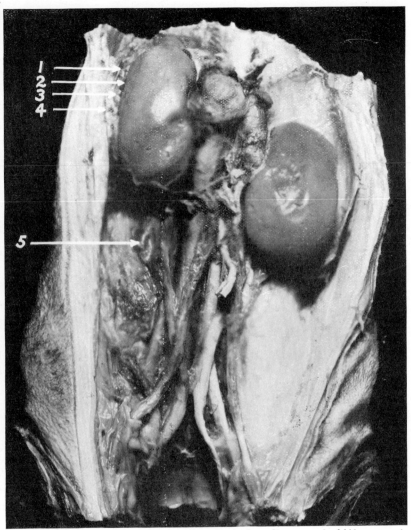

FIG. 230.—Author's Technic No. 2. 1, Gerota's capsule; 2, fibrous capsule of kidney; 3, perirenal fatty capsule; 4, peritoneum; 5, transplant vascularized by the 3rd lumbar vessels. Transplant is situated subperitoneally in fat between the peritoneum and the endo-abdominal fascia.

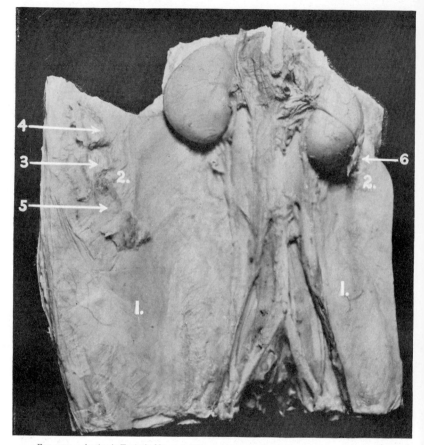

FIG. 231.—Author's Technic No. 1 and No. 2. 1, peritoneum; 2, peritoneum cut away, exposing muscle; 3, transplant situated in anterior abdominal wall (Technic No. 1); 4, sagittal section reflected upward; 5, section reflected downward; 6, transplant (Technic No. 2) posterior to left kidney. The anterior transplant is vascularized through the inferior and superior epigastric vessels.

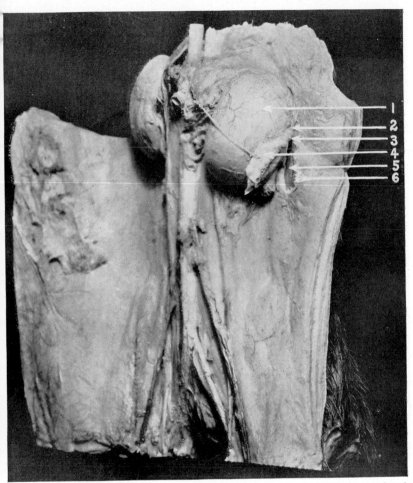

FIG. 232.—Author's Technic No. 1 and No. 2. 1, fibrous capsule of left kidney; 2, perirenal fatty capsule; 3, Gerota's capsule; 4, sagittal section reflected upward and secured by thread; 5, transplant situated posterior to left kidney; 6, blood vessels of lumbar origin.

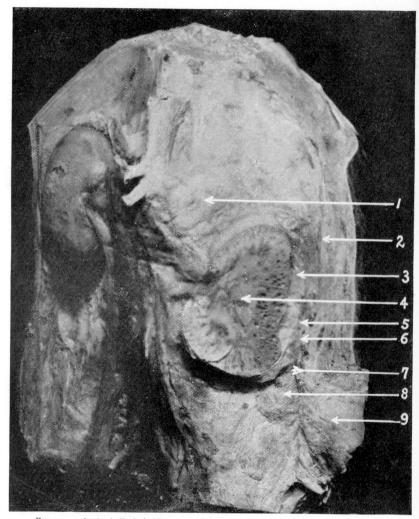

Fig. 233.—Author's Technic No. 2. 1, adrenal gland; 2, peritoneum; 3, fibrous capsule separated from kidney; 4, left kidney; 5, perirenal fatty capsule; 6, Gerota's capsule; 7, new blood vessels originating from 3rd lumbar vessels; 8, transplant situated subperitoneally and beneath fascia; 9, flap reflected outward, consisting of peritoneum and subperitoneal fat.

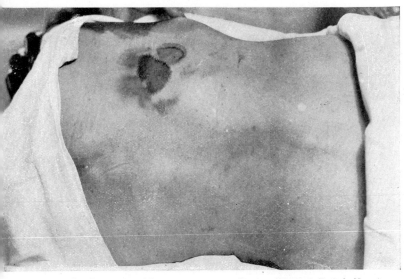

FIG. 234.—Patient in proper position to expose retrorenal space. (Author's Technic No. 2.)

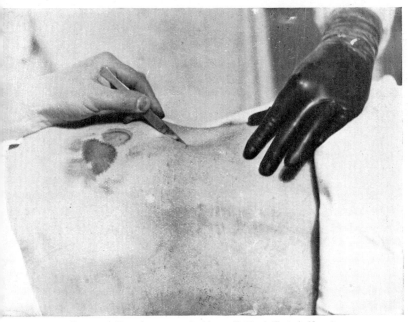

FIG. 235.—Line of cutaneous incision. (Author's Technic No. 2.)

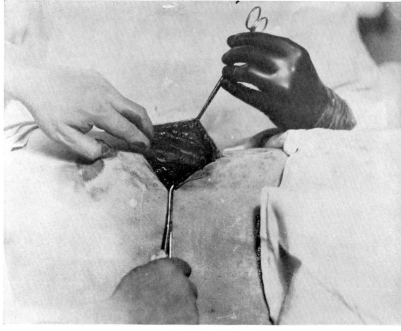

FIG. 236.—Blunt dissection of fascial and muscular planes. (Author's Technic No. 2.)

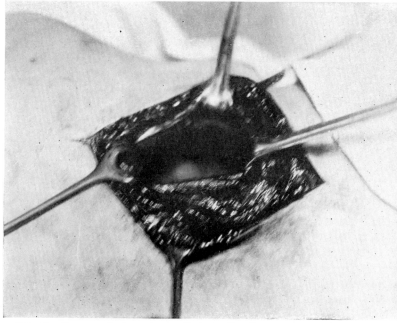

FIG. 237.—Exposure of retrorenal space, displaying Gerod's capsule and perirenal fat cushion, (Author's Technic No. 2.)

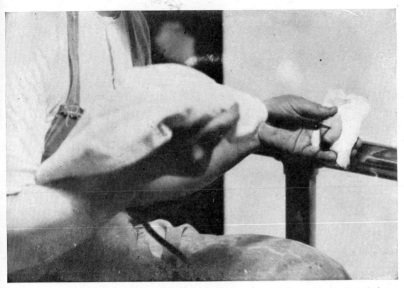

Fig. 238.—Cauterization of tunica albuginea to expose tunica vasculosa. (Author's technic.)

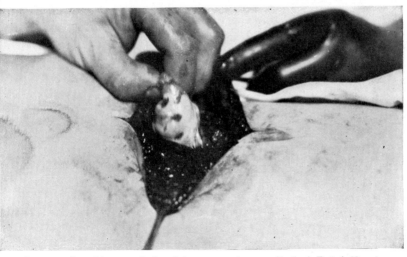

Fig. 239.—Depositing cauterized testis into retrorenal space. (Author's Technic No. 2.)

27

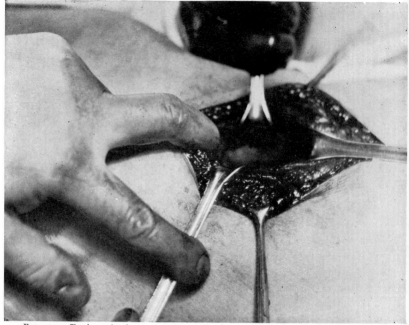

FIG. 240.—Testis resting in retrorenal space free from pressure. (Author's Technic No. 2.)

FIG. 241.—Catgut sutures loosely uniting lumbar muscles and fascia. (Author's Technic No. 2.)

CHAPTER XIX

CLINICAL CASE REPORTS

SPACE forbids the recitation of all cases observed and operated upon by the author and others. Only a series of typical cases can, therefore, be given which follow below:

Dr. Wm. J. Robinson,[1] in commenting on sex gland transplantation, quotes the work of Lydston and Voronoff in the following terms: " The first experiment by Lydston in transplanting testicles from one human being to another was performed by Lydston *on himself*, on January 16, 1914. The testicle was taken from a young man, eighteen years of age, who committed suicide by shooting. The operation of transplantation was performed twenty-four hours after the death of the boy. The operation was performed by Doctor Lydston himself on himself under local anesthesia.

" He made an incision into the scrotum and implanted the testicle directly upon the spermatic cord. There was considerable edema of the penis and scrotum, also pain, and some saprophytic infection; the experiment was considered a failure, and it was decided to remove the foreign testicle. During the operation of removal the implanted gland split, and only one-half was removed; the other half was left, and it seemed to become adherent to the spermatic cord. It gradually decreased in size until after eighteen months it could hardly be felt. The author is convinced that during that time the portion of the testicle was functioning and secreting hormones.

" Doctor Lydston has performed a number of transplantations which turned out more successfully. I shall reproduce here the report of two cases which will demonstrate the status of the procedure, and the results, when successful.

" **Case One.**—The author considers this the most remarkable of all his cases of transplantation, and it is to his mind as conclusive evidence of the value of the procedure as a single case could possibly be.

" A man, aged twenty-nine, sustained an injury to his testes while playing football, twelve years before he consulted the author, in July, 1915.

His right testicle was enormously swollen (probably hematocele) and very painful. When the swelling subsided, the gland had entirely disappeared. The remaining testicle atrophied to a moderate degree. Virility was unimpaired, and the patient married three years later. One child was born of the union.

" About two months prior to the examination, the patient, without preceding trauma or known infection, suddenly developed pain in the left iliolumbar region, left spermatic cord, and the remaining testicle. The testicle did not swell, but, the patient stated, the veins above it were swollen. There were no urinary symptoms. At the end of three weeks the testicle had completely atrophied, and some weeks later the case was referred to the author.

" On examination, we found a healthy-looking subject, over-fat, with moderately feminine secondary sex characteristics. The beard was almost negligible; the mammæ moderately large, and the pelvis distinctly broader than the normal masculine type. The patient stated that his physique had shown these peculiarities increasingly since his injury, twelve years before, but that his sexual power had been " satisfactory " until after the loss of the second testicle. During all these years he had not been physically as fit as before, and for about a year he had with difficulty met the physical and mental exigencies of his business, this lack of efficiency having rapidly increased since the loss of the remaining testicle. Since the loss of the second testicle there had been complete impotence.

" Palpation showed scarcely a vestige of tissue at the end of the spermatic cords—nothing, indeed, that could be accepted as even a remnant of gland tissue. The penis was of only moderate development, with a long prepuce, but otherwise normal.

" August 1, 1915, the author implanted on this patient both testes taken from a boy of fourteen, dead of a crushing injury. The subject was just approaching puberty, and not well developed. The testes were removed six hours after death, and kept on ice in sterile salt solution until the operation, thirty-nine hours after the death of the boy. The implantation was made in the scrotal sac on each side, at the normal site of the testes. The glands were implanted entire, the epididymes not being removed. Healing was prompt; there was only one degree of transient febrile reaction, and very slight inflammatory swelling about the implanted glands. Five days after the implantation circumcision was performed. The patient returned home in two weeks. Vigorous and painful erections occurred after the eighth day, and required an ice bag. Successful coitus was practiced three weeks after dismissal from the hospital. Seven months after operation, the patient reported that he was perfectly normal, was taking active gymnastic exercise, and had lost nearly twenty pounds of his flabby fat. Erections vigorous and more frequent than in the average normal subject of similar age. The patient laid especial stress on his mental and physical fitness for business. The implanted testes had atrophied only moderately, and were of relatively fair size and fairly normal consistency. The epididymes were plainly distinguishable. As Dr. William T. Belfield, who examined the case and questioned the patient, remarked: ' The testes, while small, are as well developed and apparently as normal as in many perfectly virile men who come under our observation.'

" In passing, I wish to state that, for a while after the implantation, the patient experienced normal orgasm without emission. He stated to Doctor Belfield and myself that after a few weeks he began to have emissions of a considerable amount of fluid, and that these emissions were almost constant. The emitted fluid, while it has not been examined, of course is not testicular secretion—no anastomosis having been done—but comes from the urethra, Cowper's glands, the prostate, and the seminal vesicles. In brief, it probably is composed of all the usual normal elements of the normal semen, save the testicular secretion, of which the spermatozoa are the important element.

" For some weeks after the implantation the patient complained of ' frightful nervousness.' As he described them, his symptoms were not unlike those produced by strychnine and similar spinal excitants. The ' nervous ' symptoms finally disappeared. The author attributed them to the unwonted dose of hormone supplied by the implanted testes, to which the nervous system gradually became accustomed.

" August 15, 1916, just one year and two weeks after the implantation, the patient reported as ' fit as a fiddle.' He stated that he sustained intercourse often as frequently as thrice weekly, and that his health was perfect. The testes still were in evidence and, although smaller when last examined, were well defined and of firm consistency.

" This case last reported to the author July 20, 1917. Drs. W. T. Belfield and J. J. Monahan examined the patient. The implanted testes were found not to have atrophied appreciably since the last examination a year before. The beneficial effects of the implantation still endured. It would appear that this case probably proves that permanency of result is possible, not only as to physiologic results, but also as to the endurance of the implanted glands.

" **Case Two.**—A man, aged fifty-eight years, commercial traveler, who, for a period of five years had been under the author's care from time to time for partial atonic impotence, consented to submit to testicular implantation. There was no local disease or abnormality. Somewhat less than half of a testis was implanted, the material used being obtained from the body of a man, aged thirty years, ten hours after death produced by contact with a live wire. The implantation was performed thirty-six hours after the death of the donor. The recipient was somewhat neurasthenic, as naturally was to have been expected, but was apparently in excellent health and well preserved for a man of his years.

" The implantation was performed, March 14, 1914, Doctor Michel assisting. The portion of the gland was partially decorticated and implanted in the left side of the scrotum, in contact with the cord, immediately posterior to the testis of the recipient. There was only moderate reaction after the implantation. This had subsided by the twelfth day, at which time a moderately firm, circumscribed, movable mass of glandular outline could be felt at the site of the implantation. During the process of healing the patient expressed himself as conscious of a remarkable stimulation of sexual activity. According to his account of the subjective symptoms, this began almost immediately—four or five days—after the implantation and continued during the progress of healing. Obviously the psychic element must be considered in connection herewith, as there was very little inflammatory reaction and the patient was not at all apprehensive of accidents. Nocturnal erections began on the second night after the operation and recurred regularly while he was under the author's observation. On the fourteenth day the patient left the city. A letter from him, June 15, was worthy of note merely as bearing upon his condition at that time. Quoting this letter, the points of interest are: ' . . . . The erections at night have continued regularly. They rarely occurred before during the past four or five years. The erections are not quite as strong as in my younger days, nor so long continued, but the sexual act is natural again and is not followed by great exhaustion as was formerly the case . . . . The lump where the piece of gland was planted has shrunk somewhat, but I feel sure that the gland is alive and hearty . . . . I am still feeling fine and much more vigorous that I have felt for years.' The evident improvement in this patient's sexual function cannot reasonably be entirely explained by the psychic effect of the implantation. Nocturnal erections dissociated from erotic dreams do not occur from purely psychic impressions. As to the influence of local irritation, this might explain the sexual stimulation occurring immediately after the operation, but naturally it would have subsided later.

" On July 20, this patient presented himself for examination. The implanted mass of gland tissue was still perceptible and about the size and shape of a good sized almond . . . . He asserted that the improvement in sexual vigor still persisted . . . .

" January 15, 1915, the patient again reported. The implanted nodule had almost disappeared, but was still perceptible on careful palpation. Improvement had been maintained and the patient was very enthusiastic.

" December 29, 1916, the patient reported himself as still doing well, and very much pleased with the results of the implantation. In a recent letter he claims to be still satisfied with results.

" Important and valuable as Doctor Lydston's work with the transplantation of human sex glands is, it is *not* of very great practical utility; and for one very simple reason: the scarcity or practical non-obtainability of material. For even under the *worst* circumstances, human testicles for transplantation into other humans are not likely to become very abundant.

" The testicles that have been used for transplantation purposes have so far been obtained from the following sources:

" Undescended testicles and testicles in hernias which their owners were willing to sacrifice as being of little or no value to them; testicles from people killed by accident; testicles from suicides; testicles from castrated or executed criminals; and in one case, we are told, a testicle was obtained by force from a man who was overpowered and mutilated. We are also told that now and then a poor fellow is willing to part with one of his sex glands for what is to him a considerable sum of money.

" Now all these sources are not likely to become more, but less abundant.

" As to undescended testicles and testicles from hernias, it is very questionable if they are qualitatively as good as normal testicles. I am inclined to the belief that they are not. Accidents and suicides, we also trust, will become less and not more frequent. The castration of criminals is not gaining but losing favor; where sterilization of undesirable people is advisable, we are more apt now to have recourse to vasectomy or to the röntgen ray. As to the execution of criminals, we hope that crime will go on diminishing instead of increasing, and that capital punishment will go out of existence within a comparatively brief period. As to people parting with their sex glands for a few dollars, that also is not likely to become a widespread practice; the sex gland is the last thing a person, no matter how poor, is willing to part with, and second, we are all hoping, and it appears not in vain, that poverty will go on diminishing instead of increasing, particularly so when birth control becomes a more or less universal practice.

" Nor is it likely that there will be many voluntary donors.

" So, taking all in all, the use of human sex glands for transplantation purposes is not of very great practical value. We therefore have to have recourse to the sex glands of animals; and the sex glands most successfully grafted and most likely to yield hormones similar to the human hormones are the sex glands of monkeys. And it is with glands of these animals that investigators, notably Dr. Serge Voronoff of Paris, have done the most important experimental and therapeutic work. As I said in the introduction of this chapter, even discounting the enthusiasm and unconscious bias of pioneer investigators, there is little doubt that the implantation of simian glands in the human male gives occasionally very remarkable results. I reproduce herewith two of the cases as reported by Doctor Voronoff.

" **Case One.**—This patient was a man of letters, a celebrated dramatic author, sixty-one years of age. He represented a most characteristic senile type, and had the appearance of an old man; flabby cheeks, wrinkled face, doubled-up body, dull eyes, and senile circle round the cornea. Every physical effort proved painful, his steps lagged, his movements were slow. Save an occasional attack of malarial fever, he complained of no particular illness; but he had no appetite, felt a great lassitude, and took cold upon the slightest cause. Thought had become slow; the happy expression hard to find; memory displayed gaps, becoming more and more numerous. Total impotence for ten years.

"Doctor Voronoff grafted on him under local anesthesia the testicles of a large cynocephalus, divided into eight fragments, carefully spaced around his testicles. Twenty-three days after the graft, the patient first experienced an erection. This fact surprised him all the more because he had hoped the graft would ameliorate his general condition only and had thought nothing of virile manifestations so long lost to him. Since that time the erections have been frequent. The patient recovered a virility such as he had about ten years before, and at the present moment, nearly two years since the graft, the manifestations of sexual energy continued. At the time, as he regained genital force, a complete change was produced in his appearance which was really astonishing. His body has become well set up, the facial muscles more firm, the eye bright, and, notwithstanding his white hair, he gives one a surprising impression of youth, vigor and energy. He resumed his former life; takes long walks, is assiduous as heretofore in his attendance at theatrical representations. But what crowns his joy is the facility with which he expresses his thought, and his renewed ability to work for long hours without fatigue.

"**Case Two.**—This case was the oldest of the author's patients, an Englishman, seventy-four years of age, and the result was the best in his experience. The patient, who was presented to the 31st French Congress of Surgery, presented the aspects of a perfect English gentleman, vigorous, robust, energetic.

"Two years ago, before the graft, this patient appeared as an old man, inert, doubled-up, obese, haggard in look, dull of eye, walking painfully with the aid of a stick. Without taking his age into account—seventy-four years—which could be reckoned as very considerable, he had passed thirty years of his life in India where he manifested a great activity, notwithstanding the depressing effect of the climate. In addition, he had contracted smallpox in India, and only two years before this transplantation he had undergone laparotomy for peritonitis, and his convalescence had been retarded by pneumonia complicated by pleurisy.

"On the second of February, 1921, the author grafted upon him, under local anesthesia, several fragments of the testis of a large cynocephalus.

Rapid cicatrization of the wound without incident. The patient left Paris twelve days after the operation, and the author saw him only eight months afterward. His assistant doctor and he were literally stupefied to see the patient appear before them, half of his embonpoint lost, his aspect jovial, his movements active, his eye clear and twinkling in appreciation of their astonishment. The body was erect, and everything combined to give the impression of a man enjoying magnificent health. He bent his head, and one could see that he did not exaggerate when he said his cranium was covered with a thick down.

" He was returning from Switzerland, where he had made several ascents, and indulged in the sports beloved of Englishmen. This man had really recovered twenty or twenty-five years of lost youth. His physical and intellectual condition, his virility, all had been radically changed under the action of the testicular graft, which transformed a decrepit old man, sexually impotent, pitiable, into a vigorous man, in the full enjoyment of all his faculties.

" According to the author, this man is the finest demonstration of the fact that modern science can victoriously combat that most deplorable state into which a man may fall, namely senile decay, physical and intellectual decadence."

Author's Clinical Observations

In all, the author performed, from 1919 to 1923, ninety-seven homo- and heterotransplantations. Only some cases of this series can be described here in detail. The reader will find a summary and analytic table on this series of cases at the end of this chapter.

Senile Asthenia; Impotentia Cœundi; Asthma; Heterotransplantation.

Scotchman, a widower, aged seventy-five, was admitted to the hospital November 7, 1920.

Family History.—Negative.

Personal History.—The patient never used alcoholic beverages; is a moderate smoker. *Anamnesis.* Until about ten years ago his sexual life was normal. Since that time there has gradually set in total impotency with extinguished *libido* and simultaneously a gradual decline in physical vigor, with the development of asthmatic attacks which rendered the patient from time to time miserable.

Physical Examination.—The patient appears a markedly senile individual; is greatly emaciated. His gait betrays weakness of locomotion. The hair is gray, the skin senile, and the skeletal muscles wasted. The pallor of the skin indicates an impoverishment of the blood. Examination of the thorax shows a senile heart and all the clinical manifestations of a bronchial irritation which is undoubtedly responsible for the asthmatic attacks of which the patient is complaining. Blood pressure, systolic 160, diastolic 100, pulse pressure 60. The palpable arteries are sclerosed. Urinalysis discloses the presence of kidney pathology, indicating an interstitial nephritis.

The patient having been under the care of a number of colleagues with the usual forms of treatment without much benefit (as a matter of fact, his condition was progressively getting worse), he requested a transplantation, to which the author acquiesced, and on November 11, 1920, the patient was subjected to testicular transplantation according to the Voronoff technic. The testicle used was from a large, mature macacus nemestrinus. The anesthetic used was scopolamin-morphin, supplemented by nitrous oxid-oxygen.

Postoperative Course.—There was a rise of temperature for the first forty-eight hours, 2° above normal, which promptly dropped. A moderate degree of suppuration of the operative field and expulsion of portions of the implanted testis followed. A sinus of the scrotum persisted, but finally was closed at the end of four weeks, at which time healing was perfect. At that particular time of the year the patient dreaded attacks of asthma which were tormenting him considerably, but six weeks after the operation he reported that not only did he not suffer from renewed attacks, but his asthmatic symptoms which were present more or less at all times, had appreciably abated. Also, that erections which he had not experienced for at least ten years, had made their reappearance and were quite violent at times. The general physical condition of the patient was improved.

A letter from him dated December 26, 1920, reads (I am quoting his words verbatim): "I have had an unusual experience last Wednesday night when I woke up with a most vigorous erection. It was not a weak erection as I have had heretofore, but strong as a person of strong powers would have." December 23, 1921, he wrote as follows: "I am just going to say that in spite of weather conditions, I seem to be taking on strength, have better balance and perhaps more energy and a marked improvement in appetite. My cough, while still persisting, is not nearly so marked. It has lost one of its bad features, the smothering feature." Again, on June 12, 1922, he wrote: " I am taking on some weight, the smothering spells have entirely disappeared and exertion does not put me out of breath as it did before."

A little over a year after the transplantation, the man felt so much improved physically that, prompted by motives of gratitude, he submitted himself for a retransplantation voluntarily for purely experimental purposes. A letter sent to the author by this grateful patient was to the effect that not only did he wish to have implantation experiments performed upon him, but he also willed his body, after his death, to the author to be used for purposes of dissection for scientific investigation. Of course, this latter offer was not accepted, but is simply mentioned to emphasize his gratitude for the relief he had experienced that prompted his action. As another implantation, after the lapse of a year could not possibly have done the man any harm, and perhaps might do him a great deal of good, the author took advantage of his offer. Keeping in mind the sloughing that resulted at the hands of the author, Lichtenstern and others, and the author having evolved his technic by experimenting on a great many animals up to that date, this patient was given the benefit of this technic, and an implantation, according to the author's method was done on August 5, 1922, the testis being taken from a cynocephalus, and the implant being placed in the right side of the abdomen.

At the time of this transplantation, the patient was in excellent physical condition, and the previous testicular transplant done by the Voronoff method, although much shrunken in size, was still slightly palpable. The last transplanted testicle was removed with the patient's consent four and one-half months later for the purpose of histologic study. The findings were as follows (Fig. 242):

1. A regression of the seminiferous tubules.

2. Proliferation of the interstitial cells of Leydig.

3. Spermatogonia and Sertoli cells could still be found, the latter in comparatively greater numbers than the former.

4. New blood vessels, macrophages and giant cells in great abundance were observed.

The patient was discharged from the hospital a short time after the operation, and has occasionally reported his continued well-being to the author. During the early part of January, 1923, he reported that the asthmatic symptoms, although occurring occasionally, were very much

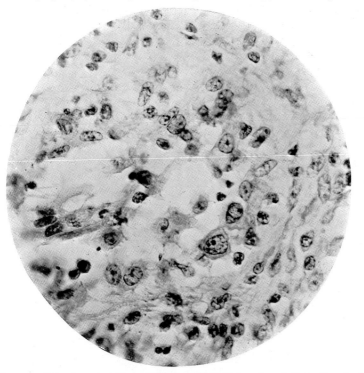

Fig. 242.—Heterotransplantation. Author's method. Four and one-half months after implantation. Obj. 7.5; ocular 2. Enlarged 965 diameters, Leitz apochromatic. Hematoxylin and osin. Observe the beautifully preserved Leydig cells; the tubular regression; the persistence of spermatogonia and Sertoli cells; the presence of new blood vessels, macrophages, etc.

ameliorated. There was marked general physical improvement and the patient could perform sexually to his entire satisfaction, having normal *libido* and normal potency. His urinalysis, however, showed that his kidney functions were bad—in fact, worse than last year. (More casts of the hyalin and granular variety being found upon repeated examination.)

Comment.—The beneficial clinical effects from sex gland transplantation were clearly demonstrated in this case. The improvement in the asthmatic attacks of the patient the author is inclined to attribute to the adrenalin content in the testicular tissue, as pointed out by Sajous. Stud of the microphotograph appended in this case offers a great deal of foo for thought. The Leydig cells were alive and proliferating, and undoubtedl contribute to the splendid results obtained in this instance. Heterotrans plantation from ape to man is not only a possible but feasible procedure as exemplified in this case, as well as in others.

General Asthenia; Senility; Complete Loss of Sexual Power Mental Depression; Hetero Sex Gland Implantation.—

Mr. J. B. T., American, a widower, aged seventy-eight years, the fathe of five children, was admitted to the hospital December 20, 1920.

Family History.—Negative.

Personal History.—Pneumonia when thirty years of age; three at tacks of gonorrhea from which he completely recovered. Smokes an drinks in moderation. Complains of general weakness, with complet loss of sexual power and *libido*. Gradual loss of memory, shortness c breath upon exertion, great mental depression with suicidal tendencies.

Physical Examination.—A poorly nourished individual, bald headec defective teeth, *arcus senilis*, flabbiness of general skeletal musculature advanced arteriosclerosis, myocarditis. Blood pressure, systolic 200, dia stolic 120, pulse 80. Second pulmonary sound accentuated. Abdome negative. Prostatic gland moderately enlarged. Hyalin casts occasionall discoverable in the urine. The patient had been in a sanitarium and ha taken rest cures, etc., etc., without the slightest relief.

The general condition of the patient being very bad, and he insistin upon a gland implantation, he was given to understand by the author tha this operation would be undertaken at his request for purely experimenta reasons. He cheerfully consented to this proposition, expressing a desir to aid in scientific investigation. The author informed him that tw testes would be implanted and that after a time, one of these implant would be removed for microscopic study, to which he asquiesced.

Operation.—On October 15, 1921, under scopolamin-morphin, nitrous oxide oxygen anesthesia, implantation of both testes of a cynocephalu by the author's method (Cf. Chapter on Technic) was done.

Postoperative Course.—The wound healed by primary union, th patient leaving the bed on the eleventh day. He returned to his home an bout ten days later began to do some light work. A month after the peration, he presented himself for observation. His general condition t that time was more buoyant, his nervous condition much more placid nd he impressed one with greater cheer. His morose depression was less aarked. He was advised to return home, to not exert himself greatly, and) return a month later, which he did. At that time his general physical nprovement was marked. The systolic pressure had dropped to 160, e was not tormented with suicidal inclinations, and his general appearnce evidenced a great deal of improvement.

True to his promise, he presented himself seven months later and reuested that one of the implanted testes be removed, as arranged for at ie previous date. This was done under local anesthesia. Examination ' the gross specimen after removal showed that implantation was an itire success. The tunica albuginea was blended with the surrounding ructures in the bed formed for the implant, and performed its functions atisfactorily. Vascularization was markedly in evidence. There was ınsiderable reduction in the size of the transplant, however. Microscopic aamination of sections taken from this specimen and stained with hemaəxylin-eosin presented the following picture:

The low power magnification at once reveals tubular regression and terstitial tissue proliferation. The interstitial elements consist of the ıme component parts as are described in the specimen removed from ıe previously reported case. The Leydig cells are clearly demonstrable ıd of various sizes, mono- and polynuclear. Giant cells and new blood ıssels abound. Some of these giant cells seem to be the result of coalition Leydig cells and other cellular elements. In some of the Leydig cells itoses (?) are seen. Careful search and special staining for crystalloids, ı described by Reinecke, could not be demonstrated in this specimen. onnective tissue cells of all varieties were present in abundance. Phago-⁻tic action is clearly demonstrated, particularly in the areas of the distegrated tubules. The accompanying illustration clearly illustrates the ıanges in this implanted testis (Figs. 243 and 244).

Seven months after the original operation, the improvement in the neral condition of the patient was evident. There was marked return ⁻ sexual vigor. The subjective manifestations complained of by the patient were on the decline, and he was, as he expressed it, " much com forted and improved."

The author had an opportunity to reëxamine this man on March 2 1923. He is doing some light work, visits motion picture shows in th evening and enjoys the performance greatly. His blood pressure at thi time is, systolic 158, diastolic 98, pulse pressure 60.

Comment.—In this case the effects of heterotransplantation from higher apes to man are clearly demonstrated. The persistence of the im

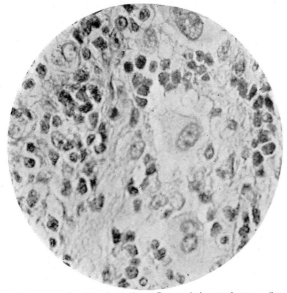

FIG. 243.—Hetero sex gland implantation. Cynocephalus to human. Seven and a ha months after transplantation. Obj. 7½; ocular 2. Leitz apochromatic, enlarged 102 diameter Hematoxylin and eosin. Leydig cells and other components about same as in previous cas Mitoses (?) Leydig cells were seen in some places.

plant after seven and a half months and the presence of the Leydig cells and above all, the general physical improvement of the patient are strik ing as well as significant of the practicability of implanting testes even i considerably advanced cases of physical deterioration.

Sexual Neurasthenia; Psycho-neurosis; Heterogenous Implantatio of Testis.—

A clergyman, aged forty-two years, presented himself for treatmen for sexual impotency extending over a period of six years. He had bee

ɔtent and very active sexually until about four years ago when a tre-
ᴍendous onrush of work caused him to exert himself in his parishional
ᴜties, and following which he noticed, with great disappointment and
ɲagrin, a decline of his sexual power. This worried him to such an extent
ᴛat he became extremely nervous, sleepless, complained of noises in his
ᴇad that interfered with his hearing and of great psychic depression.

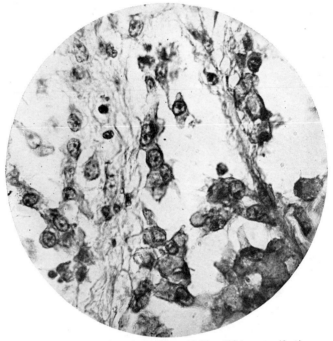

Fɪɢ. 244.—Same as foregoing—different field and higher magnification.

Physical Examination.—Examination revealed a well-built man, in-
ᴄlined to be adipose, of pallid complexion, in which pallidity all the visible
ᴍucous membranes shared. The reflexes both superficial and deep were
ᴍarkedly exaggerated. The urine was negative, the cardiovascular sys-
ᴇm normal. Hemoglobin was 72 per cent.; blood pressure systolic 100,
ᴅiastolic 70, pulse pressure 30.

The patient insisted upon an implantation, and this was done on
Ⅎebruary 8, 1921, by the Voronoff method. There was a mild degree of
ᴤuppuration of the wound for about a month, after which closure took place.

28

Postoperative Results.—The patient left the hospital in the same frame of mind as when admitted, introspective, pessimistic and worried over his sexual decline. The results of the operation in this case were practically *nil*.

Communications from the patient six and eight months and a year and a half respectively, after the implantation reported no improvement whatsoever in his mental, physical or sexual condition.

Comment.—In this case, the pessimistic attitude of the patient and constant brooding over the inability to perform as much sexually as he wished to, and the constant drain upon the nervous system through worry and resulting insomnia, have marred, in a measure, the results of the gland therapy, and prevent, therefore, an unbiased conclusion as to whether or not any benefits were gained from the implantation. The patient works hard in his parish and is able to do so constantly in spite of the strain, but complains bitterly of his impotency. The author is inclined to believe that we are dealing here with a form of psychic impotence which could be more benefited by a neurologist if the patient were willing to submit himself to a prolonged course of conscientious neurological observation and neuropsychic therapy. We must conclude, however, that subjectively at least, the implantation in this case was a rank failure.

Precocious Senility; Heteroimplantation.—

V. H., admitted to the hospital December 19, 1920, aged fifty-five years, American, an ex-soldier, now employed in a commission house. Complained of general weakness, total loss of *libido* and sexual power during the last five years; cardiac palpitation, inability for sexual exertion and periods of mental depression.

Physical Examination.—The patient presented the appearance of a man away past sixty, although only fifty-five years of age. With the exception of exaggerated reflexes, the findings were negative aside from the visible signs of premature senescence. The Wassermann reaction on blood and spinal fluid is negative; urinalysis negative.

There was nothing of importance in the family or personal history except that the patient had malaria and an attack of something that from his description suggests amebic dysentery.

Transplantation was desired, and the testis of a cynocephalus was implanted according to the author's technic.

Postoperative Course.—The patient stated that two days after the operation erections took place and recurred every day as long as he remained in the hospital, their character being strong and lasting. The wound healed by primary intention and the patient was discharged.

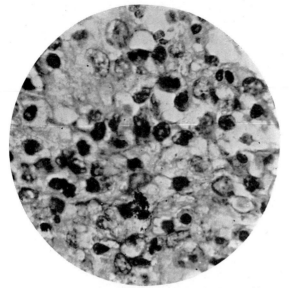

FIG. 245.—Eight months and fifteen days after implantation. Ocular 8x; obj. 2; magnified 1021 diameters. Leitz apochromatic. Hematoxylin and eosin.

By mutual consent, the patient submitted to a removal of the implant eight months and fifteen days after the operation (Fig. 245) the testis of another cynocephalus being implanted in its place.

Postoperative Results.—The sensation of fatigue gradually abated; the patient arises refreshed in the morning and is continuing his work with a much brighter outlook on life. Sexually he is, as he expresses it, " perfect."

The last examination of the patient was made a year and a half after the operation, and his physical, mental, and psychic improvement remains very marked.

Comment.—This case clearly illustrates the beneficial results of sex gland implantation in precocious senility provided no organic disease is present. Although the patient gave a history of malaria and dysentery these maladies did not leave him in any way impaired organically so far as could be ascertained by physical examination.

Precocious Senility; Implantation.—

M. P. A., aged fifty-five years, a vessel pilot, was admitted to the hospital February 7, 1921. Aside from having lost a finger in an accident and having had gonorrhea in his younger days and an attack of malaria twelve years ago, the previous history of this patient was negative. There was no hereditary taint. The present complaint is chiefly that of complete loss of sexual power and *libido,* with a decline of physical power and endurance. The patient cannot ascribe any cause for his physical condition, which came on gradually. He has always been moderate sexually.

Physical Examination.—Examination reveals no organic defect, although the patient appears much older than his actual age, his appearance being that of sixty-five rather than fifty-five. He is much emaciated. The Wassermann reaction is negative. Cardiovascular and renal signs (objectively) are absent.

Operation.—Transplantation under scopolamin-morphin ether anesthesia, the transplant being a testis from a youth dead from accident (fall from height).

Postoperative Course.—The patient was out of bed on the twelfth day, the wound healing by primary intention. He was discharged with instructions to report, and was last heard from on August 2, 1922, when he reported his sexual *libido* and power much improved. In his own language: " With reference to my sexual power I want to say I am not as active as when a youth, but am sufficiently so to make me feel much improved and to gratify my sexual desires to my entire satisfaction. Physically I am also much better in every way."

Comment.—This case is recited to show the great similarity to the previous one reported and to emphasize that in precocious senility with physical and mental decline homotransplantation will give, in well selected cases—particularly those with freedom from organic disease—excellent results.

Senility; Male Climacterium; Homotransplantation.—

T. T. T., aged sixty-four years, an American, musician. Family history negative. A moderate drinker; denies venereal infection, but indulged excessively in sexual relations with women while young. Complains of inability to work, insomnia, attacks of cardiac palpitation, sweating, constipation, gastric disturbance in the form of pyrosis and eructations of gas, spots before the eyes, and periods of irritability alternating with attacks of mental depression.

Physical Examination.—Examination reveals an individual bearing all the earmarks of precocious senility, giving the appearance of a man in the seventies rather than his real age of sixty-four. Wassermann reaction on blood and spinal fluid negative. There is total absence of *libido,* and complete extinction of *potentia cœundi,* which has lasted for twelve to fifteen years. Sexual organs cold and flabby. Hypotension, systolic 105; pulse pressure 30. Urinalysis negative. The patient has been married twice; has one daughter by the first wife, and a son by the second. Divorced from the first wife; the second wife died. He is very much disturbed over his lack of power of concentration, and extinction of *vita sexualis.*

The oral administration of testicular extract followed by the subcutaneous injection of a preparation consisting of a testicular emulsion over a period of six weeks was tried, without the slightest benefit. Implantation was then recommended, and the material for the implant was obtained from a man thirty-four years of age. The interesting part of this case was that the patient himself arranged with the donor to part with a portion of his testis. Evidently there was some close relationship existing between the two, the nature of which I could not ascertain, but the donor was most cheerful after having matters explained to him.

The operation was performed on November 5, 1921, by the author's method. On the fourteenth day after the operation, the patient was discharged with the wound completely healed. He promised to keep in touch with the author for the purpose of checking up the clinical findings, but he was not heard from for two months after leaving the hospital when, without previously announcing his arrival, he appeared upon the scene. The following findings were then noted:

On January 10, 1922, increased potency and better mental attitude. The blood pressure, which it will be recalled was 105 on the first examination, had mounted to 118 at this examination. Adrenin contents of testes (Sajous) (?).

There was no discomfort in the area operated upon.

The psychic condition was very much improved and the attitude of pessimism and mental depression had not been noted in the last two months. The crying spells did not recur. Libidinous dreams on the average of once a week, with emissions, were noted by the patient, the first one occurring three-and-a-half weeks after his discharge from the hospital and about every week thereafter.

On July 18, 1922, the patient reported continuous improvement.

Comment.—The results of homotransplantation in this case were all that could be desired. The oral administration of extracts of testicular preparations and subcutaneous injections of testicular emulsion as suggested by some authors (Cf. Chapter on Opotherapy), were followed by negative results. The psychic element in this case could be eliminated as a factor with a certain degree of reasonableness.

Homosexuality; Heteroimplantation.—

L. D., aged forty-one years, a German-American, baker by occupation.

Family History.—His father died insane; his mother died of apoplexy. Two brothers are normal sexually: one sister has homosexual tendencies.

Personal History.—Patient has had inclination toward men since very early life. Has no desire to associate or cohabit with the opposite sex, but is drawn strongly toward men, particularly those of large stature.

Physical Examination.—Examination reveals a proportionately built, normal individual, effeminate in type, in whom the experienced sexologist would at once recognize a homosexual individual. Examination of the chest, abdomen, kidney function, negative. Wassermann reaction on blood and spinal fluid negative. The genitalia were normal with the exception of being undersized for a man of his age and stature. The frame of the body revealed feminine characteristics.

The patient had taken a number of courses of psychotherapy in an effort to rid himself of his affliction, but without success. Implantation was advised and the operation was performed May 11, 1922. Under general anesthesia a testis of a cynocephalus was transplanted according to the author's method.

Postoperative Course.—There was primary union of the wound, but no symptoms pointing to change in the sexual manifestations were noted.

At the present time, seven months after the implantation, the patient reports his condition unchanged.

Comment.—In this instance complete failure is in all probability due to the age of the patient, the complete somatic and psychic establishment of homosexuality and, perhaps, improperly selected therapy. In view of the fact that some authors reported good results following sex-gland implantation in homosexuals, no results at all were obtained in this case. Further study and research in this field is urgently indicated.

Senility; Transplantation.—

Mr. W. L., aged seventy-two. Family history negative. Actor.

Personal History.—Pneumonia in 1893. Wassermann reaction negative. Complained of gradual physical decline accompanied by extinction of sexual *libido,* and power. Has always led a very active life out of doors. At the time of admission, the blood pressure was, systolic 160, diastolic 90; pulse pressure 70; coagulation time six minutes; leukocytes 15,000. There was a slight degree of aortic incompetency which was well compensated. The urine showed an occasional hyalin cast. The motor power, particularly of the lower extremities, was very much impaired. The patient was of tall stature, six feet four inches, and showed distinct evidence of senility. The hair, fingernails, skin, ocular symptoms, panniculus adiposus, carriage and vascular system all bespoke advanced senile retrograde changes. The reflexes, both superficial and deep, were somewhat exaggerated. Implantation was advised.

Operation.—January 4, 1922, under scopolamin-morphin anesthesia. The patient did not require any additional anesthetic, being sound asleep under the influence of the scopolamin. Implantation was carried out by the author's method, the testis of a cynocephalus being used.

Postoperative Course.—The patient left the hospital three weeks after operation, the wound having healed *per primam.* Gradually he improved, his general physical condition being benefited immensely. He reported regularly for a year for blood pressure determinations, the last reading being taken on February 24, 1923, more than a year after the operation. At that time the systolic pressure was 120; diastolic 80; pulse pressure 40. His carriage became more youthful, the body contour more rounded by reason of the deposition of fat and a marked change was noted by his friends in his general physical appearance. However, while his organic functions have gained perceptibly following implantation, there has been no improvement whatever in his sexual condition. While his *libido* was increased, as noted by his behavior toward the opposite sex, he stated that his sexual power did not improve. This statement the author took *cum grano salis*, for he was observed while still at the hospital to violently masturbate. Pressed closely on this question, he

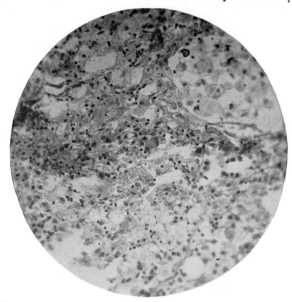

Fig. 246.—Heterotransplantation, M. L. W. One year after implantation. Enlarged 110 times.

admitted that he had libidinous dreams with emissions. A year and a month after the transplantation the patient developed symptoms of appendicitis for which he was readmitted to the hospital and was operated upon for this condition, the author entering the abdomen by way of the incision through which the transplantation was carried out. The implant was found to be reduced to the size of a hazelnut. Large vessels were found coursing in its periphery, and to all appearances, the implant was alive. A small portion was removed for microscopic study, sectioned and stained with hematoxylin and eosin. The following findings were observed (Figs. 246–248):

The Leydig cells are alive and functioning, apparently. The outlines, both of the cell body and nucleus, are distinct. The granular body proto-

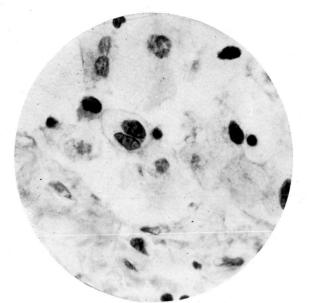

Fig. 247.—Same as preceding; higher magnification. Note Leydig cells splendidly preserved. Enlarged 1021 times.

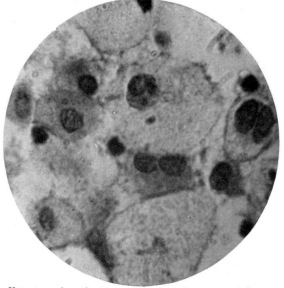

Fig. 248.—Heterotransplantation (same as preceding), from cynocephalus to human one year fter implantation, M. L. W. (senility). Enlarged 1536 diameters. On the photograph of small nagnification the disposition of interstitium to surrounding tissues is clearly shown. A study of the ceydig cells in the higher magnifications shows: Outline of cell body; granular protoplasm; vacuoations; nuclear chromatin; double nuclei.

plasm, vacuolations of cytoplasm are very clearly shown. A close study of the microphotographs depict conditions better than any description could

Comment.—In this case general physical vigor has been the pronounced feature in the results, with marked reduction in the systolic blood pressure and general improvement of physical tone, although subjectively the patient is not pleased with his sexual improvement.

Neurasthenia Gravis; Cachexia: Heterotransplantation.–

F. A., aged fifty-six years, a professional man. Family history negative

Personal History.—Patient has always led a strenuous life. Smokes in moderation; never drinks any alcoholic beverages; has always been moderate in his sexual life with the exception of his student days when he dissipated sexually to no small degree. No hereditary taint.

Because of the cachectic condition of the patient, his loss in weight and subicteric color, grave apprehensions were entertained as to the possibility of some form of malignancy. After consultation with a number of colleagues and subjecting the patient to a most thorough and painstaking diagnostic régime, a diagnosis of neurasthenia gravis was arrived at by exclusion. Implantation was advised, and the transplantation of a human testis into his scrotum was carried out about nine months ago, without any noticeable good effects.

Secondary Eunuchoidism; Homotransplantation.—

Mr. A. L., aged twenty-five years, a business man, sustained an injury to his testes during an accident, with complete atrophy of both glands, when he was twenty-one years of age. At that time he had attained full sexual maturity, was cohabiting regularly, and was very libidinous and active sexually. This period was preceded by a period of active masturbation. After the accident alluded to, the testicles shrunk perceptibly His *libido* decreased, at the end of a year his erections were only occasional and weak, and within another half year, he was completely impotent. Aside from putting on a great deal of fat, no other characteristics observed in the eunuch were evident. In November, 1921, the patient submitted to transplantation of the refrigerated testes of a young man dead of violence.

Both testes were implanted according to the author's technic. Follow-

ng this great improvement in the *vita sexualis* of the patient was observed,
o his great satisfaction.   At this time, a year and four months after the
peration, the patient is having erections regularly, and has an orgasm
with mucoid discharge which undoubtedly springs from the prostate, Cow-
er's gland and urethral mucus, intermingled with some products from
he seminal vesicles.   He has lost some of his surplus weight and feels
enerally very much improved.

    Comment.—In this class of cases with secondary eunuchoidism result-
ng from atrophy of the testes as the result of trauma or pathology, im-
lantation offers a very fertile field for good results.   This has been
bserved not only by the author, but by other investigators in this field
f research.

RESULTS OF NINETY-SEVEN TESTICULAR TRANSPLANTS OBSERVED OVER A FOUR-
YEAR PERIOD (1919-1923).

No. of cases	Type of cases	Type of transplant	Results for both types of transplants
69 (A)	*Senility*, physiological and precocious, representing all degrees of clinical manifestations, including the male climacterium and chronic constitutional diseases	29 homotransplants 40 heterotransplants	31 symptomatic restorations to normal. 13 markedly improved. 12 slightly improved. 13 failures.
11 (B)	*Loss of testes* from trauma, tuberculosis, sarcoma or suppuration of various types	3 homotransplants 8 heterotransplants	8 markedly improved. 3 failures.
8 (C)	*Neurasthenia gravis;* sexual neurasthenia; impotency at early age not due to organic diseases	3 homotransplants 5 heterotransplants	5 markedly improved. 3 failures.
5 (D)	Dementia precox 3 Other psychoses 2	1 homotransplant 4 heterotransplants	2 markedly improved. 1 slightly improved. 2 failures.
2 1 1 (E)	*Glandular syndrome* Fröhlich's disease Eunuchoidism Hypogenitalism	All heterotransplants	1 slightly improved. 3 failures.

RESULTS OF NINETY-SEVEN TESTICULAR TRANSPLANTS OBSERVED OVER A FOU**R** YEAR PERIOD (1919-1923).

Results	Group A senile atrophy		Group B trauma and pathology		Group C functional disorders		Group D psychoses		Group E glandular syndromes		Total	
	No.	%	No.	%	No.	%	No.	%	No.	%	No.	%
Complete symptomatic recovery...	31	45.0	0	0.	0	0.	0	0	0	0	31	32.0
Marked improvement...........	13	18.8	8	72.7	5	62.5	2	40	1	25	29	30.0
Slight improvement.	12	17.4	0	0.	0	0.	1	20	0	0	13	13.4
Failures...........	13	18.8	3	27.3	3	37.5	2	40	3	75	24	24.6
Total cases........	69	100.	11	100.	8	100.	5	100	4	100	97	100.
Type of transplant..												
Homo-..........	29		3		3		1		0		36	
Hetero-.........	40		8		5		4		4		61	

Conclusions.—

In my opinion, based upon the studies herein set forth, there are clear-cut indications and contraindications for sex gland transplantation as shown above. (See Chapter on Indications and Contraindications.)

I emphatically object to the term " rejuvenation." It is misleading particularly to the laity who gain from such terminology the impression that by certain procedures the old can be made young. This is erroneous No organ, or set of organs can be returned, by any method known thus far, to a juvenile state when pathologic changes have made inroads on the structures and rendered them senile, in the accepted form of the term I would suggest the substitution of the term " Therapeutic Gonadal Implantation " in place of the promiscuously used term " rejuvenation." The field of usefulness for such implantation is varied and includes many conditions. Improvement in certain well-defined pathologic states can be anticipated in properly selected cases following the use of proper material and the employment of proper technic. Undoubtedly further research and the accumulation of clinical data will place therapeutic gonadal implantation more firmly as a valuable addition to the armamentaria of the progressive physician.

BIBLIOGRAPHY
[1] ROBINSON, WM. J.: Sexual Impotence, 1923.

CHAPTER XX

THE INTER-RELATION OF THE GLANDS OF INTERNAL SECRETION

THE endocrine glands of the human body should be considered as a ɔ-related whole, and not as an agglomeration of individual glands. The iterrelationship must be judged from the point of view that the glands ltogether form a system, like the lymphatic or nervous system, and that there is any deficiency or any superabundance in the activity of any one land it calls for regularization of the endocrine system at large.

Williams thinks that the endocrine system should be considered as whole and not in terms of any particular gland. That such is the roper course is obvious when it is considered that toxins are the main nemies of the human organism and that the main defences are the duct- ss glands. In this sense life may be looked upon as a war between toxins nd the endocrines; and in the decline of vitality, with the advent of rteriosclerosis and other degenerative changes, the endocrines retreat efore the advancing toxins and the struggle for life is soon ended. But ɔoked at also in the same sense and judging from the time necessary for man to arrive at maturity there is no valid reason why he should not ve until one hundred years or more rather than be senile and effete at eventy years. It is a matter of correct physiological living and prevention f toxin supremacy, and if such would threaten we should endeavor to bviate it.

Williams says that, " it is an interesting fact that the glands in both exes which show the first signs of fatigue are those which seem to have he closest connection with the gonads—namely, the suprarenal in man, and 1e thyroid in woman. In woman the reproductive capacity is definitely rought to a close at the menopause, and it does not surprise us, that the ecessity for redressing the endocrine balance consequent upon the with- rawal of the ovary from practical politics should give rise to considerable ɔnstitutional disturbance."

There appears to be no reason why a man should lose his sexual potency ɔ long as his gonads retain their efficiency, but this efficiency is usually impaired about the sixties, because of the failure of his endocrine system and the accumulation of poisons in his organism. At such a time there is often an atrophy of the seminal tubules, and hypertrophy of the interstitial gland which is probably an effort on the part of this gland to repel toxemia. This senile hypertrophy of the interstitial gland is aided by the hypertrophy of other glands, notably by that of the prostate, hypertrophy of which with advancing years is constantly observed.

With our present knowledge it is impossible to say how far the functions of any particular gland may be associated to dealing with particular toxins, but the obvious rational course is to preserve the integrity of all glands as far as possible, and husband these resources, so that by their correlated action they may protect the organism from the action of accumulating toxins.

While this view regarding the integral correlation of the whole endocrine system is fairly generally conceded as correct, each gland has apparently its own special field of activity, while still retaining its place and exerting its influence in the endocrine chain.

In the present chapter we are principally concerned with the interstitial structures of the testicle—a ductless glandular tissue which forms its secretion, and sends it directly into the blood vessels to act as a hormone.

Wheelon and Shipley think that it cannot be assumed that the internal secretion of the gonads alone is sufficient to establish and maintain sexual characteristics, but that the influence of the adrenals, thyroid, hypophysis and thymus upon the development and maintenance of sex and sex-characters, cannot be ignored. We shall, therefore, glance at the relationship of the sex gland, with the other internal secreting glands, with which it is co-related.

First, with the suprarenal which appears to be a predominantly male gland. The suprarenal cortex seems to supply a combative element to the character, a male-sex characteristic. When the suprarenals are well developed and active the trunk is normal in development and hirsute, and the individual possesses normal sexuality.

Apert, in 1910, collected thirty cases of suprarenal hypertrophy or tumors of the suprarenal cortex, which had given rise to a masculine appearance in women. In 1916, Blanchard, in a study of suprarenal

virilism, came to the conclusion that this condition was due to changes in
the interstitial gland of the ovary.

In a case reported by Mauclaire a woman, aged thirty-eight years, had
six years previously developed an abdominal tumor, and her menses had
then ceased. Her face, neck, and chest became covered with long hairs,
the face became elongated, the breasts atrophied, etc. Laparotomy disclosed a tumor of the right suprarenal. The patient was treated with
ovarian extract and her menses reappeared.

That there must be a close interrelationship between the testicles and
suprarenals seems to be obvious, and the question has been fully investigated by Leupold. Leupold weighed adrenals and testicles obtained at
autopsies, and found a constant relationship between the two values. When
the weights did not correspond there probably was atrophy of the testicle
or hyperplasia. This hyperplasia combined with hypertrophy of the adrenal
is observed when a persistent thymus is present. When the adrenals contained much fat there was also an increased quantity of fat in the testicle.
All causes giving rise to a decrease of fat in the adrenals tend also to
diminish the amount of fat in the testicle. The testicle, however, generally
contains less cholesterol than does the adrenal, and when cholesterol
diminishes in the testicle and in the adrenal it generally is first decreased
in the testicle, thus proving that the adrenals have a higher function in
this regard than the testicle. Leupold also found that when saponin was
injected subcutaneously into cats, cholesterin was partly removed from the
cortex of the adrenals and from the interstitial cells of the testicle. In
animals, extirpation of both adrenals produced, if the animal survived,
degeneration of the secretory cells of the testicle. The same facts can be
verified in human adults, but in young children the relation between the
adrenals and testicles is less intimate.

Faught and Ryan remark that the close relation between the adrenals
and sex glands is well known. Such association is well supported clinically
by the fact that in cases of sexual precocity the adrenal cortex has been
shown to be hypertrophied, while certain tumors of the adrenal cortex in
young children, not producing destruction of the gland, are generally
associated with premature development of the secondary sexual characteristics. Hypertrophy of the adrenal cortex during pregnancy is an estab-

lished fact. Furthermore, in hyperplasia of the adrenals changes occur in the testicles, particularly in the interstitial cells.

In regard to the relation between the interstitial gland structure and the pituitary gland it is generally accepted that there is a connection between the anterior lobe of the pituitary and the establishment of puberty and sexual maturity. In the Chapters on Dystrophias we have already dealt with the changes observed in the sexual glands in pathological conditions of the pituitary gland.

Fichera,[1] had observed earlier that in castrated fowls (capons) there was hypertrophy of the pituitary body and of its eosinophil cells. The hypophysis of the capon is far richer in eosinophil cells than that of the rooster; it is also more hyperemic. Fichera's results will be referred to again.

Massaglia's experiments showed that not until the atrophied testicles were removed were the changes in the pituitary observed subsequent to castration found, but after removal of the atrophic testicle, the interstitial or Leydig cells, being then in good condition, the same pituitary changes were found as those observed in the capon. Apparently, then, the hypophyseal changes were due to loss of the internal secretion of the testes.

When the testicles of roosters were removed from their normal situation in the scrotum and scattered, after division, upon the peritoneum, if the grafts took, the pituitary body showed an increase of eosinophil cells.

The effects of the abolition of the internal secretion of the testis upon the hypophysis are very important because, as Massaglia observes, it shows that there exists through this internal secretion a functional co-relation between the testis and hypophysis cerebri. It lends support to the view that the pituitary body has the function of ruling the skeletal growth and perhaps throws some light upon the obscure etiology of gigantism and acromegaly. In the acromegalic there is found marked hypertrophy of the hypophysis with eosinophilia of its cells and deficient development of sexual organs according to the findings of several investigators. But in the acromegalic the most important fact is that there is some lesion of the pituitary body, whereas in the castrated it is the loss of the internal secretion of the testis, which secondarily produces hypertrophy of the hypophysis.

In Fichera's experimental investigations in regard to the connection between the hypophysis and testicles he found that after castration of nimals the weight of the hypophysis was constantly increased; in castrated nimals this weight was almost double that of normal animals. This is ot the expression of a difference due to the more notable development of he different organs seen in castrated animals. While there is a skeletal, nuscular and adipose increase of growth in castrated animals this increase loes not apply to internal organs.

In one series of young roosters, Fichera totally removed the testicles ome time after which the animals were killed. In another series, three oung adult capons had testicular extract injections. The histological nodifications of the hypophysis were studied in each series. In the castrated roosters the histological picture could not be distinguished from hat of ordinary capons. But in the capons which had received testicular xtract injections the histological picture of the hypophysis showed changes rientating toward that of the hypophysis of an entire animal. Fichera hinks that such changes must be the work of the internal secretion of the esticle because such changes ceased when the injections were stopped. Thus, a close relationship between the testicle and pituitary was experimentally established.

Hypertrophy of the hypophysis is also observed in acromegaly and gigantism, but in these conditions it is not a constant finding, whereas with astration hypertrophy of the hypophysis is constant. Fichera, therefore, concludes that the greater functional activity of the pituitary gland, following ablation of the sex glands, exercises a favorable influence on the conditions of development and of nutrition of the different tissues, and especially of the osseous tissues.

Massaglia [2] made a number of experimental investigations on the interelationship between the pituitary and the sex glands.

In a number of cases of experimental ligation and resection of the *ductus deferens* in roosters, Massaglia examined the effects on the *ypophysis cerebri*. In the rooster the anterior lobe (glandular part) constitutes the major part of the organ.

The same effects ought logically follow any condition besides castration which interferes with the functioning of testicular secretion. Inversity also, according to Fröhlich and other writers, and hypophyseal injury is usually followed by testicular aplasia. Many clinical and experimental studies of pituitary lesions have also shown that when there was deficiency

29

or absence of pituitary glandular secretion an atrophy of the testicle followed with sterility, impotency, and the constitutional changes associated with absence of testicular secretion. (See Fröhlich's Syndrome.) Citelli's findings of tonsillar defects originating in hypophyseal disturbances, have also demonstrated that such were causative of feminism and lack of sexual capacity in male subjects. On the other hand, it has been shown elsewhere that hyperactivity of the hypophysis produces precocious puberty, and that hyperactivity of the testicular elements results in the same effects. The same is true of tumors associated with the pituitary.

The pituitary gland seems to preside over the type of the bony skeleton and is, therefore, presumably under the direction of the appropriate sex gland, male or female, as the case may be. It seems to have a peculiar connection with the ovary, since ordinary amenorrhea is more surely cured according to some observers by oral administration of pituitary extract than by any other ministrations of the gynecologist. But its connection with the male gland is no less certain since Fröhlich's syndrome (*dystrophia adiposo genitalis*) shows a direct and intimate relationship between the pituitary and the male interstitial gland, and this dystrophia has been observed to result in the male by oral administration of extract of the whole gland.

Izumi has experimentally demonstrated that the pituitary of castrated rats were larger than normal, and that this was due clearly to the appearance of " castrate cells " in the anterior lobe.

Respecting the interrelationship between the sex glands and the thyroid, Hoskins [3] points out that hypothyroidism, either clinical or experimental, results in a sex depression that may be so pronounced that it amounts to complete impotence. Hoskins cites two clinical cases reported by Gaudy in which the patients, men of twenty-five and thirty-three years respectively, after having attained a normal adult sexual condition developed myxedema. This was followed by reversion to a sexually infantile condition, indicated by atrophy of the genitalia and impotence. Many similar cases are on record. The fact that in endemic goitrous regions menstrual irregularities are frequently among the females and subnormal genital development among the males is well known. A great deal of work on the interrelation of the endocrines has been done by Hoskins.

In experimental investigations thyroidectomy has resulted, in the
ands of various observers, in a depression of the sex function with atrophy
r degeneration of the gonads.   So well established is the idea that thyroid
eficiency results in sexual depression that observers who have made
hyroidectomies in recent years have usually not considered it worth
vhile to report specifically upon sexual activities.   Whether the sexual
nanifestations in thyroid disturbances are due to general metabolic reac-
ions or to some direct action in the sex glands the end result is the same.

In regard to the thyroid, Williams remarks that it seems to exercise a
articular effect upon the sex glands in the male, inasmuch as when
xtract of this gland is administered orally it causes the descent of a
idden testicle in young adults.

The thymus and pineal glands seem in some measure to act as drags
r checks upon the activities of the gonads.

Hoskins states that, in view of the fact that a certain degree of involu-
on of the thymus gland occurs at about the time of puberty, a theory
as gained considerable credence that an important relationship subsists
etween the thymus and the sex glands.   As far back as 1898, Calzolari
ad found, experimentally, that in rabbits previously castrated the thymus
as much larger than in normal animals.   In 1904 Henderson compared
ie weight of the thymus gland in one hundred castrated male cattle with
ie normal weight for this species, and found evidence of persistence of
ymus.   Henderson also found that in cattle of both sexes, that had
ercised the reproductive function, thymus involution was accelerated.
milar findings have been registered by other investigators; and on the
her hand, that thymectomy causes a more rapid growth of the testes
an normal.

BIBLIOGRAPHY

ICHERA, S.: Sur l'hypertrophic de la glande pituitaire consecutive a la castra-
    tion. Arch. ital. de biol. Turin, 1905, xliii, 405–426.

MASSAGLIA, A. C.: The internal secretion of the testic Endocrinology. Los
    Angeles, 1920, iv, 547–566.

HOSKINS, R. G.: Congenital Thyroidism. An experimental study of the thyroid
    in relation to other organs of internal secretion. Am. Journ. Physiology,
    Boston, 1910, xxvi, 426–438.

HOSKINS. R. G.: Editorial on etiology of Graves disease Endocrinology. Los
    Angeles, 1918, ii, 456–459.

[5] Hoskins, E. R. and Hoskins, H. M.: The interrelation of the thyroid and hypophysis in the growth and development of frog larvæ Endocrinology 1920, iv, 1–30.

[6] Hoskins, R. G.: Thyroid secretion as a factor in adrenal activity. Journ. Am Med. Assoc., Chicago, 1910, iv, 1724–1725.

[7] Hoskins, R. G.: The interrelation of organs of internal secretion. Am. Journ of Med. Sci., 1911, cxli, 534–545.

Author's Experiments

The author's experiments to determine the rôle played by the teste on the other endocrines have been rather voluminous and therefore onl the most important experiments and deductions will be cited i this chapter.

The animals used for these experiments were dogs and monkeys. Hal a dozen of each were selected of approximately the same age and weigh which were kept under the same conditions, and fed the same pabulum and which were all castrated at about the same time. For purposes c elucidation let us inspect Fig. 249. In this photograph the dog marke " A " is a normal animal that was kept for purposes of comparison. " B and " C " are castrates, five months after ablation of the testes. Let be remembered that these animals were all of the same size and weight a the beginning of the experiment. Observe the tremendous increase in siz in dog " B " and the considerably increased adiposity in dog " C " a compared with the normal animal " A."

As the necropsy findings in all the dogs experimented upon, as we as on the monkeys subjected to the same treatment, disclosed approx mately the same conditions and results, I will cite the findings in onl four of the dogs and two of the six monkeys observed.

Necropsy on Dog No. 26.—Castrated five months before death. Kille March 27, 1923. Injected with formalin March 27, 1923, 5:00 P.M examined March 28, 1923, 5:00 P.M. Thyroid glands markedly enlarged adrenals also larger than normal. The hypophysis was removed later ar found large, hyperemic and unattached to the base of the brain. There wa a noticeable increase in the white subcutaneous fat as well as of the mo yellow fat of the mesentery and omentum.

Necropsy on Dog No. 27.—Castrated six months before death. Kill with ether March 31, 1923, at 11:00 A.M. and immediately inject

hrough the aorta with formalin (watery solution, 10 per cent.). Examined
April 3, 1923, 10:00 A.M. Fat everywhere markedly increased. Hypophy-
is, thyroids and adrenals markedly enlarged, especially the thyroids.

Necropsy on Dog No. 30.—Castrated seven months before death.
Killed with ether March 31, 1923, at 11:00 A.M. and immediately injected

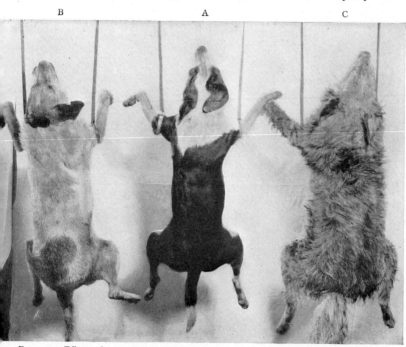

Fig. 249.—Effects of castration in the dog. *a*, normal dog; *b* and *c*, castrates five months
ter ablation of the testes. *b* and *c* were of the same weight as *a*, the control animal, prior to
peration. These dogs were all kept under the same living conditions and on the same diet.
Author's observations.)

hrough the aorta with 10 per cent. formalin. Examined April 3, 1923,
:00 P.M. Fat everywhere markedly increased and very pale, almost
hite. Thyroids very large; hypophysis and adrenals moderately enlarged.

Necropsy on Dog No. 31.—(Control animal). Normal and healthy.
illed with ether March 31, 1923, 2:00 P.M. and immediately injected
hrough the aorta with 10 per cent. watery solution of formalin. Fat
resent only in moderate amounts. Hypophysis normal, smaller than
os. 26, 27 and 30. Thyroids normal, very small compared to Nos.
5, 27 and 30; adrenals normal, somewhat smaller than Nos. 26, 27 and 30.

Necropsy on Macacus Rhesus.—Castration performed November 1922, died May 19, 1923 (seven months), examined May 20, 1923. The inner surface of the dura mater is covered everywhere with a thin layer of organized blood. The soft meninges are highly hyperemic, but show no evidence of hemorrhage. There is no liquid blood between dura and soft meninges. The brain substance is hyperemic, but shows no evidence of hemorrhage or of tuberculosis. The cerebellum, pons and medulla oblongata are normal. The pineal gland is a small, elongate, pale body of 2 mms. length and 1 mm. width and thickness. The hypophysis is apparently larger, measuring 5–4–3 mms. The thyroid is paler, of some what larger size than normal. The thymus is enlarged by the presence of a cherry-sized cheesy node in its upper aspects. The left adrenal is some what larger, both apparently free of pathological changes. Both kidney are of normal size, pale but otherwise unaltered. The prostate is apparently larger, firm and pale. The seminal vesicles are decidedly larger and firmer the vasa deferentia atrophied, threadlike. The lymph nodes everywhere in the body are markedly enlarged, some showing only medullary infiltration; others, such as the bronchial, tracheal, retroperitoneal, show in addition cheesy degeneration. The stomach and bowels are free of noteworthy changes.

Anatomical Diagnosis.—Cicatrix post castration in menses sex ante mortem effectam. Generalized chronic and subacute tuberculosis. Acute hemorrhagic pachymeningitis. Acute hemorrhagic pericarditis. Hyperplasia of the *hypophysis, pineal gland, left adrenal, seminal vesicles, prostate* and atrophy of *the vasa deferentia.*

Necropsy on " Mike."—Large monkey upon which bilateral castration was performed eight months ago. The animal was always well, and was killed with ether May 23, 1923, for the purpose of study of the effect of castration upon the endocrine glands. Examined May 23, 1923, at 5.00 P.M.

There was an ancient scar in the lowermost aspect of the anterior wall of the abdomen. The body is well nourished, and of strong bone structure. On opening the abdominal cavity old fibrous adhesions are found between the omentum and peritoneum, between the liver and diaphragm, and among the intestinal convolutions. There are no pathological changes the meninges or cerebrum. The *pineal gland* represents a small, oval white body of 4–2–1 mms. The *hypophysis* is enlarged, measuring 4½–4–3 mms. The *thyroid* is rather large, very pale, both lobes alike in size, 11–4–3 mms. The *thymus* is absent, and in its place a thin transparent curtain of fat is found.

The lower border of the liver upon the a n t e r i o r surface appears very finely granular, the rest of the liver capsule and the parenchyma in g e n e r a l are unaltered. The *spleen* is *larger* than normal, its edges are rounded, the surface is coarsely granular w i t h distinct, deep reaching, white furrows between the protrusions. On palpation the liver is very firm, elastic. Its color is very pale pink. On cut section the parenchyma is pale, firm, cornified and entirely bloodless. The trabeculæ are increased, f o r m i n g irregular white small islands contrasting with the reduced pale pink pulp. The *pancreas* is unchanged. The *right adrenal* is somewhat smaller than the left, but both are larger than usual, and apparently free from pathological changes. Within the spongiosa of the penis, extending midway into the glands there is a

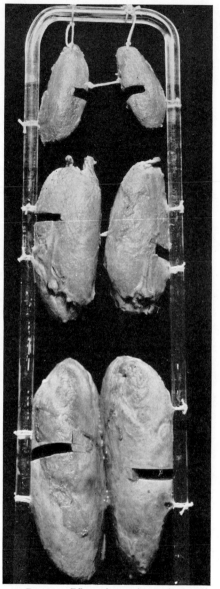

FIG. 250.—Effects of castration on the thyroid. Uppermost specimen, thyroid of normal dog, No. 31; middle, castrated dog, No. 27; lower, castrated dog, No. 30. Observe tremendous increase in size of thyroids in castrated animals. (Author's observations.)

rod-shaped, bony structure imbedded, which is 2½ cms. long and of a uniform diameter of 3 mms. The *prostate* measures up to two joined navy beans, is very pale and larger than usual. The *seminal vesicles* are large, each the size of a date seed and very pale. The *vasa deferenti* are of normal dimensions. The organs not specifically mentioned are normal.

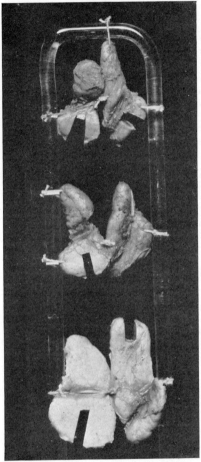

Organs in Bouin's solution submitted for microscopic examination

Let us now scrutinize Fig. 25, representing the thyroid glands of the dogs depicted in preceding illustrations. The uppermost of the pictures is the thyroid of dog No. 3 (control animal); the middle is the thyroid of dog No. 27 (a castrate), and the lower is the thyroid of dog No. 30 (also a castrate) The visual exemplification of the effects of castration upon the thyroid gland is certainly most remarkable in this series. The tremendous hypertrophy of the thyroid tissue leaves an indelible impression upon even the casual observer.

If we now turn to study the effects of the ablation of the testes upon the adrenals of the same animals, we find upon inspecting

FIG. 251.—Effects of castration on the suprarenal bodies. Uppermost specimen, suprarenal of normal dog, No. 31; middle, castrated dog, No. 27; lower, castrated dog, No. 30. Observe the marked increase in the size of suprarenals in the castrates. (Author's observations.)

Fig. 251 a concomitant enlargement of the suprarenal bodies apparently keeping pace with the hypertrophic metamorphosis of the thyroid. In other words, we find here a simultaneous enlargement of the suprarenal with that of the thyroid. The degree of hypertrophy being apparently commensurate

with the time elapsed since the date of the ablation of the testes so
that the middle adrenal depicted in the picture, belonging to castrated
dog No. 27, and the lower adrenal in the picture, belonging to castrated
dog No. 30, typify the changes better than verbal description and emphasis
can possibly do. The upper adrenal is that of the normal dog No. 31.

Fig. 252 shows a set of pituitary bodies removed from castrates. The
uppermost is the hypophysis of the normal dog (No. 31). The following
ones from above downward belong to
dogs No. 26, No. 27, and No. 30,
respectively. Here also, we encounter
a synchronous hypertrophic reaction
similar to the gross changes, observed
in the adrenals and in the thyroids of
castrated animals. While the position
of the pituitary in the sella turcica is
necessarily hampered by its osseous
encasing, preventing extension, nevertheless, an appreciable enlargement
can be discerned here also by even
casual scrutiny of the appended
photograph.

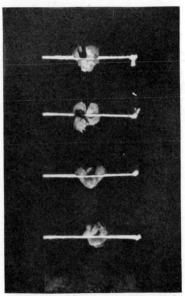

The study of the changes in the
endocrines in the higher monkeys has
divulged practically the same conditions that were observed in the dogs.
A striking example of these changes
will be seen in Fig. 253. These
monkeys were castrated seven and

Fig. 252.—Effects of castration upon the
hypophysis. Uppermost specimen hypophysis normal dog, No. 31; middle, castrated dog,
No. 26; next, castrated dog, No. 27; lowermost, castrated dog, No. 30. Observe here
also increase in size of hypophysis in castrated animals.

eight months respectively before death. On the right is observed
half of the skull of " Billy," a macacus nemestrinus, and on the
left is shown the skull of " Doughnuts," an animal of the same variety
that was castrated at the same time. In the latter, however, the
testes were reimplanted into the abdominal wall (author's implantation
technic). " Billy " was about half the size of " Doughnuts." In the
picture we see on the right side, the left half of " Billy's " skull with half
the hypophysis in situ. Note the enlargement of the pituitary body

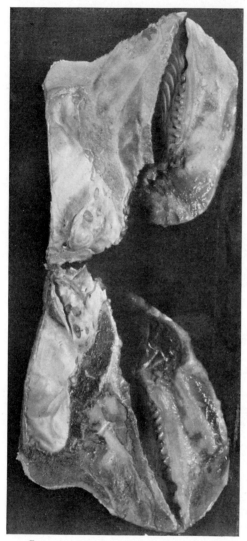

FIG. 253.—Effects of castration upon hypophysis in monkeys. The upper is the left half of skull of monkey, "Billy," with half the hypophysis *in situ*. Note enlargement of pituitary body occupying substantially the entire sella turcica, eight months after castration. The lower is the right half of the skull of the monkey "Doughnuts," twice the size and weight of "Billy," showing half the hypophysis *in situ*. Castration in "Doughnuts" was followed by immediate reimplantation of his own testes. No effect upon the size of the pituitary can be noted.

occupying substantially the entire sella turcica. The opposite half of the picture represents the right half of the skull of "Doughnuts" who, as already stated, was twice the size of "Billy," also showing half of the hypophysis *in situ*. In comparing the size of the pituitaries it will be observed that in the small monkey who was castrated the enlargement of this gland is marked, while in the large monkey, castration with reimplantation of the testes was followed by no apparent changes in the size of the hypophysis.

Fig. 254 shows the skull of "Doughnuts" exposing the position and size of the hypophysis seen from above. Fig. 255 depicts the hypophysis of the castrate "Billy" from above. Fig. 256 shows the effects of castration on the thyroid as well as the regenerative power of the thyroid tissue. In this macacus, the right lobe of the thyroid was entirely removed and only one-third of the left lobe was permitted to remain, two-

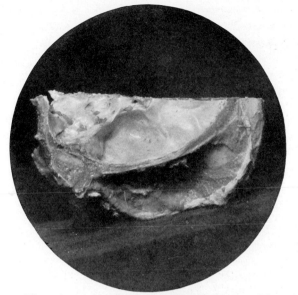

FIG. 254.—Effects of castration upon pituitary. Skull of "Doughnuts" from above.
Arrow points to hypophysis.

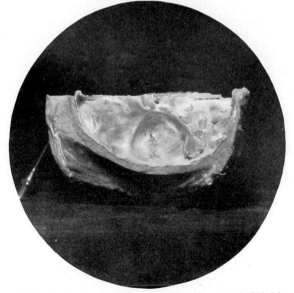

FIG. 255.—Effects of castration upon pituitary. Skull of castrated "Billy" from above.
Arrow points to enlarged hypophysis.

thirds of that lobe also being ablated. However, the thyroid has regenerated following ablation of the testes as is beautifully demonstrated in the

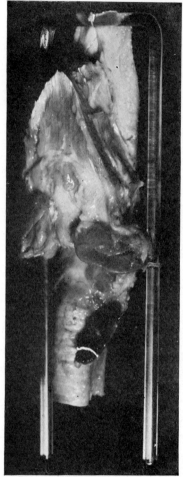

FIG. 256.—Effects of castration on thyroid. In this macacus the entire right lobe and two-thirds of the left lobe were removed. Simultaneous bilateral orchidectomy. Note remarkably regenerated tissue above white line. Below white line quantity of thyroid tissue left at operation.

accompanying photograph. The line at the lower third represents the thyroid tissue which was permitted to remain. Above that line we see more than two thirds of the newly regenerated hypertrophied thyroid tissue.

Recently there have appeared in the literature some suggestions that there is a possibility of an endocrine function of the seminal vesicles. The author has performed a bilateral partial epididymectomy on a macacus rhesus weighing about 9000 grams. Shortly after the operation the animal died, and necropsy revealed a tremendous enlargement of the seminal vesicles. Fig. 257 depicts the anterior view, and Fig. 258 the posterior view of these seminal vesicles. They are at least ten times the size of the normal seminal vesicles of animals of that type and weight.

For purposes of comparison we reproduce here a photograph of the seminal vesicles of a normal macacus rhesus of the same size and weight. Fig. 259 depicts the anterior view, and Fig. 260 the posterior aspect.

As previously stated, a more detailed description of the gross findings in this large series of experiments would prove too voluminous, and, therefore, only the essential features have been emphasized, to be followed by the microscopic description of sections removed from the gross specimens described.

Histological examination of the *thyroid* of the castrated animals (dogs,
>es) shows that the vesicles were of irregular outline, frequently pointed

FIG. 257.—Seminal vesicles from epididymectomized macacus rhesus.   Posterior
view.   (Author's observations.)

FIG. 258.—Seminal vesicles from epididymectomized macacus rhesus.   Anterior
view.   (Author's observations.)

partly oblong.   The colloid substance was normal in color in all speci-
ens examined.   The epithelial cells were cubical and of normal appear-

ance and were increased neither in size nor number. There was observe
a very marked proliferation of the blood vessels, which were large ar
apparently hyperæmic. No specific changes to contrast with normal spec
mens of thyroid tissue could be discovered in the specimens examined.

FIG. 259.—Genital apparatus of normal macacus rhesus. Anterior view. 1, prostat
2, seminal vesicles; 3, bladder. Compare the size of the seminal vesicles depicted here with tho
shown in Figs. 257 and 258.

The *adrenals* were found to be normal in appearance. There was
complete balance between the cortical and medullary substance. Her
also digressions from the normal appearance of the cellular elements c
cortical and medullary substance were absent.

The *kidneys* were of normal size and structure.   Equally, no obvious
anges were noted in the *spleen* or *liver*.

In the *hypophysis* the eosinophile cells were found to be markedly

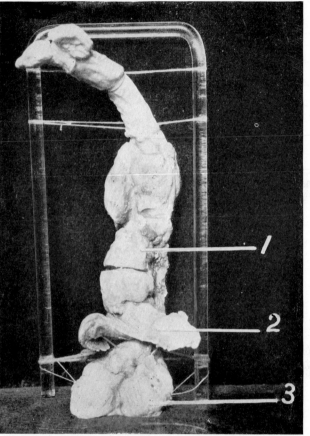

FIG. 260.—Genital apparatus of normal macacus rhesus.   Posterior view.   1, prostate;
eminal vesicles; 3, bladder.   Compare the size of the seminal vesicles here with those shown in
s. 257 and 258.

creased in number.   Its component parts were well balanced.   The *pineal*
s found to be normal.

Examination of the *prostate gland* disclosed an increase of connective
sue and decrease of glandular substance.   The *seminal vesicles* showed
idences of degeneration and simultaneous increase of the connective
sue elements.

It is the opinion of the author that the hypertrophic changes observe in the endocrines of castrated mammals examined are reactionary i character and the response to the loss of testicular incretion. It seem as long as the testicle functionates normally that there is a harmoniou coöperation between the other endocrines and as soon as that power regulation is lost, through castration or pathology of diverse nature, a endocrine discord is created, clinically evidenced by the manifestations *dyshormony.* The biochemical changes taking place in the endocrir system after ablation of the testes are still extremely obscure but furthe research will undoubtedly throw additional light upon the question at issu All experimental proof thus far points definitely to the well established fa that normal endocrine function requires normal internal secretion on th part of the testes, and that for the well-being of the individual every glam of internal secretion must be *at par* and functionating in a normal manne

CHAPTER XXI

TREATMENT

THE THERAPEUTIC AND OTHER EFFECTS OF TESTICULAR EXTRACTS

(Opotherapy)

For a long time past it was generally believed that the semen, besides
s generative function, was directly instrumental in producing and main-
aining virility. For this view, however, there was no scientific basis of
roof until late in the nineteenth century.

In 1889, Brown-Séquard [1] made his first communication to the
cademy of Science of Paris, giving the results of certain experimental
vestigations which he had carried out upon himself, *viz.*, the subcutaneous
jection of the expressed juice of the testes of dogs and guinea pigs. Brown-
équard, who was then seventy-two years old, stated that for many years
reviously he had experienced a great diminution in his physical and men-
l vigor; and that, as the result of the injections of testicular extracts,
e felt ten years younger, his capacity for both physical and mental work
as increased, and that efficient bowel movements, which had been absent
r years, were restored. Brown-Séquard further stated that he believed
he action of the testicular extract to be dynamogenic in nature.

Brown-Séquard's announcement came as a sensation throughout the
cientific world. His experimental work was repeated by Variot, [3]
asteur,[4] Bogroff,[5] Boch,[6] Zenetz,[7] and a host of other workers
ho generally confirmed the original findings of Brown-Séquard, although
here were some who disparaged the results. The investigators, in addi-
on to the original findings, discovered other effects of the orchitic extract
n the human organism as well as discovering many clinical conditions
which the extract could be used clinically. These effects will be re-
erred to later.

Brown-Séquard prepared his extract by crushing an animal testicle and
dding to it 2 or 3 cc. of glycerine and water. The resulting fluid was fil-
red and sterilized. The injection, amounting to about 1 cc., was made

30

subcutaneousiy in the abdomen, in the shoulder, or in the buttocks, an in his own case, was made once a day continuously for eight days. Brow Séquard recommended that the injections should, as a general rule, I carried out daily, or at least several times a week, a total quantity of 2 to 30 gr. of the fluid being injected. The fluid was so slightly toxic tha Brown-Séquard [2] had been able, in twenty-four or twenty-five hours, an in a number of cases, to inject with impunity in small animals up to on eighth or one-tenth of their body weight of the fluid, which, in a ma weighing 60 kilos, would be proportionately represented by a daily do: of 5000 to 6000 gr. Brown-Séquard's extract was prepared in the labor tory of the College of France under the direction of d'Arsonval. It wa an extract containing all the testicular elements, tissues, blood and glandu lar secretions.

Normal, fresh orchitic extract is alkaline in reaction and decompose very rapidly. Fresh testis contains about 13 per cent. solid matter i the case of the ram, but less in the guinea pig and rabbit. Of the protei matter, nucleo-proteid forms by far the largest bulk. Whole orchit extract, therefore, contains three groups of bodies: (1) proteids; (2) o ganic substances; (3) inorganic salts.

Brown-Séquard thought that orchitic extract acted on the organism i two ways: (a) by its effect on the nervous system, especially the spin cord, ameliorating the dynamic or organic condition of diseased part: (b) by actually bringing into the blood new materials which furnish ne cells or other anatomical matter. Brown-Séquard did not think that should be considered in any way astonishing that the introduction int the blood of matters coming from the testes of young animals shoul be followed by an increased vigor; but that rather, such an effect shoul be anticipated and looked for. Everything shows that the power of th spinal cord, and of the brain, even to a certain degree, depended upo the activity of the testicles, and facts showed that besides its generativ function, the testicle had a dynamogenic function of the highest impo tance to man; decay and impotence in old men depended upon two causes organic changes, and the absence of the stimulation exercised over th nervous centres by the active testicle.

Brown-Séquard and d'Arsonval [8] reported results obtained by more tha 200 practitioners to whom they had supplied orchitic extract for clinic use. These results supported the claims already made in regard to the beneficial effects of the medication. The diseases in which the extract was stated to be especially efficacious were those of nervous origin, loco-motor ataxia especially, pulmonary tuberculosis, superficial cancer, etc. Of 405 cases of locomotor ataxia, in 342 of which there could be no doubt of the diagnosis, 91 to 92 per cent. were reported as greatly ameliorated, if not cured. In 117 cases of sclerosis of the spinal cord there were 8 to 10 per cent. ameliorations or cures. There were astonishing results in 27 cases of paralysis agitans, 25 of which showed great amelioration. Great improvement also followed in pulmonary tuberculosis, diabetes mellitus, arteriosclerosis, chorea, neurasthenia and neuralgias. While the orchitic extract did not appear to exert any specific action its efficacy appeared to be due to a renovatory energy effect on the organism. In locomotor ataxia the different results reported from various quarters to Brown-Séquard clearly showed that the effect produced by injections of orchitic extract were far more favorable than those which followed other forms of treatment.

Brown-Séquard's [9] personal clinical experience showed also that in old men, whose spermatic glands had notably lost their functions, injec-tions of orchitic fluid furnished what was lacking in regard to the power of the central nerves; all types of diseases due to organic weakness were benefited.

Dixon [10] subjected the action of orchitic extracts to a thorough critical investigation comparing his results with those found by others. Normal orchitic extract, according to Dixon, produces a fall in blood pressure after a somewhat lengthy latent period; this effect is mainly the result of cardiac inhibition and can be well observed in cats. Small injections produce a quickening of respiration, but large injections cause a temporary absence of all respiratory movements. Respiration begins again gradually and ultimately assumes a condition both quicker and deeper than that which was present before injection. The effect is associated with some dilatation of the splanchnic area, spleen and testis, but the kidney always shows a very considerable and prolonged constriction.

Injections of testicular substance give rise to a prolonged hypoleucocy-tosis followed by hyperleucocytosis which is the effect, mainly, of the nucleo-proteid in the extract.

Several authors have made testicular extract injections in castrated animals. Bouin and Ancel [11] remark that while in castrated animals the long bones are abnormally lengthened, and the genital organs remain infantile, in young castrated animals having been treated with testicular extract, the long bones were shorter than in uninjected control castrates, and that the genital organs of injected castrates were well developed. These authors concluded that the effects of castration could be modified by testicular extracts even of heterogeneous origin. Dor, Maisonnave and Monziols [12] clinically verified that in children whose testes were not well developed, but who grew rapidly up to the age of puberty, the injection of testicular extract checked the skeletal growth.

Bogoslovsky and Korentchevsky [13] found that injections of testicular extract stimulated metabolic exchanges of proteins especially.

Since the recrudescence in very recent years of interest in testicular therapy, Stanley [14] has tried the effect of injections of testicular substance in bringing about this result. Stanley thinks that there is a positive advantage in using the whole testicular substance instead of the extract as used by Brown-Séquard. The whole substance-injection is absorbed much more slowly, and in this process the hormone is gradually given off, producing a continuous effect. Semi-solid testicular substance, obtained from rams, goats, and deer, was injected by force subcutaneously into the abdomen. By this method Stanley made 1000 injections of testicular substance in 656 subjects, most of whom were inmates of a prison. Only one injection was made in some, but in others, the number of injections was as high as seven. From his observations on these cases, Stanley concludes that testicular injected substances do have a decided effect on conditions of general asthenia. Improvements followed from the first week following injection. Three hundred and five out of 326 " run-down " subjects were markedly benefited. Eighty-one reported increased sexual stimulation, but in a small percentage there was decreased sexual power following injection. It can hardly be said that this treatment cures impotency. Improvements following testicular substance injections were generally observed in asthenia, acne vulgaris, senility, rheumatism, neurasthenia, and a few other conditions. In general, testicular substance injections seemed often to have a beneficial effect in relieving pain of obscure origin, and promoted bodily well-being.

Closely connected with the question of orchitic extracts is that of the value of injections of the organic substance named spermine.

In 1878, Schreiner [15] discovered needle-shaped crystals in the sperm, which Charcot and Leyden had previously isolated from the expectoration of the asthmatic. Schreiner called the substance of which the crystals were composed, spermine, and stated that it corresponded to the formula C_2H_4N. Poehl [16] Petersburg, in 1897, isolated *spermine* as one of the basic constituents which preside at oxidations of the organic tissues having been met in the testicle and ovary, pancreas, spleen, lymph, etc. Poehl corrected the chemical formula to $C_5H_{12}N_2$. Poehl obtained his spermine especially from the testicles of horses and used it in a 4 per cent. alcohol solution. The substance was stated to have a tonic effect upon the muscle power and on the nervous condition of debilitated men; it is also said to be antagonistic to adrenalin.

Poehl demonstrated that his *spermine* contained the so-called Charcot-Leyden crystals and called these *inactive spermine*. The ingestion of spermine increased the oxydizing power of blood; it played the part of a catalytic ferment and regulator of interorganic oxidations in the animal economy. Spermine is especially constantly present in tissues rich in nuclein. Its use is indicated in all conditions in which it is desirable or necessary to raise the tonus; among other effects it is said to increase the sexual capacity or energy.

Dixon, in addition to his investigation of the effects of orchitic extract upon the organism, also investigated the physiological value of spermine. According to him, spermine produces a fall in blood pressure, recovery from which is rapid and normal is again soon reached. This effect is largely cardiac, but is also due to vascular dilatation. Spermine, also, produces a slight gradual rise in the body temperature.

The chief interest of spermine depends upon the fact that it is constantly present in all tissues of the body; and in certain pathological conditions, such as leucocythemia and certain nervous diseases, its amount is increased. In the normal animal, it is stated to be most abundant in the testicular and nervous tissues.

Keeping in mind the excellent results obtained by sex gland transplantation in indicated and well selected cases, a number of clinicians have endeavored to get similar results by administering to the patient sex gland preparations by the oral route. Basing their reasoning by analogy of the splendid results obtained in feeding patients thyroid extract after thyroidectomy, with positive results, the logical conclusion was apparent that individuals suffering from various clinical manifestations by reason of losing their testes through one cause or another should be equally benefited by the administration of testicular extracts or similar preparations per os. However, these results were not forthcoming, and clinical data from various authorities record their disappointing findings and absolute failures. While there are some investigators who believe to have seen good results following testicular extract feedings, the majority have found the reverse to be true.

Steinach [21] castrated a number of rats at the age of four weeks. These animals were fed the testes of freshly-killed young rats that were sexually matured. Occasionally these feedings, which were given daily, were supplemented with testicles of guinea pigs. To this diet was added bread and milk, but soon the animals preferred the testicular feedings, of which they were allowed liberal quantities. These experiments lasted for three months but not the slightest favorable results were observed after the lapse of this time upon the animals experimented upon with reference to the development of secondary sex characters and other results looked for, and which were obtained in cases of transplantation. The animals remained morphologically and functionally genuine castrates. Why the oral administration of ovarian substances should be followed by good results in cases of climacteric disturbance as has been verified by clinicians all over the world, and why no such results are obtained through the administration of testicular substances is a question that has not, as yet, been decided. Future investigations promise much in this fertile field of research and will, undoubtedly, throw some light on this interesting question. Victor Vecki [22] of San Francisco reports to have had good results with testicular opotherapy in well selected cases.

W. Harms, who has done a great deal of experimental work with reference to the internal secretion of sex gland preparations, in summing up this question says: " Let us see how our results compare with those of modern organotherapy. It is very evident that all the attempts to obviate or to improve the results following castration by giving testicular substances or extracts of testes per os, offer a very gloomy outlook, particularly so when the testicular extracts are taken from the lower animals as is usually he case in oral organotherapy. Injections of testicular emulsions or xtracts can undoubtedly cause a transitory improvement, particularly in nimals where the effects of castration have not become too permanently stablished. After such manifestations have become permanently nrooted—in other words, where the animal has been castrated for a long ime—the centres in the brain of the animal will gradually become altered hrough disuse. An abolition or prevention of the results of castration hrough organotherapy has thus far not proven to have had a successful ssue and to our view is a hopeless proposition. In order to mitigate the haracteristic changes that occur after castration in vertebrates only one nethod remains open and that is sex gland transplantation."

Mauclaire [20] in a recent contribution expresses himself as follows on he question at issue:

Mais avant de pénétrer plus avant dans l'étude de la greffe glandes ndocrines, il convient de se poser une question préalable. Au lieu de se lonner la peine de faire une greffe, ne serait-il pas plus simple de fournir u sujet déficient de simples extraits glandulaires hétéroplastiques? Je ne e crois pas. Sans doute, les extraits glandulaires, même hétéroplastiques lonnent des résultats indiscutables, mais ceux-ci sont loin d'être aussi angibles que ceux obtenus par la greffe des organes eux-mêmes. D'autre bart, il n'est peut-être pas inutile de combiner les deux procédés quoique :ertains expérimentateurs aient constaté que l'ingestion d'extraits gland- llaires ne soit pas propice à la réussite de la greffe dans le cas de thyroïde. Juant aux résultats extraordinaires annoncés en 1921 par Stanley a San Juantin, consécutifs á des injections sous-cutanées de tissu testiculaire dans liverses maladies, ils ont besoin d'être confirmés.

In English: " Before entering more deeply into the study of the endo- :rine glands, it is essential to propound a preliminary question: Instead of taking the trouble of grafting a gland, would it not be more simple to give the afflicted patient simple glandular extracts. I do not think so. Doubtless glandular extracts produce undisputed results, but these are by far not as pronounced as those obtained from the grafting of the organs themselves. On the other hand it is probably possible, and perhaps, not useless to combine the two procedures, although certain experimenters have established that the ingestion of glandular extracts is not propitious to the success of the graft in the case of the thyroid. As regards the extra- ordinary results announced by Stanley of San Quantin resulting from the subcutaneous injection of testicular tissue in diverse diseases, there is need of them being confirmed.

BIBLIOGRAPHY

[1] BROWN-SÉQUARD: Des effects produits chez l'homme par des injections sous cutanées d'un liquid retiré des testicules frais de cobaye et de chien. Comp rend. Soc. debiol., Paris, xli, 415, 1889.

[2] BROWN-SÉQUARD: Comp. rend. Soc. de biol., Paris, 1892, xliv, 505; xlv, 307.

[3] VARIOT: Comp. rend. Soc. de biol., 1899, p. 451.

[4] PASTEUR: Cited by Dixon.

[5] BOGROFF: Vratch., 1890, xiv, 367.

[6] BOCH: Cited by Dixon.

[7] ZENETZ: Cited by Dixon.

[8] BROWN-SÉQUARD and D'ARSONVAL: Effects physiol. et. thérap. d'un liquide extrai de la glande sexuelle male. Comp. rend. Acad. d. Sci., Paris, 1893, cxvi, 85(

[9] BROWN-SÉQUARD: Gaz. des hop., Paris, 1892, lxv, 645.

[10] DIXON: Jour. of Physiol., 1900, xxv, 356.

[11] BOUIN and ANCEL: Comp. rend Acad. d. Sci., Paris, 1906, cxlii, 232.

[12] DOR, MAISONNAVE and MONZIOLS: Comp. rend. Soc. de biol., Paris, 1905, lix, 673

[13] BOGOSLOVSKY and KORENTCHEVSKY: Comp. rend. Soc. de biol., Paris, 1920, lxxxii 718.

[14] STANLEY: Endocrinology, 1922, vi, 787.

[15] SCHREINER: Cited by Dixon.

[16] POEHL: Comp. rend. Acad. d. Sci., Paris, 1897, cxxv, 959.

[17] DIXON: loc. cit.

[18] NOE: Arch. gén. de méd., Paris, 1903, p. 1757.

[19] SMAUCH: Interstate med. Jour., 1910, xvii, 92.

[20] MAUCLAIRE: Revue Française D'Endocrinologie Tome, 1, No. 1, Feb., 1923.

[21] STEINACH: Geschlechtstrieb etc., Zentralblatt für Physiologie, Bd. 24, 1910

[22] VECKI: Medical Life, New York, 1923.

CHAPTER XXII

TESTICULAR PROSTHETICS

DISEASES and anomalies of the male genitourinary organs which interfere with the function or configuration of the organs have a peculiarly depressing psychic effect on the individual, which arises from the feeling of deficient sexual power and, perhaps, from a deficiency in the secretion of the testicle which furnishes the psychic stimulus corresponding to full virility. These psychic effects often, or almost always, follow castration. The hypochondria of castrated individuals is well known; and in certain well-marked cases has been sufficient to drive the individual to suicide. It is not confined to the young and robust, but is found even in old men, whose sexual activity might be assumed to be decadent.

For the foregoing reasons, in cases where a uni- or bilateral castration has been done for tuberculosis or any other cause, it has long been customary to place artificial testicles in the scrotum in order to prevent postoperative mental reaction as well as for esthetic reasons. Silver, glass, ivory, celluloid, rubber, etc., have been used as materials from which to fashion such testicles; and in a few cases, recourse has been made to paraffin injections as reported by Carnabel.[5]

With castrated patients two conditions may arise: either the patient may not ask for a prosthetic operation, or he may demand such. In the first case the man is probably of a slight, or deficient sexuality and has no psychic feeling regarding the loss of the testicle. In such case, there may be no indication or object in doing a testicular prosthetic operation.

When the patient demands of the surgeon the supply of an artificial testicle distinctions must be made according to the nature of the case. If the patient is deprived congenitally of his testicle, being a cryptorchid, and if his mentality has been morbidly affected by the deficiency, it is very probable that he would be greatly improved psychically by the supply of an artificial testis. A case of this type was reported by Hermance[3] in a young man of twenty-five, whose left testicle had never descended, and who had been advised that nothing could be done for him surgically to remedy the condition. The result was a mental depression which was of such a morbid type that it bordered on insanity. Finally, this patient had a silver testicle substituted in the place of the missing one, the wound healing by first intention. The man recovered his mental poise, carried the

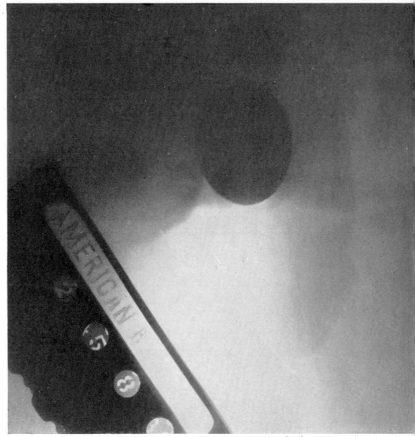

FIG. 261.—Testicular prosthesis of silver in scrotum. X-ray outlines foreign body, penis and scrotum very distinctly. (Author's observation.)

testicle without any trouble, married and had several children. Similar cases have been reported in the American literature by Guiteras [1] and Weir [2] among others, celluloid testicles being used in each case. Picqué [4] had a similar experience in a case of bilateral testicular ectopia which several surgical attempts had failed to relieve and which ended in the patient becoming profoundly melancholy. The man avoided the society of omen in every way as he imagined that they knew and made fun of is deficiency. Picqué says that if at the time the method of testicular rosthetics had been known to him it would have saved this patient many ears of misery.

Picqué also reports the case of another patient who was differently ffected. In this case a castration had been done in the radical treatment

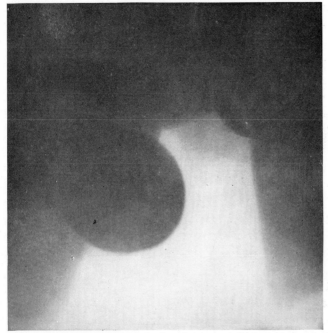

Fig. 262.—Testicular prosthesis of aluminum in scrotum. (Author's observation.)

f a hernia. A short time later the patient demanded to be supplied with n artificial testicle on account of the gibes of his companions and a rubber esticle was satisfactorily installed. Two years later the patient came to icqué, and demanded that the testicle be removed, declining to state ie circumstances under which it had been implanted or the surgeon's ame. He seemed to be obsessed with shame on account of the presence f this artificial testicle and desired to be rid of it with the greatest rgency. He left the hospital immediately after its removal; it was erfectly normal and had caused no trouble. The man's urgent request or removal was based entirely on psychic reasons.

Morestin [6] recommends the use of vulcanite which is easily molde to shape, and becomes very hard when cooled. It is easily asepticised an is well tolerated by the tissues. In a case of castration for tuberculos Morestin supplied a vulcanite testicle fixing it in place with some silkwor gut sutures. There was no trace of inflammatory reaction and the pos operative course was simple. The patient has never had any pain or swel ing and the foreign body is well tolerated in the scrotum.

The author had the opportunity to substitute testicular prostheses i an instance where the testis had been lost and observed great psychic reli of the patient. Fig. 261 shows the X-ray picture of a testicular prosthe sis. A perfectly normal man, twenty-seven years of age, lost one of h testicles through a gunshot injury which tore the testicle and part of th scrotum off. The mental condition of the patient, as a result of th loss of his testis, was pitiable. An artificial testis (silver) was implante and plastic reconstruction of the scrotum effected with splendid results t the patient's psychic condition. He has carried this substitute succes fully in the scrotum for the last five years without the slightest signs c irritation or inconvenience. In the second case, depicted in Fig. 262, th patient never had a normal testis in his scrotum; cryptorchidism (inguinal was the cause. A prosthetic appliance of aluminum was successfully in bedded into the scrotum with splendid cosmetic and psychic results.

BIBLIOGRAPHY

[1] Guiteras, R.: Amer. Med. Surg. Bull., 1894, vii, 534.
[2] Weir, R. F.: Med. Record, N. Y., 1894, xlvi, 161.
[3] Hermance, E. M.: Amer. Jour. Insan., 1894–5, li, 510.
[4] Picqué: Progrés méd., Paris, 1905, xxi, 145.
[5] Carnabel: Bull. et mém. Soc. de Chir. de Bucarest, 1903–4. v. 107.
[6] Morestin: Bull. et mém. Soc. de Chir., de Paris, 1907, xxxiii, 1286.

CHAPTER XXIII

INTERTESTICULAR ANASTOMOSIS AFTER SECTION
OF ONE VAS DEFERENS

WHEN the two testicles become fused, no matter from what cause, the ondition is called *synorchidia*. The condition is extremely rare, and in ue orchidia each testicle has its own independent vas deferens, blood apply, etc. Sometimes an artificial synorchidia may be employed in the eatment of ectopic testicle; in this there may be vascularization obtained etween the tunica albuginea of both testicles, but there is no real anasmosis between the tubules of the testicle proper.

It may happen that the vas deferens of a testicle may become destroyed r accidently sectioned without the corresponding testicle being involved. n such a case it would be considered desirable for many reasons to preserve he testicle *in situ* if possible. This would be more particularly desirable on ccount of the secretional value of the testicle, not alone for spermatoenesis, but also, for the special internal secretion of the gland and its ffect upon the male organism. In the past, therefore, surgeons have sought r some route of emission of the testicular secretion in such circumstances, ection of the spermatic cord being an occasional happening in operations r varicocele, hernia and the removal of tumors. Some, such as Poggi [1] nd Durante, [2] executed a termino-terminal anastomosis of the vas deferens; thers, such as van Hook,[3] did a termino-lateral anastomosis; while still thers, such as D'Urso,[4] did a latero-lateral anastomosis. Bardenheuer[5] ailed in his attempt to anastomose the superior end of the deferent canal vith the Highmore body of the testicle, but Scaduto [6] seems to ave succeeded.

In 1903 Gatti [7] reported his first attempts at the direct anastomosis f one testicle to the other, *i.e.*, the surgical establishment of communicaion between the excretory canaliculi of a testicle disconnected from its as deferens with the canaliculi of the internal face of the other testicle, o that there would be an uninterrupted outlet for the secretion of the rst testicle through the tubuli of the complete testicle and canal. The function of a testicle, the route of emission of the secretion of whic was interrupted, could be preserved by such an operation.

This procedure of Gatti's practically amounts to an autogenous gra of one testicle upon the other, and he states that the studies of Maximov and others, show that when the sectioned surfaces of the two testicles ai placed in contact they possess the power of proliferating and of creatin anastomoses between the seminiferous tubuli placed in the vicinity of eac other. In Gatti's method the vascular and nervous connections of th testicle are, of course, undisturbed unless insofar as they are affected b the section of the vas.

By a series of animal experiments Gatti established the fact that th intertesticular anastomosis between the tubuli of such approximate testicles did, as a matter of fact, take place. The operation of graftin one testicle on the other, was followed first by some degeneration prol ably due to operative trauma; this, however, was soon followed by regene ation, both vascular and nervous, of the tissue of the two testes. In som of the cases spermatogenic power from the incomplete testicle wa: undoubtedly, preserved.

From his experimental work on intertesticular anastomosis Gat concludes:

(1) That this anastomosis, viz., the grafting of a testicle, with if deferent canal sectioned upon the other testicle, with its deferent cana intact, with the object of anatomical preservation, and functioning o the emission of sperm, is an operation which causes a traumatism to whic both testicles may react by phenomena of degeneration.

There is practically no degenerative phenomena when the operativ trauma is slight.

In anastomosed testicles immediate or later section of a deferent cana carefully dissected from the connective and other tissues surrounding if does not cause any phenomena of degeneration.

When phenomena of degeneration are not marked the two anastomose testicles react by a renewed production in which all the tissues of botl share. The process of epithelial regeneration not alone tends to recon stitution of glandular tissue on the mass of the testicle, but also tends t create a tubular anastomosis between the glandular portions of the tw fused testicles. This process is effected by epithelial offshoots in the firs instance which ultimately canalize. This epithelial regeneration is preceded and accompanied by an active vascular and nervous regeneration through the line of anastomosis, which puts the vascular and nervous systems of each testicle in direct communication with each other. In the line of anastomosis there is only a thin and insignificant proliferation of connective tissue, when the operation is carried out without resection of the glandular tissue, but only with incision and detachment of the vaginal and albuginea and freshening slightly with a fine knife the glandular surfaces to be approximated. In order to avoid the independent vaginals fusing in the line of anastomosis between the glandular tissue and causing a separation of the latter by proliferation of connective tissue, Gatti found a special crucial incision effective.

Intertesticular anastomosis done in the necessary way not only preserves the vitality of the glandular tissue of the testicle, even in the most differentiated epithelial element of the walls of the seminiferous tubuli, but also the function of spermatogenesis with the presence of abundant spermatozoa showing normal movements. The operation is to be recommended in cases of operative or traumatic injury to the deferent canal of a healthy testicle; but it is not indicated after an epididymectomy for tuberculous or similar epididymitis.

Reconstruction of the Vaginalis of the Testicle with Peritoneal Strips.—

The tunica vaginalis of the testicle besides its protective action on the organ has, according to the experiments of Charrin,[9] and others, also a trophic influence on the testicle. Animal experiments have shown that when testicles were deprived of this covering they became smaller and harder in consistency in less than a year. Histological examination showed atrophy of the seminiferous tubules with degeneration of the cellular elements. These results had been found by the experiments of Alessandri,[10] in 1897, but were not in accordance with the findings of Rolando [11] (1902), who believed that after a maximum period of three months following ablation of the vaginal, the epithelial and other changes in the seminiferous tubules, which were only transitory, ceased, and the organ became restored to its normal anatomical and functional conditions.

with the exception that there was a certain amount of hyperplasia o peritubular connective tissue.

The divergence of opinion between several of those who investigate this matter led Libroia,[12] in 1912, to institute a new series of experiments especially since partial resection of the vaginal is a procedure forming par of certain surgical operations, such as the treatment of hydrocele. Libroia's experiments were based on the substitution of parietal peritoneal strips fo the removed vaginal, as this might be considered a more or less homologou transplantation. These experiments were made on dogs.

The experiments carried out by Libroia demonstrated to him tha transplantation of a serous strip upon the testicle in the place of th parietal vaginal always "took," provided that the operation was execute under strict asepsis. In seven experiments there was only one in whicl there was thickening of the transplanted strip and epithelial changes, anc this was probably due to manifestative maltreatment of the strip.

The transplanted strip assumes all the functions of the vaginal; i forms a serous sac about the testicle, exercising both the protective anc trophic functions of the vaginal. After eight months of transplantation the disturbances in trophism noted by other preceding investigators, such a atrophy of the seminiferous tubules and degeneration of the cellular ele ments, etc., could not be observed. Libroia, therefore, concludes tha peritoneal serosa strips (or the sac of a hernia), may be employed as a substitute for the vaginal of the testicle whenever it may be necessary to remove it.

BIBLIOGRAPHY

[1] Poggi: Rivista clin., 1886.

[2] Durante: Trat. di Patol. e. terap. chir., Rome, 1895, v, iii, p. 100.

[3] v. Hook: Medical News, June, 1894.

[4] D'Urso and Trocello: Policlin, Rome, 1900, sez. chir., p. 291.

[5] Bardenheuer: Mittheal. a. d. Kölner. Burger. hosp., 1886, xliv, H.3.

[6] Scaduto: Ann. d. mal. d. org. gén. urm., 1900, p. 257.

[7] Gatti and Ferrari: Policlin. Rome, sez. chir., April, 1903.

[8] Maximov: Beitr. z. path. Anat., xxvi.

[9] Charrin: Bull. Soc. anat. de Paris, May, 1906.

[10] Alessandri: Policlinico, Rome, Sez. Chir., April, 1897.

[11] Rolando: Clin. Chirug. Milan, 1902.

[12] Libroia: Riforma med., Naples, 1912, xviii, 57.

CHAPTER XXIV

NEUROSES OF THE TESTICLE

NEURALGIAS of the testes are of rare occurrence and include a group of conditions thus far but imperfectly recognized, although the symptomatology is quite clear. The condition is variously known as *irritability of the testis*, or *neuralgia of the testis and cord*.

Etiology.—There may be a local irritation due to congestion in some part of the seminal apparatus, but the absence of definite anatomical or physiological facts renders the ultimate cause doubtful. In some cases there is a history of an initial lesion, an abscess of short duration, an orchitis, an enlargement of the prostate, a cystitis, or a hernia (Andrews). In others, there is a nodulous development on the cord or in some part of the scrotum. Again, distinct neuromas have been reported in connection with hypersensitiveness of the testicle, and in this event the nerve lesion is apparently responsible for even a complicated and very persistent irritable state of the scrotum and its contents.

Pathology and Symptomatology.—Three different conditions are recognized: 1, neurosis without demonstrable pathological change in the testis; 2, symptomatic neurosis in connection with a local lesion within the testis or its appendages; 3, neurosis due to a peripheral, or remote nervous lesion.

The *first type* is characterized by severe pain, general or localized about the testicle and epididymis. This pain may be constant or broken by intervals of peace. It occurs in children and then is characterized as similar to hysteria with its typical aspects: limited cutaneous anesthesia, reduction of the field of vision, pharyngeal anesthesia, etc. Whether in children or adults, however, the condition may be interpreted as a spasmodic retraction of the testis, originally a functional process but here degenerated into a form of chorea.

The *second type* may be the result of an inflammation of the epididymis of urethral origin, causing a development of palpable nodules along the organ, or a general thickening. Fibrous tumors are known to cause similar

31

distressing, radiating pains, and the same is true of cysts and sperma
tocele. A continued sensitiveness of the testes frequently is a result of
orchitis. Atrophy, especially consequent upon trauma, often causes an
intense irritability of the testes, sufficient to induce the patient even t
demand orchidectomy in order to gain needed relief.

The *third type* includes the sequelæ of varicocele, hydrocele, also pro
static disturbances and diseases of the kidneys.

Hernia, as a contributing cause, should not be overlooked, especiall
when an ill-fitting bandage may give rise to a pressure directly or indirectl
involving the scrotum.

The pain in neuralgia of the testes may be only mild or agonizing in it
intensity and often is observed to be associated with tonic or clonic spasm
of the cremaster muscle. The testis during a paroxysm of pain may be s
sensitive that the friction of the trousers causes severe suffering.

Treatment.—The so-called anti-neuralgic medicinal substances invari
ably fail to give other than passing relief. Absolute rest in a horizonta
position, with proper support to the testicles may obviate any exacerbatio
of the pain for a long time. The emptying of the large intestine, of fece
and gas, regularly, in order to avoid pressure in the iliac region, also mus
be insisted on. Local applications very often give prompt relief, not onl
at the time, but for several days after. Electricity likewise, one pole a
the scrotum, the other at the lumbar region, may be of some benefit.

Prompt and permanent relief has been attained by the application o
mechanical pressure by a clamp applied to the cord high up in the scrotur
(Hammond) firmly enough to stop circulation. This procedure not onl
relieves the pain completely but in time induces a return of the sensibilit
of the testis and cord. The pressure, fairly strong, is applied for abou
five minutes, interrupted and resumed if necessary.

In extreme cases, orchidectomy was indicated, yet opinions differ as t
its justification. If extensive atrophy of testis and cord are present, th
problem is not difficult; otherwise, a conservative procedure is preferable

Resection of the nerves involved, or portions of them, has been done i
some cases, and successfully as regards the immediate results, but atrophy
follows, and the subjective condition may not become desirable.

It is needless to emphasize that all existing and discoverable predisposing causes (varicocele, toxæmias of various sorts, hernia, etc.), should be eliminated by proper treatment. Sexual hygiene should be insisted upon. The author disagrees with the advice given by some to do an orchidectomy in cases of neuralgic testes. As a *dernier resort* only, after all attempts at palliative therapy have summarily failed, should one think of sacrificing a testis. In some cases the author has seen splendid results by resorting to *neurectomy* or *dividing the vas.*

BIBLIOGRAPHY

ANDREWS, E.: A study of a few suggestive cases. Chicago Medical Recorder, viii, 1895, 1–8.

HAMMOND, WM. A.: Neuralgia of the testis. St. Louis Courier of Med., iii, 1880, 429–438.

MONAD and TERRILLON: Traité des malad. du testicule, 1889.

TERRILLON, O.: De la néuralgie du tubercule. Bull. et mém. Soc. de Chir., 1886, 797.

ROUX, G. F.: De la néuralgie du testicule. Thèse. Paris, 1876.

PATUREAU, H.: Contribution a l'étude de la néuralgie testiculaire et de son traitement par la resection nerveuse. Paris, 1901.

CHAPTER XXV

TRAUMATIC INJURIES OF THE TESTES

INJURIES of the testes, while less common than certain functional or infective disorders, are important not only in themselves but also on account of the fact that they, like all other forms of traumatism, form the subject of occasional controversies in legal medicine. They include the following groups of pathological conditions:

Torsion.

Dislocations.

Wounds and Contusions.

Traumatic sequelæ.

The activity of all testicular structures in recovering from a mechanical injury, other things being equal, has been the subject of extensive morphological and histological study of A. Maximov.

1. **Torsion** has been fully described in this work (see Chapter IV). However, to recapitulate; in torsion the twisting of the cord is of obscure origin. It may occur as an acute affection or persist, usually in a less degree, as a chronic condition, perhaps due to traction of the gubernaculum or incomplete descent of a testis. In the acute form pain is a characteristic phenomenon, also nausea. The condition usually is unilateral; the scrotum becomes congested, and the testis is pulled upward and drawn closely up against the cord.

Treatment should be effected as promptly as possible. An incision is made into the sac and the inguinal canal, whereupon the cord is pulled back and the testis liberated. To restore circulation, after closing the wound, hot compresses are applied. If the case is of long standing, and the organ has degenerated, or if gangrene sets in after operation, the only possible procedure is orchidectomy. The prognosis usually is favorable.

Care should always be taken to establish a sure differential diagnosis with reference to strangulated hernia.

2. **Dislocations.**—Dislocations generally are of traumatic origin, the testis being displaced by squeezing or by severe falls causing a sudden

484

npact on the scrotal region. The organ may be displaced into the peri-
eum, or in under the abdominal wall, or into the upper part of the thigh.
Whatever is the character of the dislocation, a suitable free incision
hould be made, the testis drawn back and replaced within the tunica
aginalis. In cases less severe, a continued manipulation may bring about
he desired result, but as a rule the pain is very intense, and no effort can
e made except by the aid of a general anesthetic. Recovery follows
romptly, but complications may occur with orchitis or epididymitis, or
ith attendant traumatic conditions in the regions of injury.

3. Wounds and Contusions.—Simple contusions, varying in severity,
ause an effusion into the body of the testis and possibly into the tunica
nd the cord. Complicated contusions involve the formation of abscess as
result of congestion, and hematocele of the sac. The characteristic
ymptoms are intense pain and nausea, swelling and fever. The treatment
alls for stimulants to restore the general condition from the shock, which
s always severe. Intestinal pressure is obviated by enemas. It may be
ecessary to allay the pain by morphine. Cold compresses are applied
nd continued until the symptoms abate. It then may be necessary to tap
he hematocele. An abscess, if forming, should be supported by hot appli-
ations and opened at the proper time.

In severe contusions involving other organs than the testes proper,
trophy commonly follows.

Wounds are treated by the usual surgical routine, which varies with
ndividual conditions. Rigid asepsis as a rule will secure autoplastic
ealing. If, as in deep injuries, such as are caused by gunshot or stabbing,
uppuration may ensue and gangrene set in. The first requirement is to
ring the organ back within the tunica and then close the tunica. This
nay not be possible. Unless it is, and if the injury will not permit of a
nion, or if circulation fails to be restored, the entire removal of the organ
s the only possible procedure.

Good bandaging supplemented by ample drainage from the wounds, is
ssential; also the proper support of the organ, to prevent inconvenience
rom the dragging of its weight.

After the immediate recovery, a supporting bandage should be worn
or some time, especially when the patient is allowed to leave his bed.

4. The Traumatic Sequelæ.—Any injury to the testicles is apt 1 cause considerable shock. Vomiting frequently occurs after a sligl injury, but we also find occasionally spasmodic twitchings due to actu nerve injury. In severe cases we find a succession, perhaps for a long perio of tonic spasms, unconsciousness, edema of the lower extremities, and gre; exhaustion. The local symptoms even may extend to the upper parts the body. The pathology of this condition undoubtedly depends upon a intoxication due to a local infection induced by the trauma, or to son obscure nerve irritation. Treatment must be expectant and directed 1 relieve the existing pathologic processes (anodynes; hot fomentations intensive nutrition).

Phlebitis is a rare complication.

BIBLIOGRAPHY

[1] Barthélemy, and Miramond deLaroquette: Les lésions traumatique testicule. Revue de chir., xliv, 1912, 791–809.

[2] Hubbard, B. R.: Nervous Disturbances following injury to the testicle. Ed Med. Jour., lvii, 1897, 67–72.

[3] Maximov, A.: Die histologischen Vorgänge bei der heilung von Hodengewel Beitr. zur Pathol. Anat. (Ziegler), xxvi, 1899, 230–319; two plates.

[4] Quesseveur, F. M.: De la contusion du testicule. Paris, 1907.

[5] Sinclair, J. A. B.: Traumatic extrusion of the testicle. U. S. Nav. Med. Bul v, 1911, 355; two plates.

[6] Weinberger, M.: Die perineale Hodenverletzung. Centralbl. f. die Krankh. Harn—u. Sexual-Organe, x, 1899, 1, 73.

CHAPTER XXVI

DISEASES OF THE SCROTUM

IN addition to accidental traumatisms which may strike the scrotum as any other part of the body, this region, apart from the organs contained in it, is by its nature subject to some special pathological conditions especially of an inflammatory nature. Of these inflammatory conditions which result from *infection, gangrene* and *elephantiasis* are the most common and best known.

No region of the surface of the body would appear to be so liable to infections as the scrotal surface. The skin is thin, it is always humid and subjected to maceration and excoriation. This condition explains *infantile gangrene, eczema* and *edema*. In all patients whose nutritional apparatus is disturbed the loose cellular tissue of the scrotum becomes edematous with the greatest facility, when its means of nutrition are disturbed.

Gangrene of the scrotum is a generic term under which is comprised all the septic inflammations which strike the region. There are two different anatomical varieties. In one the skin is primarily affected and the disease spreads to the underlying tissues. In the second type the teguments are only secondarily involved, the process commencing in the deep cellular tissue.

Scrotal gangrene may or may not be accompanied by phlegmon. *Phlegmon* is observed when there is infiltration of urine, in ruptures of the urethra and when there is lymphangitis. Phlegmon does not usually accompany gangrene of the scrotum connected with general toxic conditions or pyrexias.

Gangrene of the scrotum may arise from a variety of causes. It may follow mechanical or chemical trauma; it may be associated with severe infectious disease or with the toxemias of chronic nephritis or diabetes; or it may be due to ingested toxins. It affects either the teguments or the underlying cellular tissue. When the condition is established it should be treated conservatively with incisions parallel to the spermatic cord, to permit egress of accumulated pus and to allow the removal of necrotic tissue. The process may involve the whole or part of one or both testes

487

and epididymes but it usually stops at the tunica vaginalis. The condition may follow the application of a carbolic acid poultice for epididymitis.

Randall [1] who reported on sixteen cases of scrotal gangrene, the great majority with success, encases the scrotum in gauze soaked in permanganate of potash solution. Deep incisions are made and irrigated with the solution. The dressings are changed daily. When the wounds are clean granulation commences and in time there is a new scrotum. Skin grafting may help the process.

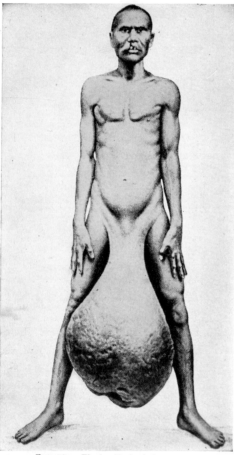

FIG. 263.—Elephantiasis of the scrotum.
(Javanese after Lexer.)

If the inflammation has spread to the inguinal canal this must be opened and drained.

The treatment of *erysipelas of the scrotum* is the same as in other parts of the body, both scarification and deep i n c i s i o n s may be necessary.

Elephantiasis of the scrotum is common in India and other warm countries, and is caused by the *Filaria sanguinis hominis*. The disease is due to arrest of the lymphatic circulation. (Figs. 263–266.) Matas [3] defines elephantiasis as a progressive histopathologic state or condition which is characterized by a chronic inflammatory fibromatosis or hypertrophy of the hypodermal and dermal connective tissue, which is preceded by and associated with lymphatic and venous stasis, and may be caused by any obstruction or mechanical interference with the return flow of the lymphatic and venous currents in the affected parts. The condition is partly due to infection with different pathogenic organisms, especially the streptococcus. It is likely that a congenital predisposition occurs and the literature shows many cases occurring in early life or even present at birth.

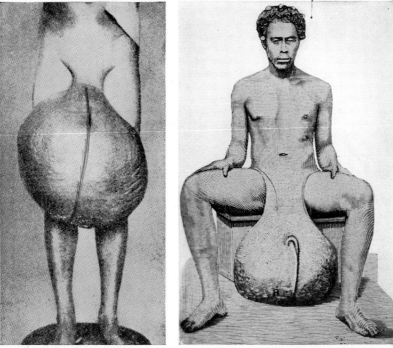

FIG. 264.—Solid form of elephantiasis of the scrotum. (After Charles.)

FIG. 265.—Elephantiasis of the scrotum. (After Turner.)

Spreese [4] reported a case of congenital elephantiasis in a child one year old; the condition had apparently been present since birth. In non-parasitic elephantiasis when the scrotum is involved an inherited defect in the lymphatic system probably exists, and in this type the factor of streptococcal infection is not usually present.

The question of operation must be determined by the amount of inconvenience caused to the patient. True elephantiasis is a chronic hypertrophy of the skin and subcutaneous tissue, following a lymphangiectasis produced by the parasite named. Elephantiasis of the scrotum is usually termed *lymph-scrotum* and when not very voluminous may be treated by massage, bandaging, etc.

Spurious elephantiasis of the scrotum may be due to chronic inflammation as in the case of a man with a urinary fistula. Rosenwald

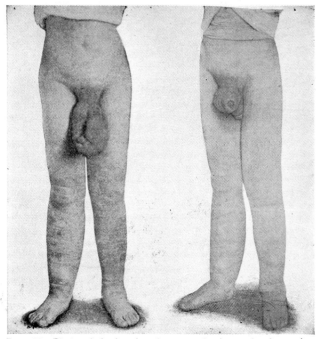

FIG. 266.—Elephantiasis of penis and scrotum, showing results of operation.
(After White and Martin.)

reported recently a case of syphilitic hyperplasia of the penis and scrotum which he termed a *pseudo-elephantiasis*.

The skin of the penis is almost always involved.

Surgery when indicated consists in resection of a part or the whole of the tumor. Enough skin must be left to cover the testicle. (Figs. 267–268.)

Such operative removal is the only rational method of dealing with a voluminous elephantiasis of the scrotum. The mortality is slight. The only difficulties presented in the operation are those of finding and preserving the testicles in the midst of the tumor, and of detaching the penis and restoring it *in situ* by an autoplastic operation. The penis and testicles

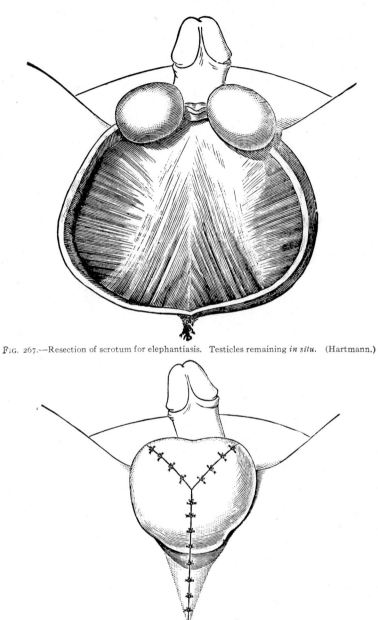

FIG. 267.—Resection of scrotum for elephantiasis. Testicles remaining *in situ*. (Hartmann.)

FIG. 268.—Resection of scrotum for elephantiasis. Testicles remaining *in situ*. (Hartmann.)

must be preserved. The vast cavity also left after the removal of voluminous elephantiastic tumor calls for all the autoplastic skill surgeon may possess.

Gas distention of the scrotum (emphysema of scrotum) either gas-producing organisms or by air passing through wound openings in t

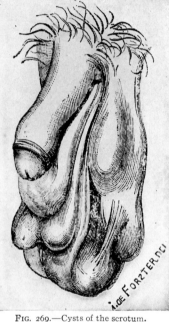

FIG. 269.—Cysts of the scrotum.
(Curling.)

vicinity, is so rare that a mere passi mention will suffice.

Benign tumors of the scrotum a mostly cystic in type. *Sebaceous cy.* are common. The best treatment excision of the cyst and skin coveri it. (Fig. 269.)

Sarcoma of the scrotum is ra but *carcinoma* is relatively commc especially that variety known as *t cancer* which occurs in men who hanc coal and its products. The conditi begins as warts which degenerate in carcinoma. The prognosis is good the warts are removed early before th have produced metastases. This canc is benign and usually remains for a lo time superficial.

The treatment of malignant tumc of the scrotum is radical extirpation, together with the careful dissecti of the regional lymph glands. If carcinoma of the scrotum has extend to the penis or testicles, these structures should be removed.

Cellulitis of the scrotum most commonly results from extravasation urine and may lead to extensive sloughs which expose the testicles.

Edema of the scrotum is usually associated with general ascites. may result in limited gangrenous patches which should be excised and tl margins of the wounds approximated.

Other conditions in the scrotum, such as *scrotal fistula, sinus of t scrotum,* and *scrotal eczema,* are of occasional occurrence and must l treated on general surgical principles.

Varices and *angiomata* may occur anywhere in the coverings of the
enis or scrotum, and have received but little attention in text-books.

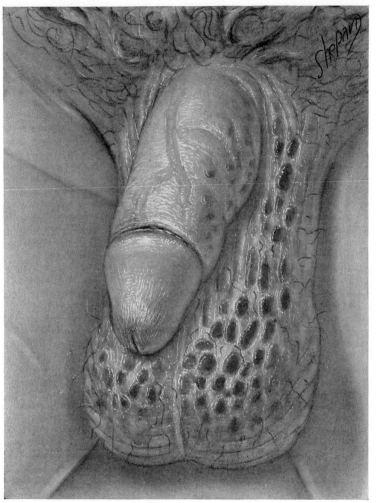

FIG. 270.—Dr. Joseph Welfeld's case of angioma of the scrotum.

Jnless of large size they do not give rise to specific symptoms; but if
mportant in size and exposed to traumatism, they may rupture or ulcerate,
iving rise to profuse hemorrhage and exposing to infection.

The presence of varicose veins in the skin of the scrotum is not unusual and does not cause particular inconvenience unless developed to a high degree. Joseph Welfeld [9] has reported a case of the latter type in which erection and coitus were followed by rupture of varicosities and profuse hemorrhages (Fig. 270.) endangering the life of the patient.

Quartz lamp or radium, so often successfully employed in the treatment of superficial angiomata, will probably be useful in urological work of this kind. Welfeld used radium with success in the case alluded to.

Syphilitic disease of testes or scrotum is amenable to specific treatment unless a sloughing gumma demands surgical excision.

BIBLIOGRAPHY

[1] RANDALL: Jour. Urol., 1920, iv, 219.
[2] "American Practice of Surgery," vi, 676.
[3] MATAS: Amer. Jour. Trop. Dis., 1913, 60.
[4] SPREESE: Internal. Clin., 1920, ii, 253.
[5] ROSENWALD: Jour. Amer. Med. Assn., 1920, xxv, 244.
[6] v. BERGMANN, ETC.: Handb. d. prak. Chir. (English transl.), v. 664.
[7] LE DENTU and DELBET: Nouveau traité de Chir., xxxii, 82.
[8] HASLINGER: Zeitschr. f. Urolog. Chir., 1921, vi, 293.
[9] WELFELD: Urol. and Cutan., 1919, xxii, 566.

CHAPTER XXVII

VARICOCELE

VARICOSE dilatation of the spermatic veins is a common affection. It
s observed especially in young subjects from fifteen to twenty-five years
ld and occurs most frequently on the left side.

Varicocele is more liable to occur in those having a lax or pendulous
crotum; it may be due to some congenital or acquired abnormality of
ascularization of the scrotum or testes, or to pressure by a hernia, tumor
r truss. (Fig. 271.)

Varicocele may be *primary* or *idiopathic; secondary* or *symptomatic.*
'rimary varicocele may be explained on the basis of two pathogenic
heories: either that it is the result of phlebo-sclerosis or of varicose dilata-
ions by sclerosis and due to parieto-venous lesions. The first theory
epends on disturbances of circulation; the second upon venous stasis.
.ittle is really known of the true etiology of varicocele.

Secondary varicocele is apparently the result of compression of the
permatic veins in some part of their trajectory. The compression may be
aused by a hernia, by various inguino-iliac conditions, by renal
umors, etc.

Whatever may be the primary underlying cause of varicocele, it is
xpressed anatomically by a varicose dilatation of the veins which constitute
he spermatic plexus. When the varicocele is total the venous flexuosities
re especially marked in the vicinity of the testicle. The varicose packet
akes the form of a cone, the apex of which is inguinal, and with the base
ying on the testicle. The funiculo-scrotal veins, connected by numerous
nastomoses, form an inextricable mass in the midst of which the deferent
anal appears lost. However, at times the varicose condition may be
nly partial, involving either the anterior or the posterior group of veins,
he anterior group being that most frequently involved.

The onset of varicocele may be brusque or insidious and the evolution
nore or less rapid, thus allowing acute and chronic types to be dis-
inguished. The scrotum may be normal in size or it may attain a con-
iderable degree of augmentation.

Clinically there is the common benign type of varicocele in which there is little or no pain, although the condition may have existed for a long time. It is only when the varicose packet attains considerable dimen-

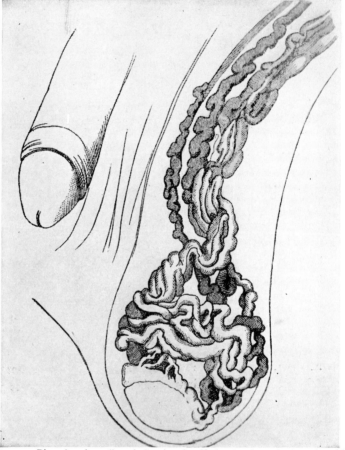

FIG. 271.—Dissection of a well-marked varicocele. Notice the almost horizontal position of the testicle with the epididymis above; its head directed forward. (von Bergmann, Bruns and Mikulicz.)

sions that the inconvenience and trouble from funiculo-testicular weight compels the patient to seek relief. This type is well supported and the genital functions are preserved. In the severe types of varicocele there is not alone permanent trouble from the weight of the venous dilated mass, but true pain as well. These pains, which irradiate in all directions, are provoked or increased by the least fatigue and are influenced by any modifications in the testicular circulation. There are, moreover, reflex disturbances of various kinds, and the condition becomes a veritable infirmity, rendering the patient unfit for any laborious occupation.

Varicocele may, as a general rule, be easily diagnosed by palpation, the conditions with which it may be confused being omental hernia, tumor of the spermatic cord or a communicating hydrocele.

Treatment

There is no uniform method of treatment applicable to all cases of varicocele. Some must be operated; some can be operated; some cannot be operated and some again should not be operated.

Large or small varicoceles ought to be operated when they are painful; when they tend to provoke testicular atrophy and disturb the genital functions; or when they interfere with the exercise of the patient's occupation.

A varicocele which is voluminous but not especially painful may be operated as well as those varicoceles which, without being painful or voluminous, constitute an infirmity which patients desire to be relieved from.

For all other types of varicocele palliative measures will generally suffice. The surgeon must use his judgment in the case of hypochondriacs as occasionally their psychic disturbances disappear after operation.

Medical measures consist in applications of cold water locally, avoidance of constipation, and the wearing of a suspensory.

Surgical procedures applicable to varicocele consist of *venous resection*, applicable in cases of pure venous ectasia; *scrotal resection* when there is orchidoptosis without venous dilatation; and *venous resection combined with scrotal resection* in cases combining both the previous conditions.

Scrotal resection was first executed by Sir Astley Cooper in 1839 and is currently employed to the present time, but only in exceptional cases when the scrotum is voluminous. The excision may be simple or made over special clamps and of both kinds many different procedures are in current use. The accompanying illustrations depict the operation well. (Figs. 272–274.)

32

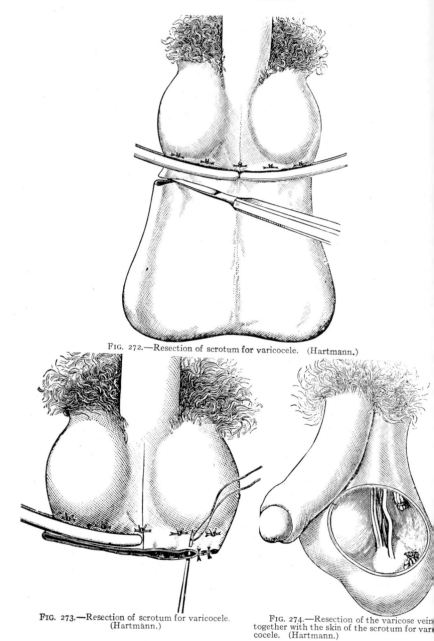

Fig. 272.—Resection of scrotum for varicocele. (Hartmann.)

Fig. 273.—Resection of scrotum for varicocele. (Hartmann.)

Fig. 274.—Resection of the varicose vein together with the skin of the scrotum for varicocele. (Hartmann.)

Venous resection comprises an incision 3 to 4 cms. long in the superior part of the scrotum; freeing the veins through a buttonhole in the cord; ligature and excision of the dilated veins and closure. Care must be taken to spare the spermatic artery and its satellite nerves in ligaturing the venous mass.

Resection may be by the low or scrotal route or by the high or inguinal route. In the latter case the technique follows the same general lines as the treatment of congenital inguinal hernia, excision of the veins, replacement, etc. In this method isolation of the spermatic vessels is easier than in that by the low route.

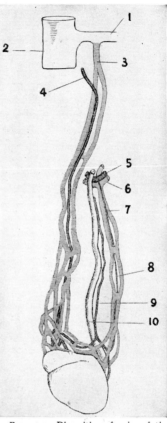

FIG. 275.—Disposition of veins of the spermatic cord. (Schematic.) 1, left renal vein; 2, inferior vena cava; 3, spermatic vein; 4, spermatic artery; 5, epigastric artery; 6, epigastric vein; 7, 8, funicular arteries; 9, deferential arteries; 10, deferent canal. (Jacob.)

The first stage of the resection varicocele operation comprises an oblique cutaneous incision in front of the external orifice of the inguinal canal; the common fibrous sheath is incised and the testicle exteriorized with the whole of the cord. Each of the three chief groups or dilated and varicose veins is then carefully dissected out. The diseased veins are resected between ligatures, two or three veins being spared to assure the circulation. The two arteries and the vas deferens are carefully avoided. If the cord is very long it is made to assume its normal length by uniting the ends of the sectioned veins. The fibrous tissue of the lower third of the cord may be sutured to the fibrous tissue of the external orifice of the inguinal, or the testicular stump of the venous mass be fixed to the inguinal ring or otherwise as the operator may select. If the skin of the scrotum is

too redundant the portion which requires removal is circumscribed by tw
strong curved forceps and resected beneath the forceps and th
edges reunited.

Like hydrocele, varicocele tends to recur after operation. Jacob
thinks that the best way to avoid recurrence of varicocele after excisic

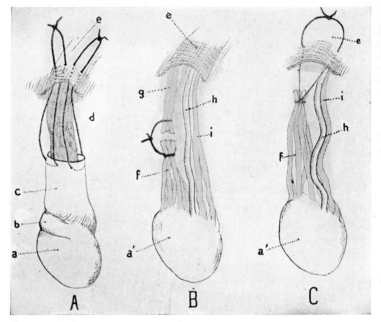

Fig. 276.—Various methods of fixation and suspension of the testicle in the surgical treatme
of varicocele. (Schematic.) *A*, method of Parona. The tunica vaginalis is opened, retracted a:
fixed at its margin to the pillars of the superficial inguinal canal. *B*, classical procedure. Both en
of the varicose bundle are united one to another after resection of the varicose mass to be remove
C, method recommended. The testicular end of the varicose bundle is resected and is sutured
the superficial ring of the inguinal canal. *a*, testicle; *b*, epididymis; *a'*, the testicle and epididym
covered by the tunica vaginalis; *c*, tunica vaginalis replaced; *d*, the spermatic cord covered b
fibrous tissue and the cremaster muscle; *e*, pillars of the external inguinal canal; *f*, testicular en
g, inguinal end of the resected veins of the cord; *h*, deferent canal; *i*, posterior venous bundle. (Jacok

of the dilated veins is to suspend the testicle from a fixed and solid poir
in such way that it can no longer exercise traction on the cord. Hi
method of operating and suturing the stump of the varicose packet to th
inguinal ring is shown in the following illustrations. (Figs. 275–282.)

Skillern [4] and others expose the inguinal canal in the varicocele opera
tion and free and remove the entire anterior vein mass from internal ring t
top of testicle, avoiding the vas and deferential vessels. McKenna [5] think

best place to make the external incision is at the junction of the scrotum
the body.

Many attempts have been made to treat varicocele by conservative
gery which does not expose the patient to section of the arteries and
consequent damage to the vitality of the testicle. These methods con-
t in various devices for suspension of the
ated mass in such a way that return circu-
ion is assured and venous stasis avoided.

The best method of surgical treatment
varicocele in young adults appears to be
nous resection followed by fixation of the
ticular venous stump to the pillars of the
guinal ring. The method is simple, rapid,
d does not expose the patient to danger.
s immediate and end results are equally
od.

Douglas [6] has recently shown that the
eration for varicocele is frequently followed by hydrocele. Out of a total of
ree hundred and three operations at St.
ake's Hospital, New York, one hundred
d six patients who were either personally
amined or reported by letter, showed that
drocele had developed, i.e., 35 per cent.
his possible complication shows that the

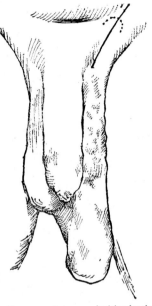

FIG. 277.—Cutaneous incision for the surgical cure of varicocele. The dotted semi-circle indicates the position of the external inguinal orifice. (Jacob.)

eration should only be performed when it is more or less imperative.

Rupture of varicocele is uncommon. Cumston [7] thinks that when it
curs it is usually the result of trauma and its infrequency is explained
/ the fact that the cord is not so situated as to be greatly liable to
auma. The scrotum becomes enlarged and violet or black in hue and
is ecchymosis may extend to the skin in the neighborhood. Pain is not
vere or may even be absent. The testicle is not usually involved. Diag-
sis is usually easy when there is the history of a previous varicocele, but
such a history is not clear the condition may be mistaken for a strangu-
ted hernia or hematocele of the vaginalis. Ruptured varicocele must be

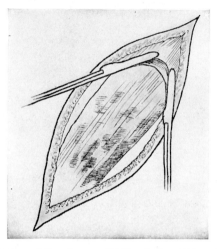

Fig. 278.—Uncovering and dissecting superficial inguinal canal, the position of which is sho
by the two artery forceps. The spermatic cord is covered by the cremaster muscle and its fibre
covering and is seen emerging from the inguinal canal, and occupying the greatest part of the illu
tration. (Jacob.)

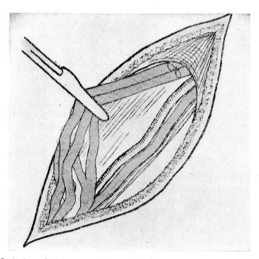

Fig. 279.—Isolation of the spermatic bundle of veins. In the back one sees the defere
canal and the posterior bundle of veins. By means of traction the spermatic bundle is brought f
ward as much as possible from its abode in the inguinal canal. The cross (x) and two small dott
circles, placed around the spermatic bundle, immediately under the border of the inguinal can
indicate the point where the ligature and section of the cord should be made. (Jacob.)

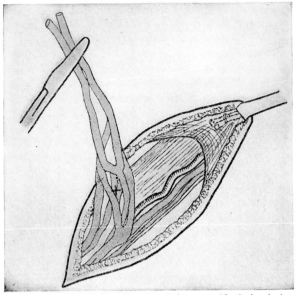

FIG. 280.—The inguinal end of the varicose bundle is retracted in the inguinal canal, as shown by the dotted outline in the figure, immediately under the retractor. The testicular end is isolated for resection. This is accomplished by throwing a ligature around it and then resecting it at the point marked by the cross. (Jacob.)

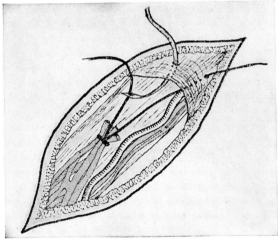

FIG. 281.—Application of the ligature to the testicular end of the resected bundle and the position where it is attached to the inguinal canal by drawing the ligature into position, as shown in the illustration. (Jacob.)

distinguished from ruptured hydrocele principally by palpation. In ruptured varicocele the testicle is usually quite distinct from the tumor but in ruptured hydrocele the testicle is lost in the midst of the tumor; often the true condition only becomes revealed after incision.

Surgical treatment consists in the removal of the blood focus, ligation of the bleeding vessel or vessels, avoiding the spermatic artery. The

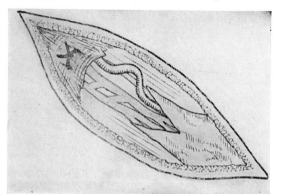

FIG. 282.—Operation completed, showing distal end of resected varices attached to sup. ring of inguinal canal. (Jacob.)

co-existence of a hydrocele and a varicocele is an absolute indication for a radical operation.

BIBLIOGRAPHY

[1] SEBILAU and DESCOMPS: Article on varicocele in LeDentu and Delbet's. Nouveau Traité de Chirurgie, xxxii, 632.
[2] JACOB: Rev. de Chir., 1919, vii, 355.
[3] v. BERGMANN, ETC.: Handb. d. prak. Chirurgie, English Transl., v, 689.
[4] SKILLERN: Internal. Clin., 1920, iv, 43.
[5] McKENNA: Surg. Clinics, Chicago, 1918, ii, 1241.
[6] DOUGLAS: Jour. Amer. Med. Assn., xxvi, 716.
[7] CUMSTON: Internat. Clin., 1923, ii, 268.
[8] FRANKE: Zentralbl. f. Chir., 1922, xlix, 45.

CHAPTER XXVIII

HYDROCELE

Hydrocele or serous vaginalitis, consisting of a collection of fluid in the tunica vaginalis, is a fairly common affection occurring about once in every one hundred and fifty ordinary hospital cases. It is more usually

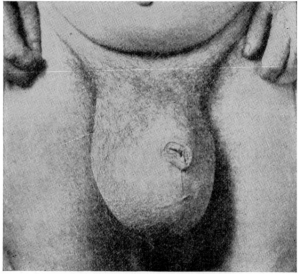

Fig. 283.—Hydrocele of the tunica vaginalis. (Horwitz.)

met between the ages of twenty-five and thirty-five years, and there are several varieties, *acute, congenital, infantile, bilocular,* etc. (Figs. 283 and 284.)

The fluid contents of a hydrocele has all the characters of an ordinary serous effusion. The tumor is translucid, of varying volume, and is independent of the scrotum from which it can be differentiated by careful palpation. Although translucidity when present is pathognomic of hydrocele (Fig. 285) its absence has not a negative significance as in a few cases hydrocele evolves toward pachyvaginalitis. The vaginal condition does not of itself affect the function of spermatogenesis.

Serous vaginalitis is of slow evolution; it very rarely cures spontaneously. But there are three kinds of complication which may possibly disturb the evolution, *viz., infection, rupture* and *hemorrhage;* the latter may change a hydrocele into a *hematocele.*

From time immemorial various treatments have been devised for the relief of hydrocele; these may be summed up as (1) *external applications;*

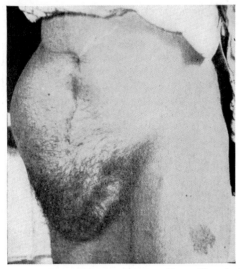

FIG. 284.—Hydrocele *en bissac.* This hydrocele extends up the cord into the inguinal canal to the internal abdominal ring. (Horwitz.)

(2) *evacuation by puncture;* (3) *artificial irritation of the interior vaginal surface;* (4) *incision and evacuation.* The external treatment comprises painting the scrotum with iodine or applying compresses steeped in various solutions, vesication, electric currents, etc.

Similarly in internal artificial irritation of the vaginal a variety of medicaments have been employed. (Fig. 286.) Both these methods of treating hydrocele have to a great extent yielded to puncture and incision. While most treatments will give temporary relief the important point is to prevent recurrence.

Chronic hydrocele is merely relieved but not cured by tapping the fluid; the fluid will usually again accumulate unless the secreting layer of serous membrane is destroyed. Destruction of the serous layer may be

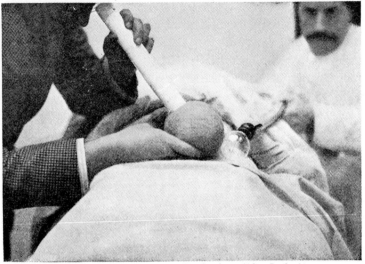

FIG. 285.—Diagnosis by transillumination. (After Sanford.)

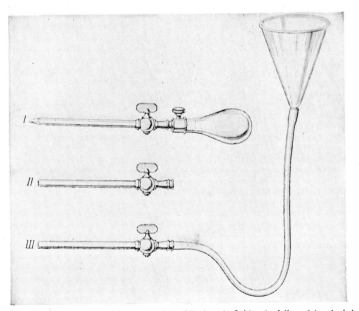

FIG. 286.—Apparatus used for evacuation of hydrocele fluid to be followed by the injection of tincture of iodine. *I*. mounted trocar; *II*, cannula and stop-cock of trocar; *III*, cannula to which rubber tube and funnel are attached to facilitate ingress of medicament. (Sebileau and Descomps.)

effected by the application to its entire surface of deliquescent crystals of carbolic acid which is injected after withdrawal of the fluid, or the parietal layer may be everted.

For evacuating the hydrocele is held firmly in the left hand. (Fig. 287.) The trocar is held in the right hand with the index finger placed upon the shaft of the needle and just as far from the point as the depth to which the needle is to be inserted. By a sudden thrust the needle is passed through the skin of the scrotum at the junction of the middle and

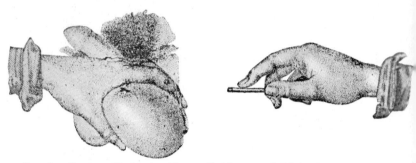

Fig. 287.—Puncture of hydrocele. Manner of holding tumor in left hand and trocar in right.
(Sebileau and Descomps.)

lower thirds of the tumor on the anterior aspect of the sac. The testes, epididymis and cord must be avoided.

Jaboulay's eversion operation for hydrocele consists in opening the tunica by a short incision and drawing the testis through the aperture. The edges of the tunica are then caught together by a stitch behind the cord. This turns the sac completely inside out, thereby bringing the secreting surfaces against a connective-tissue layer. The method has the advantages that it can be done through a short high incision, that local anesthesia or at most a very short general anesthesia is sufficient, and that the wound can be closed tightly. (Fig. 288.)

In Jaboulay's operation the smooth endothelial surface of the tunica will be in contact with the raw scrotal tissue and will adhere to it.

Doyen gives the following operation for the radical cure of hydrocele by inversion of the tunica vaginalis.

The liquid is evacuated by a small incision and the tunica vaginalis is then everted. The skin is distended over the hydrocele, the transparency of which has been verified by means of an endoscope in the dark room. An incision 3 cms. long is made over the upper anterior part of the tumor; the tunica vaginalis is exposed and seized in two Doyen's ringed forceps. The tunica is punctured and the contained fluid evacuated. The testicle is immediately drawn outside with its serous envelope and liberated from surrounding cellular connections. The orifice in the tunica is enlarged by divulsion and the serous membrane is turned completely inside out. It is fixed in this position by several fine silk sutures placed above the testicle.

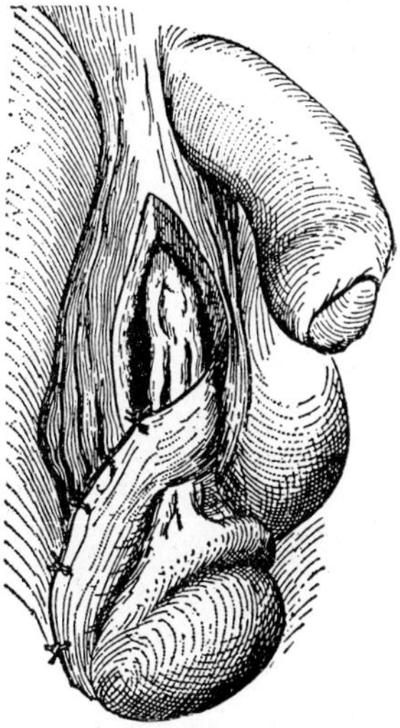

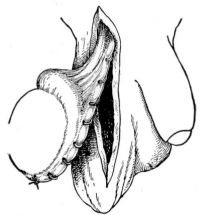

The last stage of the operation consists in reduction of the testicle which remains outside the serous coat. The skin is sutured with clips.

The hydrocele sac may be entirely excised. An incision 5 to 10 cms. long is made in the outer anterior aspect of the scrotum and carried

FIG. 288.—Jaboulay's operation. (Duval.)

down to the sac. The sac, with the testes and cord, is delivered through this opening and the parietal layer trimmed away close up to the testes and

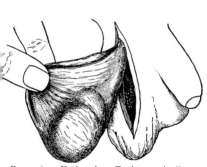

FIG. 289.—Hydrocele. Tunica vaginalis reflected and turned back ready for suturing. (Bottle operation.) (A. T. Osgood.)

FIG. 290.—Everted sac sutured back behind the spermatic cord and epididymis. (Bottle operation.) (A. T. Osgood.)

epididymis. Care must be taken to avoid injury to the vessels and not to allow the testicle to be revolved upon the cord, as it may persist when the testis is returned to the scrotum, resulting in necrosis of the testis. The "Bottle" operation for hydrocele is illustrated in Figs. 289 and 290. Von Bergmann's operation is depicted in Figs. 291 and 292.

When hydrocele is secondary to some other condition the essential treatment must be directed toward that condition.

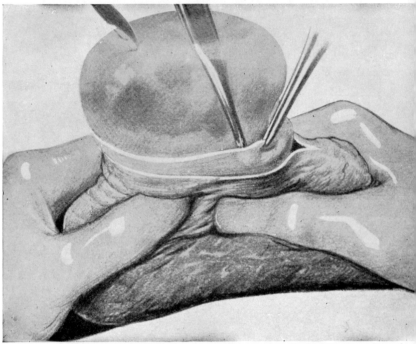

FIG. 291.—Radical operation for hydrocele. von Bergmann's method. (After Oscar Rempel.)

Vaginal hematocele is due to the collection of blood in the tunica vaginalis due to a traumatism, a tumor, or the tapping of a hydrocele.

Hematocele of the cord is a hydrocele of the cord into which bleeding has occurred.

Hematocele of the testicle is due to the effusion of blood into a hydrocele of the testicle.

Parenchymatous hematocele is extravasation of blood into the substance of the testicle.

The general treatment of these conditions consists in putting the patient to bed, supporting the scrotum, and applying ice over the tumor.

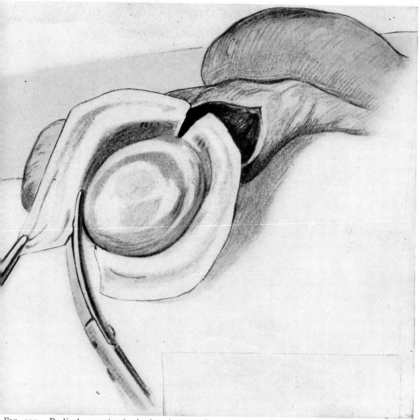

FIG. 292.—Radical operation for hydrocele. von Bergmann's method. (After Oscar Rempel.)

BIBLIOGRAPHY

JOHNSON: Operative Therapeusis, Vol. IV. Article on hydrocele. American Practice of Surgery, vi, 684.

DOYEN: Surgical Therapeutics and Operative Technique, iii, 451.

DA COSTA: Modern Surgery. 8th Edit., 1546.

SEBILEAU and DESCOMPS: Article on hydrocele in LeDentu and Delbet's. Nouveau Traité de Chirurgie, xxxii, 1916, 118.

CHAPTER XXIX

VASOTOMY

INFECTIONS of the epididymis and other parts connected with the testicle often call for treatment in the form of vasotomy with injections of

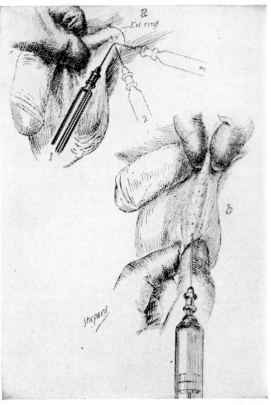

FIG. 293.—*a*, injecting novocain about the cord just below external ring; *b*, injecting novocain into skin along the line to be incised. (Herbst and Thompson.)

antiseptics. This mode of treatment and credit for pioneer work in vasotomy is due to Belfield of Chicago.[1, 2] Vasotomy is especially applicable to recent infections as well as to old cases in which changes are not too marked, such as for instance where parts of the tortuous tubules have

ecome walled off from the rest by inflammatory changes making those
arts inaccessible to injected antiseptics. Instead of opening the vas freely

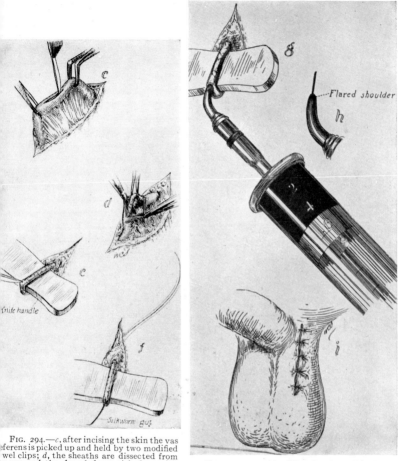

FIG. 294.—*c*, after incising the skin the vas
eferens is picked up and held by two modified
wel clips; *d*, the sheaths are dissected from
e vas and the denuded vas picked up with
tissue forceps; *e*, the sheaths are pushed
vay from the under surface of the vas and a
rector slipped between them and the vas. A
nall longitudinal nick is made penetrating
e lumen; *f*, a strand of silkworm gut is
ssed into the lumen of the vas to determine
s patency. (Herbst and Thompson.)

FIG. 295.—*g* and *h*, a Ricord syringe with blunted
curved dental needle is used for injecting the collargol solution. From 5 to 30 cc. of freshly prepared
3 to 5% solution of collargol are injected into each
vesicle; *i*, after waiting a moment to see if any of
the collargol leaks back, the vas is dropped back into
the scrotum and the wound is closed. (Herbst
and Thompson.)

ome prefer to do a vas puncture; but this has the objection that it exposes
o back infiltration and infiltration of the scrotum unless the operation
s conducted with the minutest care and precision.

33

The technique of vasotomy, as described by Herbst and Thompson of Chicago,[3] consists of incision of the skin, picking up the vas deferens and holding it by clips; the sheaths are dissected from the vas, and the denuded vas picked up with a tissue forceps; the sheaths are pushed away from the under surface of the vas and a director slipped between them and the vas;

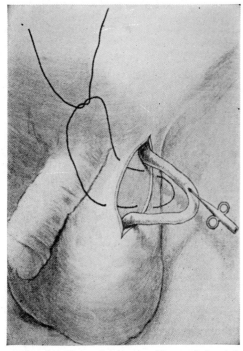

Fig. 296.—Kidd's operation of vasotomy, showing vas with cannula inserted and mattress suture passed and about to be tied so as to sling the vas just below the level of the skin edges.

a small longtitudinal nick is made penetrating to the lumen; a strand of silkworm gut is passed into the lumen of the vas to determine its patency.

A Ricord syringe with a blunted curved dental needle is used for injecting the antiseptic solution. If collargol is employed, from 5 to 30 cc. of a freshly prepared 3 to 5 per cent. solution are injected into each vesicle. The vas is dropped back into the scrotum and the wound closed. (Figs. 293–295.)

In Kidd's [4] (Fig. 296) vasotomy technique the vas is dissected clear of all connective tissue. A small incision is made into its lumen and the atency tested by a piece of silkworm gut passed through it. A special annula is used, warm sterilized water first and then colloid silver olution are used for lavage. Kidd makes a few fine silkworm gut sutures ight through both sides of the skin and fascial incision and beneath the as. These sutures are again returned and pass back again half an inch elow through both layers of the skin and fascia beneath the vas and tied. ach of the two rings on the cannula are fixed by fine suture to the skin n each side. The vas is then securely fixed in place ready for the next ash out.

BIBLIOGRAPHY

BELFIELD: Jour. Amer. Med. Assn., 1905, xliv, 1277.
BELFIELD: Surg. Gynec. & Obst., 1906, iii, 656.
HERBST and THOMPSON: Illinois Med. Jour., 1920, xxxviii, 214.
KIDD: Lancet, Lond., 1923, ii, 214.

CHAPTER XXX

VAS DEFERENS—ANASTOMOSIS

OCCASIONS may arise in surgery of the male genital organs where the vas deferens becomes torn, and an end-to-end or other anastomosis is

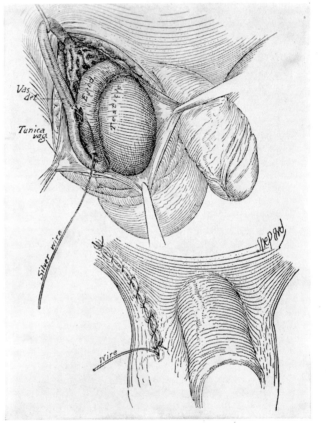

FIG. 297.—McKenna's operation for short circuiting of the vas deferens; anastomosis of vas and epididymis; placing of silver wire.

necessary. This appears to have been first done by Parlavecchio owing to a surgical accident. Some years later Lydston [1] devised a method cutting the ends off square, then introducing a filament of silkworm gut on a filiform bougie through an opening in the side and sewed the two square cut ends together. The sheath of the cord was then sewed around the point of the suture and the bougie withdrawn after ten days. Later on Lydston [2] reported that this method was not feasible when the distal end of the vas atrophied, and that in such case the anastomosis of the proximal end must be made direct to the epididymis.

In Davis' technique [3] the proximal end is cut off obliquely and pointed, the distal end being cut off on a short bevel. A piece of catgut threaded on a fine needle is passed through the tip of the proximal end, then introduced into the lumen of the distal end and made to pierce the wall well beyond the opening. A second needle on the catgut was similarly brought out near the first. Traction is made on the threads and the pointed extremity of the proximal end enters the lumen of the distal end without trouble until its apex enters the point of emergence of the needles. The catgut is then tied and the apex fixed in place. The distal end is fixed by a few fine sutures to the side of the proximal end. This operation is a modification of Poggi's ureteral anastomosis.

For " short-circuiting " the vas to the epididymis (especially for cases of male sterility) McKenna [4] cuts down on the vas about two inches above the testicle, isolates and exposes the vas, and then slits and anastomoses it with the middle third of the epididymis. (Fig. 297.)

Salvo [5] has described a method of latero-lateral anastomosis of the vas. Salvo's experimental work has been carried out on animals and he claims 50 per cent. success.

BIBLIOGRAPHY

LYDSTON : Ann. Surg., 1906, xliv, 92.
[2] LYDSTON : Amer. Jour. Surg., 1918, xxxii, 224.
DAVIS : Ann. Surg., 1908, xlviii, 793.
MCKENNA : Surg. Clinics, Chicago, 1919, iii, 145.
[5] SALVO : Policlin. Rome, 1923, xxx, sez. prat., 521.

CHAPTER XXXI

CRYPTORCHIDISM AND ITS TREATMENT

UNDESCENDED testicles are found to occur once in about every five hundred males. The great majority of cases are of the unilateral type. With the deformity there is always a great risk of hernia, of traumatism and of subsequent malignancy.

Operation is accompanied by little or no mortality. But operation though successful in restoring the testicle to its proper normal position in the scrotum, does not always succeed in keeping it there. Bevan, who studied the various operative methods of treating undescended testicle was satisfied that the reason why it was generally impracticable to keep the restored testes in the scrotum was due to the shortness of the spermatic vessels of the cord and that the vas and the vessels of the vas were in all cases practically of sufficient length. He considered that the nutriment of the testes was only partly dependent upon the spermatic supply. In his technique, therefore, Bevan sections the spermatic vessels when necessary but he points out that it is only necessary in about ten per cent. of the cases.

Arrested migration of the testicle gives different indications for treatment according to the position reached by the testicle.

If the testicle has cleared the external ring of the inguinal canal surgery is only indicated if there is a concomitant hernia. At any rate it is only necessary to assure the complementary migration of the gland and its fixation if necessary.

But if the ectopia is supra-inguinal, operation is almost always imposed as non-operative methods, massage, traction, etc., have but little chance of success. Operation is usually justified, even if there is no hernia, on account of the possible complications and especially when the malformation is bilateral.

Another consideration is that in the child and in the adolescent operation always leads to the probability of a normal development of the aberrant testicle, and in the adult the risks of complications, more especially neoplastic degeneration, is avoided.

518

The general concordance of surgical opinion is that second childhood is the period of choice in which to operate for testicular ectopia; but some surgeons operate much earlier. If the condition has been allowed to continue till adult age is reached the indications for operation no longer arise so much from the testicle as from the intestine and in a radical operation the question of conservation or removal of the atrophied testicle must depend upon its state and functional value. If the ectopia is bilateral every effort should be made to preserve at least one testicle. The surgeon must carefully weigh the effects of castration with the risks of leaving the testes remain. The author advises operation at the earliest moment consistent with safety.

The general surgical treament of imperfectly descended testes includes the radical cure of the hernia, which usually accompanies it, liberation of the testicle and of its appendage, and its fixation in the scrotum.

A multitude of operation fixation methods have been devised, but as a general rule the majority give unsatisfactory results owing to the testicular pedicle comprising the spermatic vessels, the lymphatics and nerves being too short to permit the testicle to be sufficiently lowered to its normal position in the scrotum. A method of fixation in which descent of the testicle was obtained by systematic section of all the vessels of the spermatic cord was first recommended by Mignon in 1902 and later elaborated by Bevan, whose technique will be presently referred to. Section of the pedicle has in a great number of cases been followed by secondary testicular atrophy and it has been proposed to section the spermatic veins alone and spare the spermatic artery, a procedure which is not usually anatomically possible.

Landz' operation was one of the earliest. Sutures were passed through the testicle and scrotum and fastened to either a cage or the thigh and continuous traction exerted on the cord.

Schueller's method consisted in dividing the tunic at the internal ring, forming a new tunic by its lower part, and anchoring the testicle to the scrotum or to its fellow by sutures.

The Keetley-Torek method of operation essentially consists in an incision in the bottom of the scrotum, through which the testicle is extruded. At a properly selected place an incision is made upon the thigh down to the fascia. The testicle is fastened to this structure and the

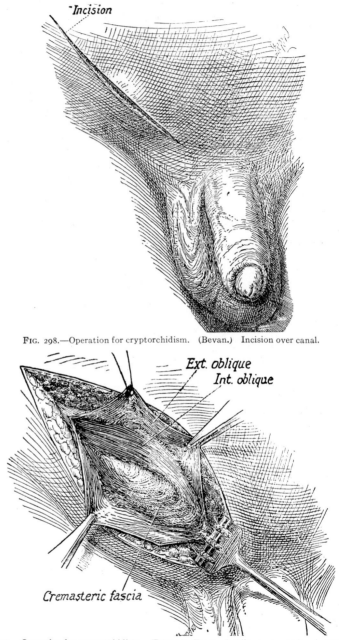

FIG. 298.—Operation for cryptorchidism. (Bevan.) Incision over canal.

FIG. 299.—Operation for cryptorchidism. (Bevan.) External oblique retracted and cremasteric fascia exposed.

rotal flaps are sutured to the flaps of the incision on the thigh. At a
ter operation the scrotum and testicle are liberated from the thigh
nd the testicle is replaced within the scrotum, the principle of the operation

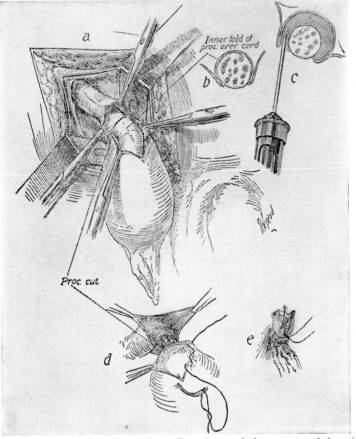

FIG. 300.—Operation for cryptorchidism. (Bevan.) *a*, vaginal process opened; *b*, section of
ord and opened process; *c*, injection of water between process and cord; *d*, vaginal process closed
ver cord; *e*, proximal end of process transfixed and tied as in a hernia operation.

eing that long continued fixation of the testicle to the thigh lengthens
he cord.

In Kirschauer's technique a bell-shaped receptacle is made for the
esticle from a piece of fascia lata of the patient and this is passed through
subcutaneous tunnel and fastened to the superficial perineal fascia.

Bevan makes a cutaneous incision similar to that for the radical cure
f inguinal hernia. (Figs. 298–305.)

The aponeurosis of the external oblique is split in the direction of i
fibers and the cremasteric fascia exposed. Retraction of the lower fla
exposes Poupart's ligament. The hernial sac which contains a quantity
fluid is now isolated from the spermatic cord. The sac is very thin and t
cord is spread out fan-shaped over the sac. The isolation of the s

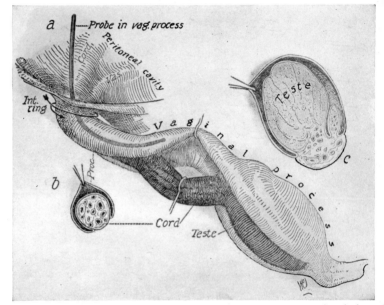

Fig. 301.—Operation for cryptorchidism. (Bevan.) Schematic representation of vaginal proc
overlying cord and testicle.

is begun at the neck and when this is completed the peritoneal cavity
closed, either by transfixion and ligation or by a purse-string sutur
The distal part of the sac may either be cut off close to its attachmer
to the testicle, or it may be cut off at some distance from the testicle an
a new tunica vaginalis constructed, or it may be everted and sutured
in the operation for hydrocele. The greatest care must be exercised i
freeing the vas deferens from the sac so that its artery may not be injure
with resultant necrosis of testes.

In Bevan's operation there is liberation of the hernial sac from t
cord closure of the sac, lengthening of the cord by incision of its coverin
and if this does not suffice ligation of the spermatic vessels.

It seems, however, from later studies that it is essential wherever possible to preserve the integrity of the important vascular connections of the testicle including the spermatic vessels.

In 1911 Davison proposed a new method. After ligating the deep

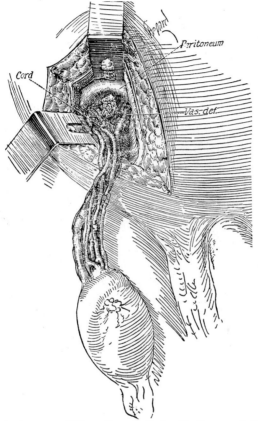

FIG. 302.—Operation for cryptorchidism. (Bevan.) Cord and testis prepared after sectioning and ligating structures above referred to, to be placed in scrotum.

epigastric vessels the posterior wall of the canal is opened thereby destroying the internal ring. After the vessels and vas are freed the testicle is put in its bed in the scrotum. The posterior wall of the canal is closed and the cord brought out through the lower angle of the incision. In 1915 this technique was modified by Wolfer who brought the cord out beneath the deep epigastrics without cutting them.

In Siever's method traction on the vascular pedicle is entirely avoided. Siever passes the undescended testicle through the obturator foramen, thus shortening its path to the scrotum instead of lengthening the spermatic cord as in other methods. In the adult, according to Welti, who had

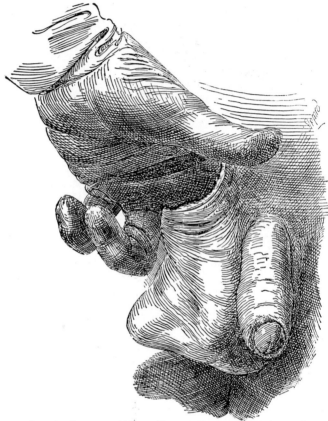

Fig. 303.—Operation for cryptorchidism. (Bevan.) Scrotum stretched to receive testicle.

applied Siever's method in thirteen cases, the cord is lengthened more than 7 cms. by drawing it through the obturator foramen. The foramen is reached after the spermatic cord is thoroughly dissected out. The incision is on the thigh, as for inguinal hernia, the adductor longus and gracilis muscles being separated. The defect of this method is that the spermatic artery and the veins of the pampiniform plexus have to be severed, although

hose who recommend it state that this has no important effect upon the
nutrition of the testicle.

Lichtenstern favors funiculopexy, suturing the spermatic cord to the
superficial fascia only the connective tissue covering of the cord being

Fig. 304.—Operation for cryptorchidism. (Bevan.)   Testicle in scrotum and retaining
sutures inserted.

involved in the suture and the sutures being continued only to the beginning of the vas deferens.

Whatever may have been the method of obtaining full descent of the
testicle to its site it seems indispensable to fix it there. Probably the best
method of fixation is that of Bevan and of Walther, who make a buttonhole
in the testicular septum and introduce the lowered testicle through it into

the scrotal sac of the opposite testicle, thus placing the two testicles side by side and then closing the orifice in the septum. The immediate and end

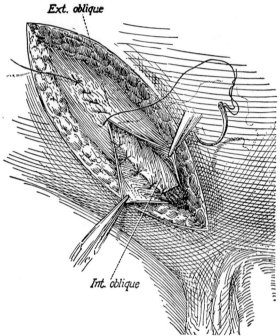

Ext. oblique

Int. oblique

FIG. 305.—Operation for cryptorchidism. (Bevan.) Closure; internal oblique sutured to sheaf of Poupart's ligament over cord. External oblique closed with continuous stitch.

results in thirty cases reported by Walther up to 1912 were very satisfactory.

BIBLIOGRAPHY

[1] BEVAN: Surg. Clin. Chicago, 1918, ii, 1101.
[2] MIGNON: Cited by LeDentu and Delbet, Nouv. Traité de Chir., xxxii.
[3] KEELTEY-TOREK: Cited in Johnson's Operative Therapeusis.
[4] LANZ: Cited in Johnson's Operative Therapeusis.
[5] SCHUELLER: Cited in Johnson's Operative Therapeusis.
[6] KIRSCHNER: Cited in Johnson's Operative Therapeusis.
[7] DAVISON: Cited in Johnson's Operative Therapeusis.
[8] SIEVER: Deut. Zeitsch. f. Chir., 1920, clx, 159.
[9] WELTI: Beitr. z. Klin. Chir., 1922, cxxvii, 410.
[10] LICHTENSTERN: Zeitsch. f. Urolog. Chir., 1922, ix, 185.
[11] WALTHER: In LeDentu and Delbet's Nouveau Traité de Chir., xxxii, 295.
[12] CAULK: Surg. Gynec. & Obst., xxxv, 641.
[13] COLEY: Surg. Gynec. & Obst., xxviii, 452.

CHAPTER XXXII

CASTRATION AND EMASCULATION

CASTRATION, by removal of the testicle, is indicated when any lesion of
ιe organ, such as abscess, neoplasm, tuberculosis or necrosis, tend to
estroy it, or which threatens the life of the individual by its presence.

General anesthesia is usually employed. A vertical incision 3 cms.
r longer is made in the scrotum from the level of the external inguinal
ng downward to the raphe of the scrotum. The incision should be long
ιough to embrace any pathological condition to be removed. The skin,
ιnica, dartos and coverings of the testicle are exposed. The cord is
xposed and drawn out and with the testis may be exteriorized through the
ιcision; and in all cases where it is a matter of a testicular neoplasm the
ιrd should be ligated and the lymphatic and vascular channels to the body
ιut off at the earliest moment with as little traumatism as possible. The
ιas should be separated from the vessels of the cord and ligated as high
s possible before removing any part of it or of the epididymis. The vas
hould be separated from the other components of the cord, ligated, and its
ιroximal stump cauterized with the actual cautery or with pure carbolic
ιcid. If the lesion is tubercular the vas should be carried to the skin
urface through a stab wound in the skin and sutured there or else it
hould be removed entire—not pulled upon and ruptured at its weakest
ιiseased point but dissected free as far as possible by opening the inguinal
anal. The vascular structures of the cord are ligated in mass, or in
eparate bundles, leaving a long stump below the ligature and by blunt
ιissection, or cutting with scissors, the lower portion of the cord and testes
s removed. The incision is then closed with a few sutures of silkworm
ιut. A rubber or tube drain is left if soiling of the scrotal tissues or oozing
ιnto the cavity of the scrotum has occurred. In malignant cases the
εchnique of Hinman (see above) should be used.

When there is no malignant disease it will suffice to clamp the cord
ιnd divide it near the inguinal ring, remove the testicle, ligate the spermatic

artery alone, and then ligate the entire thickness of the cord with chromic gut. Drainage is not necessary.

Total emasculation when necessary includes:

Section and ligature of the spermatic cords;

Total ablation of the penis and scrotum;

Dissection of the root of the corpora cavernosa and suture of urethral section to the perineum;

Removal of lymph glands in the vicinity and closure.

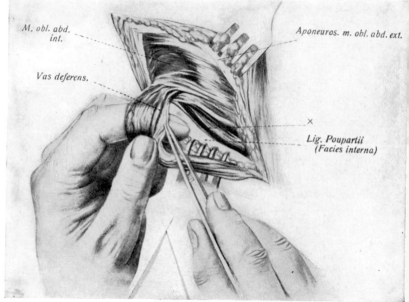

Fig. 306.—Technic of castration. (Axhausen.)

The accompanying illustrations depict G. Axhausen's [2] procedures for castration. The first stage of the operation consists of exposure of the spermatic cord. To accomplish that the skin in the inguinal region is divided during which two blood vessels are encountered which are ligated and divided. As in the operation for herniotomy, the external abdominal ring is exposed and the inguinal canal opened. Thorough exposure of the entire spermatic cord is essential. (Fig. 306.) Deliver the cord from the inguinal canal; trace its entrance into the internal inguinal canal; grasp cord in left hand; incise its fibrous tunic and recognize the vas deferens

nd isolate it from its surrounding structures by blunt dissection. Trace
t to the internal abdominal ring; divide the cord close to the internal
ring, after thorough ligation of the component parts of the cord. In this
procedure the vas is not included. Axhausen recommends that we now
grasp the vas deferens with both hands as shown in Figure 307 and deliver

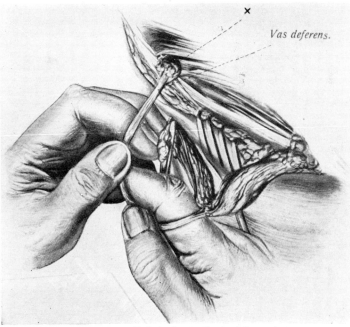

Vas deferens.

FIG. 307.—Technic of castration. (Axhausen.)

it by traction from the depth of the wound. Traction is now continued
until the vas tears off beyond the point of ligation at the internal ring.
Axhausen hopes to remove a greater portion of the vas through traction.
The author does not advise this procedure for fear that a hemorrhage from
the arteria deferentialis may be the result. The inguinal canal is now
closed in the usual manner. The testicle is now removed (Fig. 308) a gauze
compress (not shown in the illustration) protects the contiguous structures
from contamination during the ablation of the testis. The operation is
completed by closing the wound. Avoid dead spaces by obliterating the
cavity left after removing the testicle with catgut sutures. Skin closure
and dressings.

34

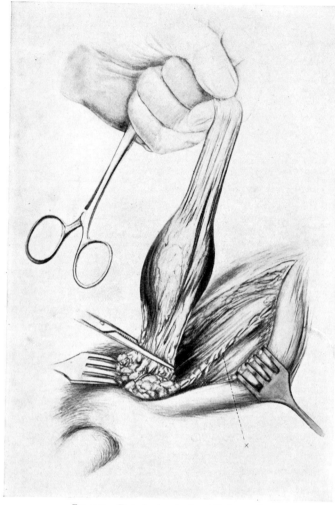

Fig. 308.—Technic of castration. (Axhausen.)

BIBLIOGRAPHY

[1] Juvara: In LeDentu and Delbet's, Nouveau Traité de Chirurgie, xxxii, 87–89.
[2] Axhausen, G.: In Lehmanns Med. Atlanten Bd. xiii, 228.

CHAPTER XXXIII

ORCHI-EPIDIDYMITIS

THE most important of the orchi-epididymites by urethral infection is that due to the gonococcus. Other inflammations of the testicle and epididymis arise from the propagation of infection by the vascular route and follow in the wake of the general infective diseases, scarlatina, measles, grippe, rheumatism, tubercular and syphilitic orchitis, etc.

Gonorrheal epididymitis has been medically treated in a variety of ways, the most recent of which seem to be intravenous injections of calcium salts or of sodium iodide. Radnal and Richter as well as Murata report good results from calcium salts. Stern and Ritter were the first to employ intravenous injections of sterile sodium iodide and Ravich reported excellent results obtained in ninety personal cases and in seventy additional cases which he had the opportunity to observe. Recently Wright reports very good results in seventy-four cases and states that the method is free from danger.

For violent orchitis or epididymitis the first indication is the suppression of pain. For this, various methods have been tried—external medication, injections, compression, electrical currents, Bier's hyperemic treatment, diathermy, vaccine treatment. Varying degrees of success are claimed by the advocates of the different methods, but the multitude of methods is a confession that there is no specific cure, nor any known definite, non-surgical method by which the infective inflammatory process can be dealt with effectively.

In the belief that the pain in orchi-epididymitis is especially due to vaginal distention, some have recommended and practised punctures or incisions of the tunica vaginalis. These operations give temporary relief, but are painful owing to the inflammatory condition of the region. Puncture of the epididymis followed by aspiration of the septic fluid and pus gives immediate relief and puts the patient in a position for rapid recovery.

The surgical method of choice in the treatment in severe cases of orchi-epididymitis with abundance of pus appears to be *epididymotomy*. This procedure fulfils the general surgical doctrine that where there is pus must be evacuated.

Epididymotomy for severe acute gonorrheal epididymitis was fir advocated by Hagner in 1902. Pathological studies of the disease, h Cunningham and Cook, have demonstrated a rapid destructive process i the tubules and intertubular tissue; and the permanent defects in th tubules argue in favor of supplying surgical drainage early if the proces is shown clinically to be severe, for upon the early termination of th destructive inflammatory process will depend the prevention of permanen impairment of the function of the ductus epididymidis.

The clinical conclusion is that epididymotomy is a rational procedur for active, acute and recurrent acute and sub-acute epididymitis, bein the application of the general surgical principle of applying drainage t an inflamed structure. Drainage of the epididymis has moreover a bene ficial influence on the inflammatory processes in the other sexual organs a they are freed from the influence of the products of inflammation drainin from the infected epididymis.

Recurrent epididymitis following epididymotomy is rare, and sterilit is not often permanent. In twenty-two patients upon whom Cunninghar did a double epididymotomy 12 or 15 per cent. were proved to have sperma tozoa, and in five others the condition was unknown. According t Cunningham the number of patients with zoöspermia following operatio is not larger than those treated by non-operative methods, and wha evidence there is, is in favor of epididymotomy. The immediate relie from pain and shortening of the course of the disease speak also well i favor of operation.

Allen reports a series of thirty-two epididymotomies for gonorrhea epididymitis with excellent results in all. The incision is made in th scrotal wall posteriorly, just above the globus minor. The globus majo globus minor and body of the epididymis are opened by puncturing ther with a pair of sharp pointed delicate scissors or bistoury held in th right hand. The instrument is pushed in one-half to one cm. into th areas to be drained. This allows the escape of the exudate and pus, relieve tension and secures drainage. Each nodular mass must be similarly treatec

The occurrence of sterility either temporary or permanent afte pididymotomy has been already alluded to, and whatever may be the surgical method adopted of opening the epididymis, this result is to be expected. That epididymal obliteration is particularly important when it is bilateral, is the main point for consideration in connection with the ater prognosis. To obviate the effects of such obliteration and provide passage for the spermatozoa still effective in the testicle various surgical methods have been devised, such as *inter-deferential, epididymary-deferento, deferento-testicular,* etc., *anastomosis.* All these methods have given more or less success.

Tuberculosis of the testicle or of the epididymis (see also Chapter on Tuberculosis of the Testes) is almost always secondary to tuberculosis elsewhere. Kocher's statistics showed that in four hundred and fifty-one cases of urino-genital tuberculosis that came to autopsy over 80 per cent. had pulmonary tuberculosis. Tuberculosis of the epididymis or testicle is very rarely primary, although such has been claimed as arising from direct trauma.

For *epididymo-testicular tuberculosis* total or partial resection of epididymis and testis, while often satisfactory, leads to frequent recurrence. Castration, either unilateral or bilateral, is to be seriously considered. Bruns has observed seventy-eight cases of unilateral and thirty-three cases of bilateral tuberculosis of testicle and epididymis for which castration was done. Of the thirty-three bilateral cases, 56 per cent. recovered, 5 per cent. died from tuberculosis in other regions, 15 per cent. developed genito-urinary tuberculosis. All these were cases of bilateral castration. Of the seventy-eight cases of unilateral castrations, 46 per cent. were cured, 26 per cent. developed tuberculosis in the opposite testicle, 15 per cent. developed pulmonary tuberculosis, 12 per cent. died of progress of the disease.

Maxeiner and Waldschmidt have observed and treated fifteen cases of tuberculosis of the epididymis, 66 per cent. of which showed prior non-genital tuberculosis. Ten cases were bilateral. These authors, from their own experience and from a study of the literature, think that the treatment of tuberculosis of the epididymis varies from the most conservative to the extremely radical. Some authors, such as Calot, employ injections exclusively and claim never to have had a failure. Others advise early operation removing the epididymis, but preserving the testicle if possible. Others still, such as Young, advocate the radical operation in cases of tuberculosis involving the seminal vesicles and epididymis. He recommends removal of both seminal vesicles and ampullæ, with resection of both lateral lobes of the prostate and removal of the vas and diseased epididymis. In the fifteen cases surgically treated by Maxeiner and Waldschmidt, a conservative operation was done; the epididymis and vas were removed and the testes preserved or resected when the disease had not advanced sufficiently to demand removal. As end results, eight patients reported their general health improved and seven reported their general health unchanged.

The conservative operation seems more logical when the local condition is pathologically and clinically a secondary process. But in well developed primary tuberculosis of the testicle or epididymis castration ought to be complete and radical. It should include not only removal of the testicle and epididymis but also of the deferent canal and even of the spermatic cord as far as the inguinal canal. The sexual deficiency due to the loss of the testicle can be supplied by a testicular transplantation.

Roentgen irradiation has also been tried in tuberculosis of the testes and epididymis. According to Freund's experience in fifteen cases (eleven with fistula) tuberculous tissue is not very sensitive to this treatment, but it may be relied on to effect a cure if the tubercular processes are confined to the testes and epididymis and have not spread to neighbouring organs. In some cases partial resection may precede roentgen-ray treatment with advantage.

The treatment of testicular or epididymal or scrotal syphilis is to a great extent the general method of anti-syphilitic treatment. Occasionally the effects of extensive ulceration and suppuration have demanded the removal of a testicle but this is exceptional.

BIBLIOGRAPHY

[1] RADNAL: Wien. Klin. Wchnschr., 1922, xxxv, 902.
[2] RICHTER: Deut. Med. Wchnschr., 1922, xlvii, 1347.
[3] MURATA: Cited by Wright.
[4] STERN and RITTER: Med. Record, N. Y., 1920, xcvii, 190.

[5] WRIGHT: New York Med. Jour., 1923, cxviii, 292.
[6] RAVICH: Med. Record, N. Y., 1922, cxv, 516.
[7] CUNNINGHAM and COOK: Jour. Urol., 1922, vii, 139.
[8] ALLEN: Miliary Surg., 1921, xlix, 439.
[9] MAXEINER and WALDSCHMIDT: Minnesota Med., 1923, vi, 492.
[10] KOCHER: Cited by Maxeiner and Waldschmidt.
[11] CALOT: Cited by Maxeiner and Waldschmidt.
[12] YOUNG: Arch. Surg., March, 1922.
[23] FREUND: Wien. Klin. Wchnschr., 1921, xxxiv, 511.

CHAPTER XXXIV

FUNICULITIS AND DEFERENTITIS

SEBILEAU and Descomps define funiculitis as an inflammation of the cellular tissue surrounding the elements of the spermatic cord. They recognize three varieties: *peri-deferentitis, peri-phlebitis* and *peri-lymphangitis*. A peri-deferentitis may complicate any urethral affection especially the gonorrheal.

The great majority of cases of funiculitis are peri-lymphangitis following accidental or surgical accidents in the region of the cord. Such accidents are frequent especially in operations for inguinal hernia.

Peri-phlebitis of the cord is rare and generally accompanies some other morbid process such as cancer of the testis. The spermatic veins may be infected from some surgical or other accident in the vicinity, or infection may spread by the blood route. Death may occur from embolism or from septicemia.

According to Wilensky and Samuels, deferentitis and funiculitis are terms which are used often interchangeably in the literature. This is, however, not correct: the vas deferens is only one constituent of the spermatic cord the funiculus spermaticus.

Various types of acute deferentitis and funiculitis are reported in the literature. Wilensky and Samuels divide them into these three main groups:

(a) Acute gonococcus deferentitis and funiculitis.

(b) Acute streptococcus funiculitis. (" endemic funiculitis.")

(c) Acute funiculitis of indeterminate origin.

Acute gonococcus deferentitis and funiculitis usually occurs about four weeks after the initial infection, and is generally associated with epididymitis, the symptoms of which dominate. But deferentitis or funiculitis may occur without involvement of the epididymis or testis, and the process may even be confined to the pelvic portion of the vas deferens.

The focus of infection is probably in the posterior urethra or prostate and spreads to the epididymis either by the lymphatics or by retrograde

536

peristalsis of the vas deferens. If the organisms penetrate the coats of the vas a deferentitis is produced; should the infection penetrate deeper a funiculitis is produced.

The process may and usually does subside without operative interference, or it may evolve to an abscess of the cord or an intra-abdominal abscess.

Endemic funiculitis, a suppurative condition of the spermatic cord, is generally observed in tropical and sub-tropical countries. The local swelling is accompanied by fever and vomiting. In almost every case a special type of diplo-streptococcus can be demonstrated in the pus, or from the blood in fewer cases. The exact etiological factor is still a matter on which opinions are divided, some claiming that it is essentially a thrombophlebitis of the pampiniform plexus, while others think it may be of parasitical origin, with the streptococcus as a secondary invader.

The treatment of endemic funiculitis is operative, and has varied from incisions of the swollen tissues, with evacuation and drainage of abscess cavities to complete removal of the cord as high up as possible.

The third group of cases of deferentitis and funiculitis—those of indeterminate nature—are interesting because of the entire absence of evidence pointing to a satisfactory etiological cause. Wilensky and Samuels think that among the factors to be considered are: (1) trauma, (2) a preëxisting infectious disease, such as rheumatism, or influenza, and (3) the presence of any focus of infection and suppuration to which the funiculitis might be considered as a metastatic phenomenon.

Wilensky and Samuels report two personal cases coming within this group. The first patient had rheumatic fever a long time back and an attack of influenza three months before the onset of pain and swelling in the cord. In the second case the only history was that of an attack of gonorrhea thirty-one years previously.

Acute funiculitis must be differentiated from: (1) abscess of the abdominal wall; (2) from irreducible hernia; (3) from appendicitis with abscess; (4) from abscess in a hernial sac; (5) from venous thrombosis or hematoma of cord; (6) from tuberculosis, gumma, or neoplasm of the cord; (7) from osteomyelitis of infected neoplasm of os pubis, or from psoas abscess. A funiculitis may simulate any of these conditions.

As regards treatment in general: in the gonorrheal type, if no pus has formed, operative treatment is contra-indicated. If pus is present incision and drainage are indicated.

In the endemic type, where the cord is riddled with small abscesses, Wilensky and Samuels recommend complete excision of the cord.

In cases of indeterminate etiology, with or without abscess formation, incision down to the cord is recommended, with evacuation and drainage of abscesses whenever present. Both the cases operated by Wilensky and Samuels recovered.

BIBLIOGRAPHY

[1] SEBILEAU and DESCOMPS: In LeDentu and Delbet's, Nouveau Traité de Chir., Paris, 1916, xxxii, 629.

[2] WILENSKY and SAMUELS: Ann. Surg., 1923, xxviii, 785.

AUTHORS CITED

INDEX OF SUBJECTS